PROBLEMS IN UNDERGRADUATE PHYSICS

VOLUME IV

MOLECULAR PHYSICS, THERMODYNAMICS, ATOMIC AND NUCLEAR PHYSICS

PROBLEMS IN UNDERGRADUATE PHYSICS

VOLUME IV

MOLECULAR PHYSICS, THERMODYNAMICS, ATOMIC AND NUCLEAR PHYSICS

BY

V. L. GINZBURG, L. M. LEVIN
M. S. RABINOVICH, D.V. SIVUKHIN

TRANSLATED BY

D. E. BROWN

TRANSLATION EDITED BY

D. TER HAAR

PERGAMON PRESS

OXFORD · LONDON · EDINBURGH · NEW YORK
PARIS · FRANKFURT

Pergamon Press Ltd., Headington Hill Hall, Oxford
4 & 5 Fitzroy Square, London W. 1
Pergamon Press (Scotland) Ltd., 2 & 3 Teviot Place, Edinburgh 1
Pergamon Press Inc., 122 East 55th St., New York 22, N.Y.
Pergamon Press GmbH, Kaiserstrasse 75, Frankfurt-am-Main

First edition 1965

Library of Congress Catalog Card No. 65-25443

This translation has been made from the Russian book
Сборник задач по общему курсу физики, часть II
(revised edition) published by Fizmatgiz, Moscow, 1960,
and includes amendments and additions supplied by the
authors during the course of the translation.

2083

CONTENTS

PREFACE

THIS set of four books of problems is based on a translation of a Russian collection which has been in use by students in physics at Moscow State University and the Moscow Physico-Technical Institute for a number of years. Where appropriate, answers and solutions to the problems are given in the second part of each volume.

During the course of the translation of these volumes, the authors provided a large list of amendments and additions to their Russian text and these have all been incorporated in this English edition. Many of the additional problems are on topics which have developed during recent years.

The standard of the problems is roughly equivalent to an undergraduate degree course in physics at a British university, or at an American university; it varies from the simple to the rather sophisticated. They can be used in conjunction with almost any textbook on physics at the appropriate level.

D. TER HAAR

PROBLEMS

CHAPTER I

MOLECULAR PHYSICS AND THERMODYNAMICS

§ 1. THERMOMETRY. CALORIMETRY THERMAL EXPANSION

1. A box containing thermometers of the Florentine Academy (1660) with 50° scales was found by chance in Florence in 1829. It was found that 50° Florence (Fl) corresponded to 44° R and 0°Fl = −15°R. Find an expression for converting degrees of the Florentine scale to degrees centigrade (°C).

2. I.N. Delil', a member of the St.Petersburg Academy of Sciences, described his thermometer scale in 1733. He used mercury as his thermometric substance and took as his zero the temperature of boiling water. He divided the volume of the mercury at this point into 100,000 parts (major thermometer) and into 10,000 parts (minor thermometer) and marked off corresponding divisions on a scale; it turned out that the mercury of the minor thermometer dropped to the 150th division in melting ice. Find the expression for converting degrees Delil' (minor thermometer) to degrees centigrade.

3. Academician I.Braun of the St.Petersburg Academy of Sciences was the first to succeed in freezing mercury, in the frost out of doors on 25 Dec., 1759, at 199° D (i.e. on Delil's scale, see the previous problem). Regarding this, B.N. Menshutkin wrote in his book *M.V. Lomonosov*:

"A mercury thermometer buried in a refrigerating mixture was broken open, and Braun obtained for the first time a ball of solid mercury. It proved to be soft, like lead, and resembled polished silver. The experiments were continued on 26 Dec., now with Lomonosov; the frost was increasing, and 212°D was reached at

10 a.m. on the 26th. A mercury thermometer was placed in a refrigerating mixture of snow, aqua fortis (nitric acid) and vitriol (sulphuric acid). Lomonosov described the further course of the experiments as follows: 'Being in no doubt that it had already frozen, I presently struck the bulb and the glass immediately shattered; the mercury came out in a solid ball with a tail formed from the mercury in the thermometer tube, and resembling pure silver wire; this latter could be bent freely like a soft metal and had a thickness of a fortieth of an inch. On striking the mercury ball with the shaft of a hammer, I felt that it had the hardness of lead or tin. The first four blows had no significant effect, but cracks began to appear with the fifth, sixth and seventh. I then stopped striking the mercury, and tried cutting it with a knife; after about 20 minutes it began to resemble an amalgam or paste, and soon regained its lost fluidity, i.e. it melted in a frost of 208 degrees'."

Find from Lomonosov's experiments the freezing-point of mercury in degrees centigrade.

4. A thermometer indicates a temperature t_0 in melting ice, and a temperature $-t_H$ in the steam from water boiling at a pressure of H mmHg. Find an expression for the true temperature t at any intermediate reading t_t of the thermometer, on the assumption that the thermometer tube is divided into equal volumes by the scale graduations. The boiling-point of water at a pressure of H mmHg is T_H.

5. A thermometer in melting ice indicates $t_0 = -3{\cdot}0°$*, whilst the reading is $t_H = 101{\cdot}4°$ in the steam from water boiling at a pressure of 760 mmHg. What temperature does the thermometer register in the vapour of boiling methylated spirits (66·9°)?

6. Two completely identical thermometers are filled at 0° with equal volumes of mercury and toluol. Find the ratio of the length l of a division corresponding to 1° on the mercury thermometer scale to the length l_1 of a division on the toluol thermometer scale. The volumetric expansion coefficient of mercury is α, of toluol α_1, and the linear expansion coefficient of glass is β.

7. Discuss the behaviour at different temperatures from 0° to 10° of a thermometer filled with water. At what temperatures will

* Wherever the temperature scale is not mentioned, degrees centigrade are to be understood.

the reading of the thermometer be the same? Use the formula

$$V = 1 - 0{\cdot}00006105t + 0{\cdot}000007733t^2,$$

for the volume V of water as a function of the temperature t. Take the volume at 0° as unity.

8. A hydrogen thermometer with a constant volume V_0 undergoes a pressure change from p_0 mmHg to p_1 mmHg on heating from $t = 0°$ to t_1. Find the gas temperature t_1 if the volumetric expansion coefficient of the vessel is α and of hydrogen is α_p.

9. A thermometer immersed in water of mass $m = 6{\cdot}7$ g undergoes a temperature rise of $\Delta t = 14{\cdot}6°$ and indicates a temperature $t = 32{\cdot}4°$. What is the temperature x^0 of the water prior to the measurement. The water equivalent of the thermometer is $k = 0{\cdot}46$ cal deg^{-1}.

10. The temperature scale of a gas thermometer is usually constructed so that equal increments of the volume or pressure of the thermometric substance correspond to equal increments of temperature. Dalton (1802) proposed a different scale, in which equal increments of temperature correspond to equal relative increments of the volume of an ideal gas at constant pressure. In the Dalton scale, as in the centigrade scale, zero is taken as the temperature of melting ice, and 100° as the temperature of steam at normal pressure. Express the temperature τ on the Dalton scale in terms of the temperature t on the centigrade scale.

11. The volumetric expansion coefficient α of mercury at 0° and atmospheric pressure is 0·00018 deg^{-1}. The compression coefficient is $\gamma = 0{\cdot}0000039$ atm^{-1}. Calculate the thermal coefficient of pressure of mercury.

12. What must be the increase in the outside pressure in order to maintain a constant volume of mercury when it is heated from 0° to 10°? (See the previous problem.)

13. Iron wire, with a resistance of 15 ohm at a temperature of 18°, is used for measuring the temperature of a thermostat. Its resistance in the thermostat proved to be 18·25 ohm. Find the thermostat temperature t if the temperature coefficient of the resistance of iron is $\varkappa = 0{\cdot}006$ deg^{-1}.

14. A linear bolometer made of blackened sheet platinum has a resistance $R = 108$ ohm. To what accuracy can temperatures be measured by using such a bolometer, if all the resistances are determined to an accuracy of $\Delta R = 0{\cdot}001$ ohm, and the temperature coefficient of the resistance of platinum is $\varkappa = 0{\cdot}0039 \text{ deg}^{-1}$?

15. Let m g ice at 0° be mixed with m' g water at t_1° in a calorimeter. Find the temperature t of the mixture if the latent heat of melting is λ, and all the ice melts.

16. What amount m of water at $t_0 = 20°$ can be frozen by vaporising $M = 100$ g of sulphuric ether, having a temperature $t_1 = 20°$, a specific heat $q = 0{\cdot}5 \text{ cal g}^{-1} \text{deg}^{-1}$, and a heat of vapourisation $r = 90 \text{ cal g}^{-1}$ (assuming that the heat of vaporisation is taken entirely from the water)? Assume that the heat of vaporisation of the ether is independent of the temperature.

17. The specific heat of zinc is determined by heating a piece of it weighting $m_2 = 235{\cdot}6$ g to $t_2 = 99{\cdot}3°$ and dropping it in a brass calorimeter. The specific heat of brass is $q_1 = 0{\cdot}093 \text{ cal g}^{-1} \text{deg}^{-1}$, the mass of the calorimeter and mixer is $m_1 = 100$ g, the mass of water is $m = 209{\cdot}3$ g; the initial temperature of the calorimeter and water is $t_0 = 20{\cdot}5°$. The temperature of the water in the calorimeter rose to $t = 27{\cdot}6°$. Find the specific heat of zinc.

18. Two liquids are heated in identical vessels by the same electric current, identical wire-wound resistances being placed in each vessel for this purpose. The liquid in the first vessel is heated from t_0 to t_1. The mass of the liquid in this vessel is m, its specific heat is q, whilst the water equivalent of the vessel is $m_1 q_1$. Find the specific heat q' of the liquid in the second vessel if it heats in the same time from t'_0 to t'_1; the water equivalent of the second vessel is $m'_1 q'_1$, and the mass of the liquid is m'.

19. Given the necessary precautions, water can be cooled to a temperature $t = -10°$. What mass of ice m is formed from $M = 1$ kg of such water when a particle of ice is thrown into it and freezing thereby produced? Regard the specific heat of the supercooled water as independent of the temperature and equal to the specific heat of ordinary water.

20. When 1 g hydrogen is burned and converted into water, 34,000 cal of heat are produced. How many grams of coal must be burned in order to dissociate 1 g water, if 50 per cent of the heat released by the coal is used? The calorific value of coal is 7000 cal g^{-1}.

21. To determine the volumetric expansion coefficient α of glass, a small glass bulb with elongated ends is weighed, first when empty, then with the amounts of mercury needed to fill it completely at two temperatures, say 0° and t. Let p_0 and p_1 be the weights of mercury at the two temperatures. Find the volumetric expansion coefficient α of glass if the volumetric expansion coefficient of mercury is α_1.

22. We are given several clocks with pendulums of the same material but different lengths. Show that, if all the clocks are regulated at a certain temperature t_1, the relative change in the running of the clocks at a different temperature t_2 is the same for all of them and independent of the length of the pendulum.

23. A glass bulb with volumetric expansion coefficient α is weighed in liquid at temperatures t and t_1. The weights of the displaced liquids are p and p_1 respectively. Find the volumetric expansion coefficient α_1 of the liquid in the temperature interval from t to t_1.

24. A picnometer at a temperature t is filled with alcohol, the weight of which is p. The picnometer plus alcohol is then heated to a temperature t_1 and the excess of alcohol above the previous level is removed by filter paper. The weight of the alcohol is then p_1. Find the mean volumetric expansion coefficient α of alcohol, if the linear expansion coefficient of glass is β.

25. A barometer has a brass scale. At a temperature $t_1 = 27°$ the height of the mercury column, measured on the scale, is $H_1 = 751{\cdot}3$ mm. Find the height H_0 of the column at $t_0 = 0°$. The coefficient of linear expansion of brass is $\beta = 0{\cdot}000019 \text{ deg}^{-1}$ and the volumetric expansion coefficient of mercury is $\alpha = 0{\cdot}000182 \text{ deg}^{-1}$.

26. The linear expansion coefficient β of German silver is determined with the aid of a lever device (Fig. 1). The length of the rod A at $t_0 = 0°$ is $l_0 = 23{\cdot}02$ cm. On heating to $t_1 = 99{\cdot}3°$ the arrow of the second lever deflects through the angle $\varphi = 9°30'$. The short arm DE of the second lever is $DE = a = 2{\cdot}5$ cm. The ratio of the arms of the first lever $BC : BD = 1 : 10$. Find β.

27. A circular plate, whose radius at a temperature t_1 is r, is cut from quartz parallel to its (optical) axis. Find the area S of the plate at a temperature t_2. The expansion coefficient parallel to the axis is $\beta_{\parallel}$, and perpendicular to the axis $\beta_{\perp}$.

28. A cylinder is cut out of quartz, its axis being parallel to the (optical) axis of the quartz. At a temperature $t_1 = 18°$ the cylinder radius is $r = 10$ mm, and its height $l = 50$ mm. Find the volume V_2 of the cylinder at the temperature $t_2 = 300°$. The linear expansion coefficients of quartz are $\beta_{\parallel} = 0{\cdot}000072\ \text{deg}^{-1}$, and $\beta_{\perp} = 0{\cdot}0000132\ \text{deg}^{-1}$.

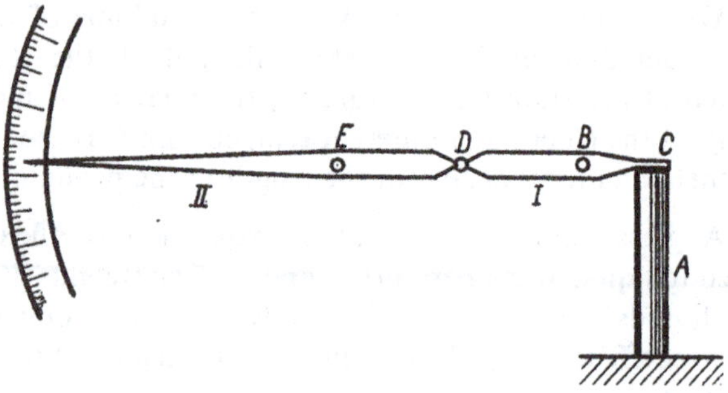

FIG. 1

29. The following method is used for determining the true volumetric expansion coefficient of a liquid. Two communicating vessels are filled with liquid, the expansion of which is to be investigated; when the vessels are at the same temperature the liquids are at the same height. If one vessel is cooled by melting ice, and the other heated in steam at standard atmospheric pressure, the liquid levels at equilibrium will be different. The difference in levels enables us to calculate the volumetric expansion coefficient α. Derive an expression for α.

30. The following method can be used for finding the volumetric expansion coefficients of different metals. A metal rod of weight p and density ϱ_0 at 0° is placed in a glass bulb with an elongated end. The bulb is filled with mercury. The volumetric expansion coefficients of mercury α and glass β are assumed known. The weights of the mercury filling the space in the bulb not occupied by the metal are P_0 and P_t at 0° and $t°$ respectively. The density of mercury at 0° is δ_0. On the basis of these data find the volumetric expansion coefficient x of the metal.

31. The wheel of a locomotive has a radius $r_0 = 1$ m at $t_0 = 0°$. Find the difference in the number of revolutions of the wheel in summer at $t_1 = 25°$ and winter at $t_2 = -25°$ over a journey of length $l = 100$ km. The linear expansion coefficient of the material of the wheel is $\beta = 0{\cdot}000012$ deg^{-1}.

32. A piece of ice floats in a vessel filled with water. Will the water level change when the ice melts, if the final temperature of the water remains 0°?

33. What force P must applied to a steel rod of 1 cm^2 cross-section, in order to stretch it as much as it would be stretched when heated through 1°. The linear expansion coefficient is $\beta = 12 \times 10^{-6}$ deg^{-1}. Young's modulus $E = 2{\cdot}1 \times 10^6$ kgcm^{-2}.

34. A steel band is driven on to a wagon wheel at $t_1 = 300°$. Find the extension force P on the band at $t_0 = 20°$ if the band cross-section is $S = 20$ cm^2. Young's modulus is $2{\cdot}1 \times 10^6$ kgcm^{-2} and the linear expansion coefficient is $\beta = 12 \times 10^{-6}$ deg^{-1}.

§ 2. Thermal Conductivity

35. A steel rod of length $l = 20$ cm and cross-sectional area $S = 3$ cm^2 is heated at one end to $t_1 = 300°$ whilst the other end rests in ice. Assuming that heat transmission occurs exclusively through the rod (without losses from the walls), calculate the mass m of the ice melting in time $\tau = 10$ min. The thermal conductivity of steel is $k = 0{\cdot}16$ caldeg^{-1} sec^{-1} cm^{-1}.

36. A copper percolator is heated on a primus. The water is brought to the boil and releases $m = 2$ g steam per minute. The thickness of the percolator base is $l = 2$ mm, and its area $S = 300$ cm^2. Find the temperature difference $t_2 - t_1$ between the inner and outer surfaces of the base, on the assumption that the base is heated uniformly. The thermal conductivity of copper is $k = 0{\cdot}92$ caldeg^{-1} sec^{-1} cm^{-1}.

37. Solve the previous problem when the base is covered on the inside by a layer of scale $l_1 = 1$ mm thick. The thermal conductivity of the scale is $k_1 = 0{\cdot}003$ caldeg^{-1} sec^{-1} cm^{-1}.

38. Three plates of the same dimensions are combined to form a small pile. The centre plate is lead, and the outer plates silver. The outer surface of one silver plate is held at a constant temperature $t = 100°$. The outer surface of the other silver plate is at $t_3 = 0°$.

Find the temperatures t_1 and t_2 at the points of contact of the lead with the silver plates. The thermal conductivity of lead is $k_1 = 30$ cal deg^{-1} hr^{-1} m^{-1}, and of silver $k = 360$ cal deg^{-3} hr^{-1} m^{-1}.

39. Find the amount of heat Q lost per m^2 of wall during a time τ equal to 24 hr when the air temperature in a room is $t_1 = 20°$ and the outdoor temperature is $t_4 = -10°$. The wall thickness is $l = 20$ cm. The thermal conductivity of the wall material is $k = 0{\cdot}003$ cal deg^{-1} sec^{-1} cm^{-1}. The external thermal conductivity at the wall–air boundary is $\alpha = 0{\cdot}0002$ cal deg^{-1} sec^{-1} cm^{-2}. Find also the temperature t_2 of the inner and t_3 of the outer surface of the wall.

40. How much coal has to be burnt in 24 hr in a central heating system if the surface area of the walls and roof of the house is $S = 10{,}000$ m^2, in order to maintain a temperature $t_1 = 18°$ in the rooms, when the outdoor temperature is $t_2 = -22°$? The wall thickness $L = 60$ cm, the internal thermal conductivity of the wall material is $k = 0{\cdot}002$ cal deg^{-1} sec^{-1} cm^{-1}, and the heat leakage per unit area of the roof surface is the same as per unit wall area. The external thermal conductivity at the air–wall boundary is $\alpha = 0{\cdot}00025$ cal deg^{-1} sec^{-1} cm^{-2}, the calorific value of coal is $r = 7500$ cal g^{-1}.

41. Two vessels, filled with liquids at temperatures t_1 and t_2, are joined by a metal rod of length L, cross-section S and thermal conductivity k. The masses and specific heats of the liquids are m_1, m_2 and c_1, c_2 respectively. The vessels and rod are thermally insulated from the surrounding medium. What is the time τ required for the temperature difference to be halved?

42. Liquid with a temperature t_1 is poured into a thin-walled closed metallic vessel. The air temperature outside the vessel is t_3. Find the temperature t_2 of the outer wall, given that the internal thermal conductivity of the metal is k, the external thermal conductivity at the metal–air boundary is α, and at the metal–liquid boundary ∞. The wall thickness is L.

Note. A vessel is regarded as thin-walled when the wall thickness is small compared with its linear dimensions.

43. Find the temperature t_2 in the previous problem in two limiting cases: (1) a very thin metallic vessel, and (2) a vessel made of material of very small thermal conductivity.

44. Liquid with a temperature t_1 is poured into a thin-walled closed metallic vessel with a total surface S. What time τ does it take the liquid to cool to a temperature t_2 if its mass is m, its specific heat c, the air temperature outside the vessel t_3, and the external thermal conductivity at the metal–air boundary α?

45. The space between two coaxial cylinders with radii R_1 and R_2 is filled by a thermally conducting uniform material. Find the temperature distribution in the space, if the temperature of the inner cylinder is t_1, and of the outer t_2.

46. Find the temperature distribution in the space between two concentric spheres of radii R_1, R_2, filled with thermally conducting uniform material, if the temperatures of the spheres are constant and equal to t_1, t_2.

47. A d.c. current of I amps flows along an uninsulated conductor. Find the conductor temperature t as a function of the distance r from its axis in the stationary state, if the conductor radius is R cm, its thermal conductivity is k cal deg^{-1} sec^{-1} cm^{-1}, its specific resistance is ϱ ohm cm, and its surface temperature is t_0.

48. The water in a pond has a temperature $t_1 = 0°$. The temperature of the surrounding air is $t_2 = -10°$. What thickness x of ice forms after 24 hr, measured from the instant when the water freezes. The thermal conductivity of ice is

$$k = 0{\cdot}0053 \text{ cal deg}^{-1} \text{sec}^{-1} \text{cm}^{-1},$$

the latent heat of freezing of water is $\lambda = 80$ cal g^{-1}, the density of ice is $\varrho = 0{\cdot}9$ g cm^{-3}.

49. The ends of a long uniform rod, the cross-sectional dimensions of which are small compared with its length, are held at temperatures t_1 and t_2, which can vary in the course of time. The temperature of the uniform medium surrounding the rod is t_3. Show that, due to conduction to the outside, the temperature in the rod is subject to the equation

$$\frac{\partial t}{\partial \tau} = a^2 \frac{\partial^2 t}{\partial x^2} - b^2(t - t_3),$$

where $a^2 = k/c\varrho$, $b^2 = \alpha p/c\varrho S$, p is the perimeter of the rod cross-section, S is the area of the cross-section, c is the specific heat of the rod material, ϱ is its density, α is the thermal conductivity to the outside, k is the thermal conductivity of the rod material, and τ is the time.

50. Find the steady-state temperature distribution along a very thin long rod of length l, if the temperatures of its ends are t_1 and t_2, and these, together with the temperature t_3 of the surrounding medium, are maintained constant. The remaining values are the same as in the previous problem.

51. Solve the previous problem on the assumption that $t_3 = t_2$. Consider the case of a very long rod.

52. Antimony and copper rods are covered by very thin layers of paraffin wax and their ends are supported in the wall of a metallic vessel filled with boiling water. During a certain time, until the stationary state is achieved, melting of the paraffin wax ceases at a distance x_1 from the wall of the vessel on the antimony rod and at a distance x_2 on the copper rod. The thermal conductivity of antimony is k_1. Find the thermal conductivity of copper k_2.

53. The thermal conductivities of liquids are found by using three copper plates, arranged horizontally, one above the other. The lower plate is washed by a flow of cold water (temperature t_1) the upper plate by warm water (temperature t_3). The space between the lower and the centre plates is filled with liquid with thermal conductivity k_1, and the space between the centre and upper plates by liquid with thermal conductivity k_2. The distance of the centre plate from the lower is d_1, and from the upper is d_2. Express the thermal conductivity k_2 in terms of k_1, if the steady-state temperature of the centre plate is t_2. In the case when the known liquid is water ($k_1 = 0{\cdot}00143$ cal deg^{-1} sec^{-1} cm^{-1}), and the unknown liquid is benzol, the distances are $d_1 = 1$ mm, $d_2 = 1{\cdot}2$ mm, the temperatures are $t_1 = 80°$, $t_2 = 68{\cdot}6°$, $t_3 = 10°$. Find k_2 for benzol.

54. The temperature of one end of a uniform rod is t_1, and of the other end t_2, the temperature of the surrounding medium being zero.

Show that, in the stationary state, the temperature $\vartheta_1, \vartheta_2, \vartheta_3$ of three equidistant sections of the rod, at distances x, $x + d$, $x + 2d$ from its origin, are connected by the relationship

$$\frac{\vartheta_1 + \vartheta_3}{\vartheta_2} = e^{\beta d} + e^{-\beta\delta}, \quad \text{where } \beta = \sqrt{\frac{\alpha p}{kS}},$$

where α is the external thermal conductivity, k the internal thermal conductivity, p the perimeter and S the area of the rod cross-section.

55. The following method is sometimes used for finding the thermal conductivity of a rod. If the temperature of the surrounding medium is taken as zero, the following relationship holds in the steady state between the temperatures $\vartheta_1, \vartheta_2, \vartheta_3$ of three equidistant cross-sections of the rod, when heated at one end:

$$\frac{\vartheta_1 + \vartheta_3}{\vartheta_2} = e^{\beta d} + e^{-\beta d} = 2n, \quad \text{where } \beta = \sqrt{\frac{\alpha p}{kS}}$$

(see the previous problem). The quantity $2n$ can be determined by direct measurements. If we are given two rods of different materials, after finding $2n$ for one of them from certain measurements, and $2n_1$ for the other, we can find the ratio of the thermal conductivities from the formula $k_1/k = \{[\ln(n + \sqrt{n^2 - 1})]/[\ln(n_1 + \sqrt{n_1^2 - 1})]\}^2$ provided the rods have the same cross-sections (S) and different external thermal conductivities (α). Deduce this formula.

56. The half-space $x > 0$ is filled with a material of thermal conductivity $a^2 = k/c\varrho$. In the plane $x = 0$ harmonic temperature oscillations of period T occur:

$$t = t_0 + t_1 \cos \omega\tau,$$

where t_0 and t_1 are constants, and $\omega = 2\pi/T$. Find the temperature of the medium as a function of the co-ordinate x and time τ.

Hint. Seek the solution of the heat conduction equation $\partial t/\partial\tau = a^2\, \partial^2 t/\partial x^2$ in the complex form: $t - t_0 = X(x)\, e^{i\omega\tau}$, then pass to the real form.

57. Experiment shows that heat waves with a period of 1 day (24 hr) are propagated inside the Earth with a velocity of 1 m per day. Find the velocity of propagation of waves with a period of 1 year.

58. Find γ_2/γ_1, where γ_1 is the damping coefficient of annual heat waves and γ_2 the damping coefficient of daily waves.

59. A uniform solid medium fills the infinite half-space $x > 0$. At the instant $\tau = 0$ the temperature of the medium is the same everywhere and equal to $t = t_0$. A constant temperature $t = 0$ is then imposed on the surface $x = 0$. Show that the temperature of the medium at any instant $\tau > 0$ is given by

$$t = \frac{2t_0}{\sqrt{\pi}} \int_0^{\frac{x}{2a\sqrt{\tau}}} e^{-\xi^2}\, d\xi. \tag{1}$$

60. W. Thomson (Lord Kelvin) calculated the age of the Earth by starting from the following assumptions: the Earth is a uniform body, the temperature of which at the instant when hardening occurred throughout its mass was equal to the temperature of rock solidification $t_0 \approx 4000\,°\text{C}$, whilst the temperature of the Earth's surface at the instant of hardening remained constant and equal to 0°C. When calculating the temperature gradient close to the Earth's surface Thomson replaced it by a uniform medium, bounded by a plane surface and occupying the infinite half-space $x > 0$ (see the previous problem). Calculate the age of the Earth (from the instant of hardening) on these assumptions; if the Earth's temperature close to its surface increases 1° per 25 m depth, and the velocity of propagation of the daily heat waves is $v = 1$ m per day.

61. A rod of cross-section S is held with its ends in solid plates, the distance L between which is maintained constant. The temperature of one plate is then raised, and a constant heat flux Q is established in the rod. What is the pressure p exerted per unit cross-section of the rod if the initial stress in the rod was zero? The thermal conductivity of the rod is k, the linear expansion coefficient is α, Young's modulus is E.

§ 3. Gas Laws. The Equation of State

62. The density of a gas may be determined as follows. A large glass bulb of capacity V is filled with the gas under test to a pressure H mm Hg and weighed. Let its weight be P. Part of the gas is now removed, so that the pressure falls to h mm Hg. The new weight of the bulb is p. What is the density of the gas at atmospheric pressure?

63. A gas-filled electric lamp contains nitrogen at a pressure of 600 mm Hg. The volume of the lamp is 500 cm³. How much water will enter the lamp if its tip is broken off under water at standard atmospheric pressure?

64. Find the number n of cycles of the piston of an air pump required to pump a vessel of volume V from a pressure p_1 to a pressure p_2, if the volume corresponding to one cycle of the piston is v. Neglect the dead space.

65. A narrow cylindrical pipe closed at one end contains air which is separated from the outer atmosphere by a column of mercury. If the pipe is turned with the closed end uppermost, the air inside it occupies a length l; whereas when the open end is uppermost, the length occupied is $l' < l$. The length of the mercury column is h. Find the atmospheric pressure.

66. A barometric tube is immersed in a deep vessel containing mercury so that the levels of the mercury in the tube and the vessel are the same. The air in the tube occupies a column of length l cm. The tube is now raised l' cm. How many centimetres does the mercury rise in the tube? The atmospheric pressure is H cm Hg.

67. A cylindrical pipette of length l is half submerged in mercury. It is closed by a finger and withdrawn. Part of the mercury flows out. What length of mercury column remains in the tube? The atmospheric pressure is H.

68. A McLeod gauge is required to read pressures up to 0·1 mm Hg. The volume of the manometer sphere must not exceed 150 cm^3, and the capillary length must not exceed 20 cm. What minimum cross-section of capillary is required?

69. In the manometer of the previous problem, how far from the end of the capillary is the marker corresponding to a pressure of 0·00005 mm Hg?

70. A badly dried flask at $t = 20°$ contains a mixture of air and water vapour, the partial pressure of which are 0·25 and 0·1 mm Hg respectively. Find the error in the reading of a McLeod gauge attached to the flask for measuring pressure, if the volume of the manometer flask is $V = 50$ cm^3, and the capillary radius is $r = 1$ mm. The pressure of water vapour at 20° is 17·5 mm Hg.

71. What volume is occupied by a gram-molecule of ideal gas at a pressure of 3 atm and temperature $T = 400$°K?

72. The density of air at 0° and 760 mm Hg is 0·001293 $g cm^{-3}$. What is the weight of a litre of air at 27·3° and 750 mm Hg?

73. An aerostat of volume V m^3 was filled with hydrogen at a temperature $t_1 = 15°$. Its temperature rose to $t_2 = 37°$ due to solar radiation at a fixed atmospheric pressure, and the excess gas escaped via an appendix, as a result of which the weight of the aerostat plus gas fell by $Q = 6{\cdot}05$ kg. The specific weight of hydrogen is $\delta_0 = 0{\cdot}000089$ gcm^{-3}. Find the volume V of the aerostat.

74. The action of acid on a certain quantity of marble ($CaCO_3$) produces $V = 1320$ cm^3 of carbon dioxide (CO_2) at a temperature $t_1 = 22°$ and pressure $p = 1000$ mm Hg. Find the mass Q of the marble entering into the reaction. The density of carbon dioxide at 0° and 760 mm Hg is $\varrho_0 = 0{\cdot}001977$ gcm^{-3}.

75. A factory chimney of height $l = 50$ m carries off smoke at a temperature $t_1 = 60°$. Find the static pressure p producing the draught in the chimney. The air temperature is $t_2 = -10°$. The specific weight of air is $d_0 = 1{\cdot}29 \times 10^{-3}$ gcm^{-3}.

76. In a mercury barometer with a regular cylindrical barometric tube, the distance from the mercury level in the cup to the soldered end of the tube is L mm. An air bubble appears in the tube at normal barometric pressure H and temperature t_1, as a result of which the length of the mercury column diminishes and becomes equal to h_1 mm. Find an expression for the correction p_1 to be added to the barometer reading h in order to be able to use it at any temperature t and any height h of the mercury column.

77. The pressure of the air contained in the closed elbow of a manometer of length l is equivalent to h mm of mercury column at a barometric pressure H_0 and absolute temperature T_0. What mercury column h_1 balances the pressure of this air at a barometric pressure H_1 and temperature T_1?

78. Nitrogen at $T = 300$°K is pumped into a thin-walled spherical bulb of weight $P = 1$ kg. Find the maximum amount of nitrogen which can be delivered to the vessel if the permissible stress in the walls is $\sigma = 50$ kgmm^{-2}. The specific weight of steel is $d = 7{\cdot}8$ kgcm^{-3}.

79. Write the van der Waals equation for a gas containing ν moles.

80. Establish the connection between the pressure, temperature and volume of a gram-molecule at the critical point for a gas obeying the van der Waals equation.

81. Find the critical pressure and critical temperature for oxygen. The constants in the van der Waals equation for oxygen are $a = 1{\cdot}30$, $b = 0{\cdot}031$ (volume in litres, pressure in atmospheres).

82. The critical temperature of carbon dioxide (CO_2) is 31 °C, and the critical pressure 73 atm. Find the critical volume V_{cr} of a gram-molecule of carbon dioxide.

83. Find the constants of the van der Waals equation for nitrogen, if t_{cr} for nitrogen is $-146°$ and $p_{cr} = 33$ atm.

84. Taking the van der Waals constant for water as $5{\cdot}47 \times 10^6$ atm cm^6 mol^{-2}, find the internal pressure p of water.

85. A.G.Stoletov (1892) first showed that, in order for a liquid contained in a given volume to be reducible to the critical state, a precise amount of it must be taken. Let us take the following example. A vessel whose volume is $V_1 = 15$ cm^3 is to be filled with water at $t_1 = 18°$ in such a way that, when it is heated to the critical temperature (after first pumping out and sealing the vessel), the critical pressure is established in the vessel. On the assumption that water obeys the van der Waals equation of state, find the volume of water that must be poured into the vessel, given that the critical temperature of water is $t_{cr} = 374°$, the critical pressure is $p_{cr} = 205{\cdot}5$ atm, the molecular weight is $\mu = 18$, and the density at 18° is $\varrho = 1$ g cm^{-3}.

86. The van der Waals equation is not quite accurate for real gases. To obtain a better agreement with experiment, Clausius proposed the alternative empirical equation

$$\left[p + \frac{a}{T(v + c)^2}\right](v - b) = RT,$$

where a, b and c are constants for the observed gas. Express the critical magnitudes in terms of these constants.

87. Express the critical magnitudes in terms of the constants of the equation of state proposed by Berthelot for describing the behaviour of real gases:

$$\left(p + \frac{a}{Tv^2}\right)(v - b) = RT.$$

88. Find the connection between the pressure, temperature and volume of a gram-molecule at the critical point on the assumption that the substance obeys the Berthelot equation of state (see the previous problem).

89. Regarding the latent heat of vaporisation λ as the work done in overcoming the internal pressure π, find the relationship between π, λ and the density ϱ of a liquid. Assume that the liquid obeys the van der Waals equation.

90. The power or pumping speed K of a pump is defined as the volume of gas pumped out per second, measured at the pressure occurring in the pump at the given instant. Generally speaking, it depends on the pressure. Assuming that K is constant, find the pressure change p in an evacuated vessel if the pump and vessel are connected by a capillary of length l' and diameter D, whilst the gas in the vessel is so rarefied that the free path of a molecule in the vessel is large compared to D. According to Knudsen, in these conditions the mass of gas flowing through a capillary, at the ends of which the pressures are p_1 and p_2, is given by $(p_1 - p_2)/w$, where $w = 2{\cdot}18 \times 10^4 (l/D^3)\sqrt{T/\mu}$; T is the absolute temperature of the gas, and μ its molecular weight. All the quantities are measured in c.g.s. units.

91. The pumping speed of a rotary oil pump is 150 $cm^3 sec^{-1}$. How long does it take to evacuate a vessel of 5 litres volume from normal atmospheric pressure to a pressure of 1×10^{-2} mm Hg?

92. What time τ is required for a Langmuir pump to evacuate a 2-litre flask containing air at a pressure $p_0 = 10^{-3}$ mm Hg to a pressure $p = 10^{-5}$ mm Hg, if the flask is connected to the pump by a tube of length $l = 25$ cm and diameter $D = 7$ mm? The pumping speed is $K = 1000$ $cm^3 sec^{-1}$. The air temperature is $t = 18°$.

93. Find the mass M of gas flowing per second from a capillary of length l and diameter d, if the gas pressures at the beginning and end of the capillary are p_1 and p_2, and the coefficient of internal friction of the gas is η. Regard the process as isothermal.

Note. The coefficient of internal friction of an ideal gas is independent of its density, and depends only on the temperature.

94. A vessel of volume V is filled with gas at a pressure p_1. The external atmospheric pressure is p_2. A tap is opened at a certain instant, enabling the gas to flow out of the vessel via a capillary of length l and diameter d. What time τ is required for the pressure difference between the vessel and the outside to be halved? Regard the process as isothermal.

95. Two vessels A and B containing air are connected by a capillary with a tap. Vessel A is immersed in a water bath at a temperature $t_1 = 100°$ and vessel B in a refrigerating mixture at $t_2 = -20°$. The vessels were originally disconnected by closing the tap, and the air pressures in A and B were respectively $p_1 = 400$ mm and $p_2 = 150$ mm Hg. Find the pressure established after opening the tap, if the volume of A is $V_1 = 250\ \text{cm}^3$, and of B is $V_2 = 400\ \text{cm}^3$.

96. Show that the resultant of all the pressure forces of an ideal gas on the walls of a vertical closed cylindrical vessel containing the gas is equal to the weight of the gas, whatever the length of the cylinder, when and only when the gas density obeys the barometric formula

$$\varrho = \varrho_0\, e^{-\frac{\mu}{RT}gx},$$

where μ is the molecular weight of the gas, R is the gas constant, T is the temperature (°K) and g is the acceleration due to gravity. The gas temperature is assumed the same throughout the cylinder, and the gas is in equilibrium.

§ 4. First and Second Laws of Thermodynamics and their Applications

97. What must be the speed of a lead bullet if it melts when striking a steel slab? The temperature of the bullet is $t_0 = 27°$, its melting-point is $t_1 = 327°$, its heat of melting $q = 5\ \text{cal g}^{-1}$, and its specific heat $c = 0{\cdot}03\ \text{cal g}^{-1}\,\text{deg}^{-1}$.

98. Express in c.g.s. units the heat Q expended in heating a lead sphere of mass $m = 100$ g through $(t_1 - t_0) = 10°$. The specific heat of lead is $c = 0{\cdot}0307\ \text{cal g}^{-1}\,\text{deg}^{-1}$.

99. Two gram-molecules of nitrogen at temperature t_0 and pressure p atm are compressed isothermally to a pressure p_1 atm. Find the amount of heat Q released by the gas to the thermostat.

100. Find the amount of heat Q released on the isothermal compression of 7 g nitrogen from normal pressure $p_1 = 1{\cdot}033\,\text{kg}\,\text{cm}^{-2}$ to a pressure $p_2 = 51{\cdot}65\,\text{kg}\,\text{cm}^{-2}$; the temperature of the nitrogen is 25°.

101. In an apparatus designed for measuring the mechanical equivalent of heat, a mixer furnished with scoops rotates in a calorimeter filled with water. The friction of the water on the walls of the calorimeter produces a force which tends to rotate the calorimeter in the direction of rotation of the mixer. The calorimeter rotation is prevented by a load of weight P, attached to a string which wraps round a pulley and fastens to the calorimeter cover on a wheel of radius R. The moment of the load is constant in this device and has an opposite sign to the moment of the friction forces acting on the calorimeter walls from the liquid. When the mixer rotates the load neither rises nor falls. Find the mechanical equivalent E of heat, if the temperature rises by Δt when the mixer has performed N revolutions. The mass of the water in the calorimeter is M, and w is its water equivalent.

102. Find the mechanical equivalent of heat, given that $c_p = 0{\cdot}237\,\text{cal}\,\text{g}^{-1}\,\text{deg}^{-1}$ for air and $\gamma = c_p/c_v = 1{\cdot}41$. The molecular weight of air is $\mu = 28{\cdot}84$.

103. A polytropic process is one which occurs with constant specific heat c. The curve representing a polytropic process is called a polytrope. Find the equation of the polytrope for an ideal gas, the specific heat c_v of which is independent of the temperature. Consider the particular cases: (1) $c = c_v$; (2) $c = c_p$; (3) $c = 0$; (4) $c = \infty$.

104. (1) Does an ideal gas get hotter or colder when it expands according to the law $pV^2 = \text{const}$. (2) What is its molar specific heat during this process?

105. Solve the previous problem for an ideal gas expanding in accordance with the law $p^2V = \text{const}$.

106. Helium is compressed in a polytropic process from an initial volume of 4 litres to a final volume of 1 litre. The pressure meantime increases from 1 to 8 atm. Find the heat capacity C of the total mass of helium if its initial temperature was 300°K.

107. Calculate the molar specific heat of an ideal gas for a process in which the pressure p is proportional to the volume V. The specific heat c_v of the gas is independent of the temperature.

108. An isotherm *TT* and adiabat *SS* are drawn through an arbitrary point *A* on the *p*, *V* diagram (Fig. 2) for an ideal gas, the specific heat c_v of which is independent of the temperature. Show that the polytrope passing through *A* and lying in the shaded region corresponds to a negative specific heat, and a polytrope in the unshaded region to a positive specific heat.

109. 97,000 cal are released when 12 g solid carbon burns to form carbon dioxide (CO_2), and 68,000 cal released when 28 g carbon

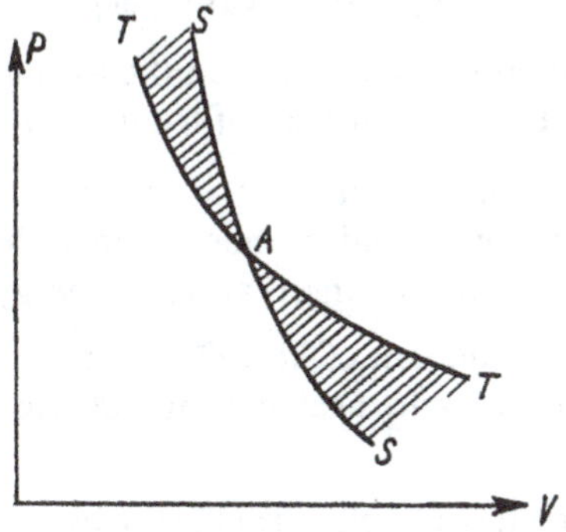

FIG. 2

monoxide (CO) are burned. What amount of heat would be released if 12 g carbon were burned in such a way as to produce pure carbon monoxide?

110. The combustion of hydrogen at 100° to form 1 mole of water vapour releases 58,000 cal. When 1 mole of steam at 100° is condensed, 9700 cal are released. Find the heat of formation of 1 mole of liquid water from hydrogen and oxygen at the same temperature.

111. Two thermally insulated vessels of volumes $V_1 = 1$ litre and $V_2 = 3$ litres are connected by a pipe with a tap. Prior to opening the tap, the first vessel contains nitrogen at $t_1 = 0°$ and pressure $p_1 = 0{\cdot}5$ atm, and the second vessel argon at $t_2 = 100°$ and pressure $p_2 = 1{\cdot}5$ atm. Find the pressure and temperature established in the gas mixture when the tap is opened.

112. A heater is switched on in a room for a certain time. The air temperature in the room rises from T_1 to T_2, whilst the pressure remains the same and equal to the outside pressure. Regarding air as an ideal gas, find the amount of heat that goes into increasing the internal energy of the air in the room.

113. Find the equation of the ideal gas process in which the specific heat of the gas varies with the temperature according to the law $c = \alpha T$, where α is a constant.

114. What is the amount of heat Q consumed in heating 1 m^3 of air from 0° to 1° at constant volume and an initial pressure $p = 760$ mm Hg? The density of air in normal conditions is $\varrho_0 = 0{\cdot}00129\ \text{g cm}^{-3}$; $c_p = 0{\cdot}237\ \text{cal g}^{-1}\ \text{deg}^{-1}$; $\gamma = c_p/c_v = 1{\cdot}41$.

115. Solve the previous problem on the assumption that the air is heated from 91° to 92°, instead of from 0° to 1°.

116. Show that Dalton's law for a mixture of gases having the same value of $\gamma = c_p/c_v$ and chemically inert to each other is a consequence of the law of conservation of energy.

117. What is the amount of heat Q that must be communicated to 75 g steam in order to heat it from 100° to 250° at constant volume?

118. A cylindrical vessel, closed at the top by a frictionless weightless piston, contains 1 m^3 hydrogen at 0°. The atmospheric pressure is 730 mm Hg. What is the amount Q of heat that must be consumed to heat the hydrogen to 300°?

119. Find the increase ΔU in the internal energy of helium when it expands isobarically from a volume of 5 litres to a volume of 10 litres. The process occurs at a pressure of 2 kg cm^{-2}.

120. A mass $m = 4{\cdot}032$ g hydrogen is mixed with $m_1 = 32$ g oxygen. Their specific heats are $c_p = 3{\cdot}50\ \text{cal g}^{-1}\ \text{deg}^{-1}$ and $c_{1p} = 0{\cdot}218\ \text{cal g}^{-1}\ \text{deg}^{-1}$, respectively. Find the decrease in the internal energy ΔU of the mixture on cooling it through $t = 20°$ at constant volume. For both gases, $\gamma = 1{\cdot}40$.

121. A volume V_0 at a temperature $t = 0°$ contains m gram-molecules hydrogen and $\frac{1}{2}m$ gram-molecules oxygen. What is the maximum steam pressure p_t obtained when the mixture is exploded, if the molar specific heat of steam is c, and the gram-molecular heat of formation of water from oxygen and hydrogen is C?

122. A closed vessel contains 1 mole (18 g) water at 0°. How much heat is required to raise the temperature of the system to

100° and at the same time convert all the water to saturated steam? The latent heat of vaporisation of water at 100° and constant pressure is 539 cal g^{-1}. Neglect the vapour pressure of saturated steam at 0° and the heat capacity of the walls of the vessel. Neglect also the volume of the water compared with the volume of the saturated steam.

123. Starting from the first law of thermodynamics, find $c_p - c_v$ for any physically homogeneous isotropic medium.

124. Show that the adiabatic and isothermal compressibilities of a physically homogeneous isotropic medium are connected by

$$\frac{1}{V}\left(\frac{\partial V}{\partial p}\right)_{\text{ad}} = \frac{1}{\gamma}\frac{1}{V}\left(\frac{\partial V}{\partial p}\right)_T,$$

where $\gamma = c_p/c_v$. Show that this relationship is a consequence of the first law of thermodynamics and the functional relationship between p, V and T (equation of state) only.

125. On the assumption that the propagation of sound in air is an isothermal process, Newton obtained the following formula for the speed of sound:

$$v = \sqrt{\frac{p}{\varrho}},$$

where p is the pressure and ϱ the density of the air. The values obtained for v from this formula were too small. Laplace regarded the process of propagation as adiabatic, and obtained a formula in agreement with experiment, namely

$$v = \sqrt{\gamma\frac{p}{\varrho}},$$

where $\gamma = c_p/c_v$. Explain qualitatively why the speed of sound from Laplace's viewpoint is greater than from Newton's. The air is heated at points of compression, with the result that its elasticity is increased as compared with what it would be if the same compression were isothermal. Similarly, at points of rarefaction the air is cooled, and its elasticity correspondingly diminished. It would appear that the effect of the heating at points of compression would compensate the effect of cooling at points of rarefaction, in which case the speeds of sound would be the same for isothermal and adiabatic processes.

126. Show that the speed of sound in an ideal gas is a function of temperature only.

127. The speed of sound in air at 0° is 332 m sec^{-1}. Find the speed of sound in hydrogen at the same temperature. The molecular weight of air is $M = 28{\cdot}8$.

128. Given the speed of sound in hydrogen (see the previous problem), find the speed of sound in helium at 0°.

Hint. Use the fact that hydrogen is a diatomic gas, and helium monatomic.

129. Find $\gamma = c_p/c_v$, if the speed of sound in air at 0° and normal pressure $H = 76$ cm Hg is $v = 332$ m sec^{-1} and the density of air is $\varrho = 0{\cdot}001292$ g cm^{-3}.

130. Find the ratio of the speeds of propagation of sound in hydrogen (v) and in carbon dioxide (v_1) at the same temperature. For the first, $\gamma = c_p/c_v = 1{\cdot}4$, for the second $\gamma_1 = c_p/c_v = 1{\cdot}3$. The density of hydrogen is $\varrho = 0{\cdot}0000899$ g cm^{-3}, of carbon dioxide $\varrho_1 = 0{\cdot}001977$ g cm^{-3} (in normal conditions).

131. What is the ratio $\gamma = c_p/c_v$ for argon, if $Q = 254$ cal are required to heat $m = 1$ kg of it through $(t_1 - t_0) = 2°$ at constant pressure $H = 760$ mm Hg, and $Q = 486$ cal heat are released on cooling argon from $t_2 = 100°$ to $t = 0°$ at constant volume $V = 5$ l. The initial pressure of the cooling argon is $H_1 = 10$ atm.

132. For argon, $\gamma = c_p/c_v = 1{\cdot}7$. Find the pressure after adiabatic expansion of this gas from a volume $V_1 = 1$ l to $V_2 = 2$ l, if the initial pressure is $p_1 = 1$ atm.

133. The following method is sometimes used for finding $\gamma = c_p/c_v$. A definite amount of gas, the initial temperature, volume and pressure of which are t_0, V_0 and p_0 respectively, is heated by a platinum wire, through which an electrical current passes for a definite time: firstly at constant volume, so that the gas reaches a temperature t_1 and a pressure p_1 (volume V_0), then secondly at constant pressure, so that the temperature becomes t_2 and the volume V_1 (pressure p_0). Show that

$$\gamma = \frac{(p_1 - p_0)V_0}{(V_1 - V_0)p_0}.$$

134. In the Clément–Desormes method for determining c_p/c_v (Fig. 3), gas is pumped via the tube B into the vessel A so that the pressure p_1 in it is somewhat above atmospheric. The tap C is then suddenly opened. The gas expands adiabatically to atmospheric pressure p_0. After a certain time, when the gas in the vessel again takes room temperature, its pressure becomes p_2. Find an expression for $\gamma = c_p/c_v$ on the basis of these data.

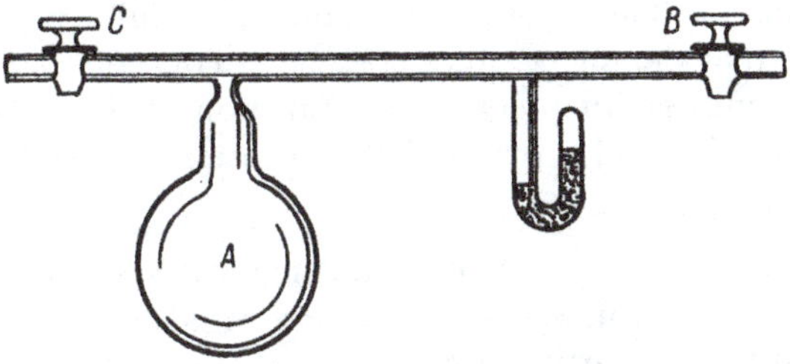

FIG. 3

135. The ratio of the specific heats c_p and c_v of a gas can be found by measuring the period T_1 of small vibrations of the mercury in a glass U-tube with open ends. Two identical large hollow glass spheres containing the gas are then mounted in the two arms of the U-tube, as a result of which the period of vibration changes and becomes T_2. Regarding the process of compression and rarefaction of the gas in the spheres as adiabatic, deduce a formula for $\gamma = c_p/c_v$. The volume of each sphere is V cm^3, the gas pressure in them in the state of rest is l cm Hg, and the cross-sectional area of the tube is S cm^2. The volume of the unfilled part of the tube can be neglected by comparison with V.

136. A device occasionally used for obtaining gases at very high temperatures and pressures consists of a cylinder barrel closed at one end and a piston bullet which enters the barrel at the open end. If the bullet and barrel are provided with a good finish the escape of gas through the gap between them can be made small. Due to the very high temperatures, the strongly compressed gases can be regarded as ideal in these conditions. Estimate the upper limit of the temperature T, the pressure p and the density ϱ of argon, subjected to compression in this device, if a bullet of mass $m = 100$ g enters the barrel, which has a volume $V = 200$ cm^3, with initial velocity

$v = 250\,\text{m}\,\text{sec}^{-1}$. The initial temperature and pressure are $T_0 = 300\,^\circ\text{K}$ and $p_0 = 1$ atm respectively.

137. If the air of the atmosphere be in stable mechanical equilibrium, what is the maximum value of its temperature gradient? Neglect the effect of humidity. The absolute temperature of the air at the Earth's surface can be taken as $T = 273\,^\circ\text{K}$.

138. Find the variation of atmospheric pressure with height on the assumption that the air temperature falls uniformly with the height, so that the temperature gradient is constant and equal to $-a$. Also find the air pressure as a function of the temperature. Hence obtain formulae for the limiting case of an isothermal atmosphere ($a = 0$).

139. What would be the height of the Earth's atmosphere if its temperature gradient were constant and equal to $-a$? Calculate this height for the particular case of adiabatic stratification of the atmosphere, assuming that the air temperature at the Earth's surface is $T_0 = 273\,^\circ\text{K}$.

140. The specific heat of cobalt is $c_1 = 0{\cdot}104\,\text{cal}\,\text{g}^{-1}\,\text{deg}^{-1}$, and of gold $c_2 = 0{\cdot}0312\,\text{cal}\,\text{g}^{-1}\,\text{deg}^{-1}$. Find their atomic specific heats.

141. Find the efficiency of the cycle consisting of two isotherms and two isobars, assuming that the operative substance is an ideal gas.

142. Find the efficiency of the ideal gas cycle consisting of two isotherms at temperatures T_1 and T_2 and two isochores with volumes V_1 and V_2 ($T_1 > T_2$; $V_1 > V_2$).

143. Show by direct calculation that the efficiency of the Carnot cycle performed with a gas which is thermally ideal but calorifically non-ideal is given by

$$\eta = \frac{T_1 - T_2}{T_1}.$$

Note. A gas is thermally ideal if it obeys the perfect gas law. A thermally ideal gas is calorifically non-ideal if its specific heat is independent of the volume but depends on the temperature.

144. Give an example of a process in which all the heat borrowed from the heat reservoir is converted into work.

145. The idea of dynamical heating, devised in 1852 by W. Thomson (Lord Kelvin), is as follows. Fuel is burned in the furnace of a heat engine, which operates a refrigerating machine. The refrigerating machine takes its heat from a natural water reservoir (say from subsoil water) and delivers it to the heating system. Simultaneously the water in the heating system is used to cool the heat engine. Find the theoretical amount of heat (i.e. discounting losses) which the heated location obtains from burning 1 kg coal, using the following data: the calorific value of coal is $q = 8000\,\text{cal}\,\text{kg}^{-1}$, the temperature in the steam engine boiler is $t_1 = 210°$; the temperature of the water in the heating system is $t_2 = 60°$; the temperature of the subsoil water is $t_3 = 15°$.

146. Show by considering an infinitesimal Carnot cycle and using Carnot's theorem that the internal energy and specific heat of a physically homogeneous and isotropic body satisfy

$$\left(\frac{\partial U}{\partial V}\right)_T = T\left(\frac{\partial p}{\partial T}\right)_V - p; \quad \left(\frac{\partial c_v}{\partial V}\right)_T = T\left(\frac{\partial^2 p}{\partial T^2}\right)_V.$$

Using these equations and the equations of state for an ideal gas, show that the internal energy and specific heat of an ideal gas depend only on the temperature, and not on the volume occupied by a given mass of the gas.

147. Prove that the specific heat c_v of a gas subject to the van der Waals equation is independent of the volume, and is a function of temperature only. Find an expression for the internal energy of a van der Waals gas, the specific heat of which is independent of the temperature.

Hint. See the previous problem.

148. Calculate the internal energy of a van der Waals gas, as the heat communicated to the gas when heated at constant volume, minus the work done by the gas on isothermal expansion. It must be borne in mind here that when a gas expands isothermally it does work against the internal pressure as well as external work. What is the defect of this method compared with the thermodynamic method of the previous problem?

149. One gram-molecule of nitrogen expands *in vacuo* from an nitial volume of 1 litre to a final volume of 10 litres. Find the temperature drop ΔT in this process, if the constant a in the van der Waals equation for nitrogen is $1{\cdot}35 \times 10^6$ atm cm^6 mol^{-2}.

150. Two vessels with volumes V_1 and V_2 are connected by a tube with a tap. The tap is closed and each vessel contains 1 mole of the same gas, which obeys the van der Waals equation. Before the tap is opened the temperature is the same (T) in both vessels. Does the gas get hotter or colder on opening the tap? Find the pressure after opening the tap. Regard the walls of the vessels and the connecting tube as adiabatic, and the specific heat c_v as independent of the temperature.

151. Two bulbs with volumes $V_1 = V_2 = V = 1$ litre are connected by a pipe with a tap. The first bulb (volume V_1) contains air at atmospheric pressure, and the second is pumped out to ideal vacuum. Assuming that air obeys the van der Waals equation, and that the bulb walls and pipe are adiabatic, find the change in the gas temperature on opening the tap. The initial temperature is $T = 290\,°K$, and for air, $a = 1{\cdot}35 \times 10^6$ atm cm^6 mol^{-2}.

152. Nitrogen at the critical temperature $-147°$ has a critical volume of $0{\cdot}12$ l. mol^{-1}. Assuming that nitrogen obeys the van der Waals equation, find the temperature drop of 7 g nitrogen on expanding *in vacuo* from a volume of 5 litres to a volume of 50 litres.

153. How much heat must be applied to one mole of a van der Waals gas in order for its temperature to remain unchanged when it expands *in vacuo* from a volume V_1 to a volume V_2?

154. How much heat must be supplied to one mole of a van der Waals gas in order for its pressure to remain constant and equal to p when it expands *in vacuo* from a volume V_1 to a volume V_2?

155. Find an expression for the heat of vaporisation of 1 mole of liquid at constant temperature T at the pressure of its saturated vapour, on the assumption that the equation of state of the liquid and its vapour is the van der Waals equation. Assume that the temperature T and the molar volumes V_l of the liquid and V_v of its saturated vapour at this temperature are known.

156. Given the equation of state of a physically homogeneous and isotropic substance, find the difference $c_p - c_v$ between its specific heats.

157. Find $c_p - c_v$ for a van der Waals gas.

158. The specific heat of mercury at standard atmospheric pressure p_0 and temperature $T = 273\,°\text{K}$ is $c_p = 0{\cdot}0333\ \text{cal}\,\text{g}^{-1}\,\text{deg}^{-1}$. Find its specific heat at constant volume c_v and the ratio $\gamma = c_p/c_v$, if the coefficient α of thermal expansion and the isothermal coefficient β of compression of mercury are

$$\alpha = \frac{1}{v}\left(\frac{\partial v}{\partial T}\right)_p = 1{\cdot}81 \times 10^{-4}\ \text{deg}^{-1},$$

$$\beta = -\frac{1}{v}\left(\frac{\partial v}{\partial p}\right)_T = 3{\cdot}9 \times 10^{-6}\text{atm}^{-1}.$$

The density of mercury is $\varrho = 13{\cdot}6\,\text{g}\,\text{cm}^{-3}$. What part of the difference $c_p - c_v$ goes into the production of external work A and what part into increasing the internal energy of the mercury?

159. It is shown in thermodynamics that the necessary conditions for stability of a physically homogeneous and isotropic substance are: (1) $(\partial p/\partial V)_T < 0$; (2) $c_v > 0$. Use this to show that $c_p > c_v$, and thus $c_p > 0$.

160. The external pressure acting on water is increased whilst at the same time heat is supplied or removed in such a way that the volume of water remains unchanged. Does the water get hotter or colder, if its initial temperature is (1) below 4°, (2) above 4°?

161. Experiment shows that a rubber strap elongates on cooling (if its tension remains constant). Using this fact, show that the strap heats up if it is stretched adiabatically.

162. The enthalpy of a physically homogeneous and isotropic material is the state function defined by $H = U + pV$. By considering an infinitesimal Carnot cycle and applying Carnot's theorem to it, show that the enthalpy H and specific heat c_p satisfy

$$\left(\frac{\partial H}{\partial p}\right)_T = V - T\left(\frac{\partial V}{\partial T}\right)_p; \quad \left(\frac{\partial c_p}{\partial p}\right)_T = -T\left(\frac{\partial^2 V}{\partial T^2}\right)_p.$$

163. By using the result of the previous problem, obtain an expression for the differential Joule–Thomson effect, i.e. for the case when the gas pressures differ only infinitesimally on either side of the "plug" in the Joule–Thomson experiment.

164. Obtain the formula for the differential Joule–Thomson effect for a van der Waals gas, neglecting squares and higher powers of the van der Waals constants a and b. Show that the gas will cool at sufficiently low temperatures.

165. Show that a gas which obeys the van der Waals equation with $a = 0$ always heats up in the Joule–Thomson experiment. Find the temperature rise on expansion.

166. Show that a gas which obeys the van der Waals equation with $b = 0$ always cools down in the Joule–Thomson experiment. Find the temperature drop on expansion.

167. Find the connection between the critical temperature T_k and the inversion temperature T_i of the Joule–Thomson effect for a substance which is subject to the van der Waals equation of state.

168. At what temperature T will helium start to cool in the Joule–Thomson experiment, given that the critical temperature of helium is $T_k = 5{\cdot}3\,°K$? Assume that the state of helium is described by a van der Waals equation.

169. The values of the van der Waals constants are given below for nitrogen, hydrogen and helium.

	a, atm cm^6 mol^{-2}	b, cm^3 mol^{-1}
Nitrogen	$1{\cdot}35 \times 10^6$	39·6
Hydrogen	0·191	21·8
Helium	0·033	23·4

Use these data to find the inversion points T_i of the differential Joule–Thomson effect for these gases. Find also the temperature change ΔT in the Joule–Thomson experiment if $T = 300\,°K$ and the pressure drop is $\Delta p = 0{\cdot}1$ atm.

170. The gases in the previous problem are strongly compressed in the initial state to molar volumes $V = 100$ cm^3 then are expanded to atmospheric pressure in the Joule–Thomson process. Assuming that the gases obey the van der Waals equation, find the temperature change $\Delta T = T' - T$ in this process.

Note. The formula for the differential Joule–Thomson effect cannot be used when the compression is so strong. The gases can be regarded as ideal at atmospheric pressure.

171. The gas expansion in the Joule–Thomson process is carried out from an initial state T, V to a highly rarefied state in which the gas can be regarded as ideal. If the initial state is represented on a T, V diagram, a curve can be drawn on it which lies in two regions of the T, V plane: points of one region correspond to $\Delta T < 0$ (the gas cools), and of the other to $\Delta T > 0$ (the gas heats up). Find the equation of this curve and draw the curves for nitrogen, hydrogen and helium, on the assumption that these gases obey the van der Waals equation.

172. By considering the Carnot cycle for a system consisting of a liquid and its saturated vapour, and applying Carnot's theorem to it, express the derivative of the saturated vapour pressure with respect to temperature (dp/dT) in terms of the specific volumes v_v, v_l of the vapour and liquid and the heat of vaporisation, q.

173. Find the pressure of saturated steam at 101°. Regard the steam as an ideal gas.

174. A closed vessel with volume $V_0 = 5$ litres contains 1 kg water at $t = 100°$. The space above the water is occupied by saturated steam (the air is evacuated). Find the increase Δm in the mass of the saturated steam when the temperature of the system increases by $\Delta T = 1°$. The heat of vaporisation $q = 539$ cal g^{-1}.

Hint. Regard the steam as an ideal gas. Neglect the specific volume of the water compared with the specific volume of the steam.

175. At 0° the water vapour pressure over ice is $p_1 = 4{\cdot}58$ mm Hg. The heat of melting of ice at 0° is $q_1 = 80$ cal g^{-1}. The heat of vaporisation of water at 0° is $q_2 = 596$ cal g^{-1}. Find the water vapour pressure over ice at $t = -1°$.

176. Find the molar specific heat c of saturated vapour, expanding (or contracting) in such a way that it remains saturated throughout the process. Neglect the specific volume of the liquid compared with the specific volume of its saturated vapour. Assume that the vapour behaves like an ideal gas.

177. Solve the previous problem without using the assumption that water vapour behaves like an ideal gas. Express the result in terms of the specific heat of vaporisation q, its derivative with respect to temperature dq/dT and the molar specific heat c_p of the liquid.

178. Saturated water vapour at $T = 300°K$ is subjected to adiabatic compression and adiabatic expansion. In which of these processes does the vapour become unsaturated, and in which supersaturated?

179. Three phases 1, 2 and 3 are in equilibrium with one another at the triple point (Fig. 4). Their specific volumes at this point are v_1, v_2, v_3 respectively. Let $p_{12} = p_{12}(T)$, $p_{23} = p_{23}(T)$, $p_{31} = p_{31}(T)$ be the equations of the curves of equilibrium between phases 1

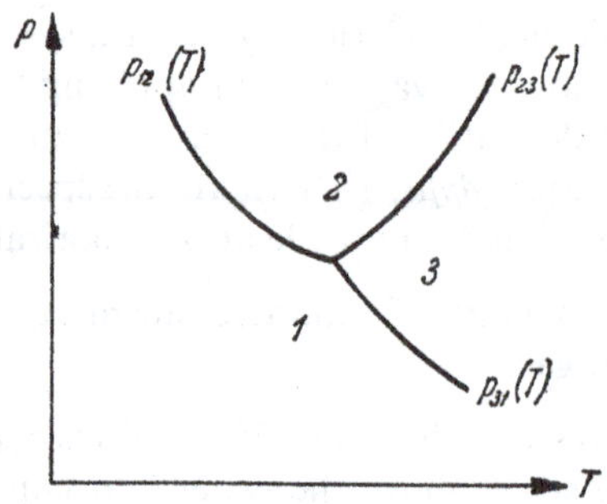

FIG. 4

and 2, 2 and 3, and 3 and 1. Show that the relationship

$$(v_1 - v_2)\frac{dp_{12}}{dT} + (v_2 - v_3)\frac{dp_{23}}{dT} + (v_3 - v_1)\frac{dp_{31}}{dT} = 0$$

holds at the triple point.

180. Find approximately the pressure and temperature (on the centrigrade scale) at the triple point of water, using the following data: the pressure of the saturated vapour over liquid water is:

$$\text{at } t = t_1 = 0°, \quad p_1 = 4{\cdot}579 \text{ mm Hg},$$
$$\text{at } t = t_2 = 1°, \quad p_2 = 4{\cdot}926 \text{ mm Hg}.$$

The specific volume of ice at 0° and standard atmospheric pressure ($p_0 = 760$ mm Hg) is $v_1 = 1{\cdot}091$ cm^{3}g^{-1}, the specific volume of water under the same conditions is $v_2 = 1$ cm^{3}g^{-1}. The heat of melting of ice is $q = 80$ cal g^{-1}.

181. A phase transition occurs at a certain temperature Θ, as a result of which a cubical crystal lattice becomes tetragonal with axes a and $c > a$. Describe qualitatively how the ratio c/a behaves when the temperature T varies in the case of phase transitions of the first and second kinds.

182. In the case of phase transitions of the second kind (which include, e.g., passage from the paramagnetic to the ferromagnetic state in iron and other ferromagnetic materials), there is no jump either in volume or entropy, i.e. $\Delta S = 0$ and $\Delta V = 0$. Show that, in a phase transition of the second kind, the jumps in the various magnitudes (indicated by Δ) satisfy the Ehrenfest relationships

$$\Delta\left(\frac{\partial V}{\partial T}\right)_p + \frac{dp}{dT}\Delta\left(\frac{\partial V}{\partial p}\right)_T = 0, \quad \frac{\Delta c_p}{T} - \frac{dp}{dT}\Delta\left(\frac{\partial V}{\partial T}\right)_p = 0,$$

$$\Delta\left(\frac{\partial p}{\partial T}\right)_V + \frac{dV}{dT}\Delta\left(\frac{\partial p}{\partial V}\right)_T = 0, \quad \frac{\Delta c_v}{T} + \frac{dV}{dT}\Delta\left(\frac{\partial p}{\partial T}\right)_V = 0,$$

where the derivatives dp/dT and dV/dT are taken along the transition curves, on which there is one additional relationship, apart from the equation of state, between p, V, T.

183. A piece of ice is placed in an adiabatic envelope at 0° and atmospheric pressure. What fraction $\Delta m/m$ of the ice melts, if the ice is subjected to an all-round compression to $p = 100$ atm, and what is the change in temperature of the system? The change in volume of the ice on compression can be neglected. The specific volumes of water and ice are: $v_w = 1\ \text{cm}^3\,\text{g}^{-1}$, $v_i = 1{\cdot}11\ \text{cm}^3\,\text{g}^{-1}$. The heat of melting of ice is $q = 80\ \text{cal}\,\text{g}^{-1}$. The specific heats of ice and water are connected by $c_i = 0{\cdot}6\ c_w$.

184. The Russian physicist M. P. Avenarius showed that the heat of vaporisation is zero at the critical temperature. Verify this by using the Clausius–Clapeyron equation.

185. Find the specific volume of water vapour v_v at 100° and standard pressure, if the boiling point of water is known to be 99·1° at a pressure of 735·5 mm Hg. The latent heat of vaporisation at 100° is $q = 539\ \text{cal}\,\text{g}^{-1}$.

186. Two bodies A and B, heated to different temperatures, are located in a rigid adiabatic envelope and are placed in thermal contact with one another. As a result, heat is transferred from the hotter to the cooler body until their temperatures are the same.

Show that the entropy of the system $A + B$ is increased in this process.

187. Temperature and entropy can be taken as the fundamental variables characterising the state of a body. Draw a graph of the Carnot cycle, taking entropy on the axis of abscissae, and temperature on the axis of ordinates. Use this graph to calculate the efficiency of the cycle.

188. Find the entropy change ΔS of a substance on heating, if its specific heat c is constant and the volumetric expansion coefficient is zero.

189. Find the entropy change ΔS of 30 g ice when it becomes vapour, if the initial temperature of the ice is $-40°$ and the temperature of the vapour is 100°. Regard the specific heats of water and ice as constant, and all the processes as occurring at atmospheric pressure. The specific heat of ice is $c = 0{\cdot}5 \text{ cal g}^{-1} \text{deg}^{-1}$.

190. Find the total entropy change ΔS (water plus iron) when 100 g iron, heated to 300°, is submerged in water at 15°. The specific heat of iron is $0{\cdot}11 \text{ cal g}^{-1} \text{deg}^{-1}$.

191. Find the entropy rise ΔS of an ideal gas of mass M occupying a volume V_1 when it expands *in vacuo* to a volume V_2 (Gay-Lussac process).

192. Calculate the change in internal energy and entropy of 1 mole of ideal gas when it expands along the polytrope $pV^k = \text{const.}$ from a volume V_1 to V_2. Consider the particular cases of isothermal and adiabatic processes.

193. Calculate the change in internal energy and entropy of 1 mole of an ideal monatomic gas and the quantity of heat absorbed when the gas expands along the polytrope $pV^3 = \text{const.}$ from the volume $V_1 = 1$ l at pressure $p_1 = 20$ atm to the volume $V_2 = 3$ l. The temperature during the process is such that we can take $c_v = 3R/2$ for the molar specific heat.

194. In a polytropic process the pressure and volume of a definite mass of oxygen change from $p_1 = 4$ atm and $V_1 = 1$ litre to $p_2 = 1$ atm and $V_2 = 2$ litres. The temperature at the start of the process is $T_1 = 500\,°\text{K}$. How much heat is obtained by the oxygen from the surrounding medium? What are the changes in the entropy and internal energy of the gas?

195. Find the entropy change ΔS of 5 g hydrogen, isothermally expanded from a volume of 10 to 25 litres.

196. Two vessels of the same volume contain different ideal gases. The mass of gas in the first vessel is M_1, in the second M_2, whilst the pressure and temperatures of the gases are the same. The vessels are connected to one another, and a diffusion process commences. Find the total change ΔS in the entropy of the system, if the molecular weight of the first gas is μ_1 and of the second μ_2.

197. Two vessels each of volume $V = 1$ litre are connected by a pipe with a tap. One vessel contains hydrogen at $t_1 = 20°$ and pressure 1 atm, and the other helium at $t_2 = 100°$ and pressure 3 atm. Find the entropy change ΔS of the system after the tap is opened and equilibrium is reached. The walls of the vessels and pipe ensure complete thermal insulation of the gases from the surrounding medium.

198. A heat insulated cylindric vessel is separated into two parts by a piston of negligibly small mass. One side of the piston is occupied by an ideal gas of mass M, molecular weight μ and molar specific heats c_v and c_p, which are temperature-independent, whilst the other side is occupied by a high vacuum. The initial temperature and pressure of the gas are T_0 and p_0. The piston is released and moves freely, so that the gas can occupy the whole of the volume of the cylinder. The piston pressure is then gradually increased, so that the gas volume slowly returns to its initial value. Find the changes in the internal energy and entropy of the gas during the process.

199. Find an expression for the entropy of a mole of van der Waals' gas, the specific heat c_v of which is independent of temperature. Obtain the equation of the adiabat for such a gas.

200. Find the equation of the polytrope for a van der Waals gas, the specific heat c_v of which is independent of the temperature, whilst the heat capacity of the polytropic process is c.

201. Find the specific entropy s of a non-homogeneous system, consisting of liquid and its saturated vapour. Regard the specific heat of the liquid as temperature-independent.

202. A gas flows adiabatically from a vessel via a small orifice. The gas temperature in the vessel is T_1, its pressure p_1, the external pressure p_2. Find an expression for the speed of the escaping gas jet. Calculate this speed for carbon dioxide (CO_2), on the assumption that $T_1 = 300°K$, $p_1 = 10$ atm, $p_2 = 1$ atm; γ for carbon dioxide is 1·30, the specific heat $c_p = 0{\cdot}202$ cal g^{-1} deg^{-1}.

203. Air is compressed in a large flask at a temperature $T_0 = 273°K$ and flows into the atmosphere via a pipe, at the end of which it has a speed $v = 400$ m sec^{-1}. Find the temperature T of the escaping air at the end of the pipe, and the air pressure p_0 in the flask. Regard the escape of the gas as adiabatic.

204. Find the maximum speed attainable by a gas when it escapes adiabatically from a flask, if the absolute temperature of the gas in the flask is T.

205. Suppose that the temperature of combustion of the chemical fuel for a rocket motor is $T = 3000°K$, that the average molecular weight of the products of combustion is $\mu = 30$ and that the flow of the products of combustion occurs adiabatically into a vacuum. Find the difference between the starting mass M_0 of the rocket and its final weight M if the rocket is capable of achieving a velocity $v = 8$ km sec^{-1}. The molar specific heat c_p of the products of combustion can be taken as 8 cal mol^{-1} deg^{-1} as a guide. Neglect the force of gravity and air friction when calculating the speed of the rocket.

206. The following expressions are derived in statistical physics for the fluctuations of the specific volume and specific entropy of liquids and gases:

$$\overline{\Delta p^2} = -kT\left(\frac{\partial p}{\partial V}\right)_s; \quad \overline{\Delta s^2} = kc_p; \quad \overline{\Delta p \Delta s} = 0,$$

where c_p is the specific heat, and k Boltzmann's constant. Use these expressions to find the ratio of the intensities of the undisplaced component I_ω to the sum of the intensities of the two shifted components $I_{\omega-\delta\omega} + I_{\omega+\delta\omega}$ when light is scattered in liquids.

§ 5. Properties of Liquids. Surface Tension. Solutions

207. Find the density δ of sea water at a depth of 5 km, if the density at the surface of the ocean is $\delta_0 = 1{\cdot}03$ g cm^{-3}, and the compressibility of water within the pressure limits 1–500 atm is equal to $\beta = 47{\cdot}5 \times 10^{-6}$ atm^{-1}.

208. The viscosity of water was found by measuring the amount of water flowing from a capillary of length $l = 10$ cm and diameter $d = 1$ mm under the action of the pressure difference produced by a column of water 50 cm high. $V = 217$ cm^3 water flowed out in a time $\tau = 3$ min. Find the viscosity η of water.

209. Find the coefficient σ of surface tension of a liquid if it rises to a height $h = 32{\cdot}6$ mm in a capillary of diameter $D = 1$ mm. The density of the liquid is $\delta = 1$ gcm^{-3}. The edge angle of the meniscus is zero.

210. The surface tension of a liquid can be determined by weighing a drop when it breaks from a capillary and measuring the neck of the drop at the instant of breaking off. It is found that 318 drops weigh 5 g, and $d = 0{\cdot}7$ mm. Find the surface tension.

211. A vertical glass capillary is attached to one arm of a balance and kept in equilibrium by weights on the other arm. What happens to the balance if a vessel containing water is carefully brought up below the capillary so that its end touches the water surface?

212. What is the difference in the levels of a liquid in two communicating capillaries of diameters d_1 and d_2? The surface tension of the liquid is σ. The edge angles of the menisci are zero. The density of the liquid is ϱ.

213. By considering the Carnot cycle for a plate of liquid on the assumption that the temperatures of the heater and cooler are infinitesimally different, and applying the Carnot theorem to this cycle, find the derivative of the surface tension σ with respect to the temperature T.

214. What is the change in the level difference $h_1 - h_2$ of water in two communicating capillaries of diameters $d_1 = 0{\cdot}1$ mm and $d_2 = 0{\cdot}3$ mm on heating from 20° to 70°, if the surface tension of water at these respective temperatures are 73 and 64 dyne cm^{-1}.

215. What is the capillary pressure p in a mercury droplet of diameter $d = 1\ \mu$ at 15°, if the surface tension of mercury at this temperature is $\sigma = 487$ dyne cm^{-1}?

216. What is the extra pressure p inside a soap bubble of diameter $d = 0{\cdot}8$ cm if the surface tension of the soap solution is $\sigma = 40$ dyne cm^{-1}?

217. There is a crack of width $a = 0{\cdot}02$ mm in the bottom of a vessel. To what height h can the vessel be filled with mercury before any flows out through the crack? The density of mercury is $\varrho = 13{\cdot}6\ \mathrm{g\,cm^{-1}}$. The surface tension (at 15°) is $\sigma = 487\ \mathrm{dyne\,cm^{-1}}$.

218. Gas bubbles of diameter $d_1 = 0{\cdot}05$ mm separate at the bottom of a pond of depth $h = 2$ m. What will be the diameter d_2 of the bubbles when they rise to the surface? $\sigma = 73\ \mathrm{dyne\,cm^{-1}}$.

219. A vertically mounted glass capillary of length l and radius r is closed at the top. To what height h does water rise in the capillary when its lower end is brought into contact with the surface of water?

220. What is the increase ΔT of the temperature inside a soap bubble over the temperature T of the surrounding air if the bubble starts to rise? The bubble radius is r, the surface tension of the soap film is σ. The mass of the film can be neglected. Assume that the air pressure inside the bubble is only slightly different from atmospheric pressure p.

221. A soap bubble of radius r, filled with air, is contained in a cylinder with a movable piston. The air pressure outside the bubble is at first equal to the atmospheric pressure p_0. On moving the piston slowly the bubble is compressed until its radius is halved. Find the pressure of the outer air in the cylinder at this instant.

222. To what height h does the water rise between two vertical glass plates partially submerged in water, if the distance between them is $d = 0{\cdot}5$ mm? For water, $\sigma = 73\ \mathrm{dyne\,cm^{-1}}$. The edge angle ϑ can be taken as zero in this case.

223. Two vertical glass plates, partially submerged in liquid, together form a wedge with a very small angle α. Find the height h to which the liquid rises as a function of the distance x from the rib of the wedge.

224. A drop of water of mass $m = 0{\cdot}1$ g is introduced between two plane parallel glass plates, wetted with water, the edge angle being zero. What is the force F of attraction between the plates if they are spaced $d = 10^{-4}$ cm apart. The surface tension of water (at 18°) is $\sigma = 73\ \mathrm{dyne\,cm^{-1}}$.

225. One gram of mercury is placed between two plane glass plates. What force F must be applied to the upper plate in order for the mercury to take the shape of a circular lozenge of uniform thickness and radius $R = 5$ cm. The surface tension of mercury (at 15°) is $\sigma = 487$ dyne cm^{-1}, and the edge angle between the mercury and the glass is $\vartheta = 40°$.

226. What is the force F of attraction between two vertical and parallel glass plates, partially submerged in water and such that their distance apart is $d = 0{\cdot}1$ mm? The width of the plates is $l = 15$ cm; $\tau = 73$ dyne cm^{-1}; $\vartheta = 0$. The height of the plates is such that the water does not reach their upper edges.

227. An infinitely long rectangular plate lies on the surface of a liquid wetting it, then is gently raised so that a certain amount of liquid is drawn up with it (Fig. 5). Find the equation of the lateral surface of the liquid, resulting from the action of capillary and gravity forces.

Hint. Take as the x axis a straight line perpendicular to the long side of the plate and lying on the horizontal surface of the liquid,

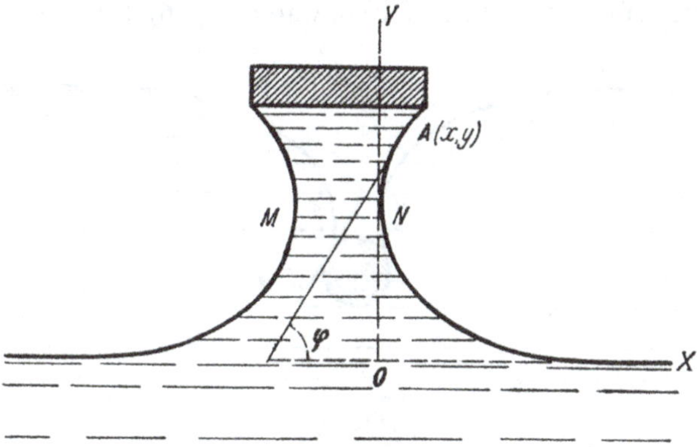

FIG. 5

and as the y axis a vertical line touching the lateral cylindrical surface of the liquid. Express the coordinates x and y of a point of the required surface in terms of the angle φ formed by the tangent plane to this surface with a horizontal plane.

228. Find the maximum height h to which the plate of the previous problem can be raised above the liquid surface and the thickness D of the corresponding liquid column at its narrowest part MN

(Fig. 5). Find also the force F which must be applied per unit length of the plate in order to remove the latter from the liquid. The weight per unit length of the plate is q, its width is a.

229. An infinitely long rectangular plate of width a is placed on the surface of a non-wetting liquid of surface tension σ. The density of the plate material ϱ_0 is greater than the density ϱ of the liquid. Find the maximum plate thickness h that can be taken without the plate sinking.

230. Find the force F needed for removing a circular weightless plate of radius $r = 8$ cm which is placed on the surface of water. The surface tension is $\sigma = 73$ dyne cm^{-1}. The plate is wetted by the water.

231. Find the height h to which liquid rises against an infinite vertical plate, wetted by the liquid. The edge angle is ϑ.

Hint. See the solution to Problem 227, page 144.

232. A steel needle (preferably first covered by a thin layer of graphite) can float on the surface of water (Fig. 6). Find the radius r

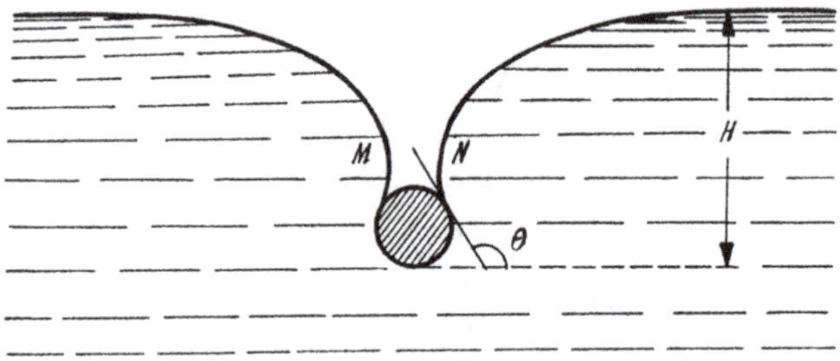

FIG. 6

of the needle, the width $D = MN$ of the gap between the side surfaces of the water at the narrowest point, and the depth H of submersion for different values of the angle ϑ between the commonn tangent to the needle surface and the water and the horizontal plane. The density of steel is $\varrho_0 = 7{\cdot}8$ g cm^{-3}, the surface tension of water is $\sigma = 73$ dyne cm^{-1}. Find the maximum possible radius before the needle sinks. Find the maximum depth of submersion corresponding to this radius. For purposes of calculation, regard the needle as an infinitely long cylinder.

233. Find the direction of the forces acting on two vertical parallel plates partially submerged in liquid in the following cases: (1) both plates are wetted by the liquid, (2) neither of the plates are wetted by the liquid, (3) one plate is wetted and the other not.

234. Find the surface tension σ of the liquid if a loop of rubber band of length l and cross-section S placed on a film of the liquid dilates to a circle of radius R after the film has been punctured inside the loop. Assume that Hooke's law holds for small extensions of the rubber and that Young's modulus for rubber is E.

235. If a soap film of thickness $l = 0{\cdot}001$ mm is at the melting-point of ice, find the temperature drop of the film when it is stretched adiabatically in such a way that its area is doubled. The density of the soap solution is $\varrho = 1\,\mathrm{g\,cm^{-3}}$, the specific heat $c = 1\,\mathrm{cal\,g^{-1}\,deg^{-1}}$. The surface tension of the soap solution falls by $0{\cdot}15\,\mathrm{dyne\,cm^{-1}}$ when the temperature rises 1°.

236. A soap bubble is blown out through a cylindrical pipe with internal radius $r = 1$ mm and length $l = 10$ cm. At the instant when the bubble radius reaches the value $R_0 = 10$ cm, the blowing stops, and the air from the bubble starts to flow out through the pipe. Starting from this instant, how long does it take for the bubble to disappear? The surface tension of the soap solution is $\sigma = 50\,\mathrm{dyne\,cm^{-1}}$, the coefficient of viscosity of air is $\eta = 1{\cdot}8 \times \times 10^{-4}\,\mathrm{g\,sec^{-1}\,cm^{-1}}$. Neglect any change in the air density during the process.

237. A circular hole of radius $a = 1$ mm is made in the wall of a spherical soap bubble (it can be made, for instance, by placing a loop of thread on the bubble and then pricking the wall inside the loop). Find the time taken for all the air to leave the bubble if its initial radius $r_0 = 10$ cm. The air temperature inside and outside the bubble is $t = 20°$. The surface tension of the soap solution at this temperature is $\sigma = 50\,\mathrm{dyne\,cm^{-1}}$. The atmospheric pressure $p = 760$ mm Hg. The mean molecular weight of air can be taken as $\mu = 29$. Regard the air as an ideal incompressible fluid during its flow through the hole.

238. A drop of incompressible fluid performs pulsational vibrations, becoming in turn lengthened, spherical, flattened, spherical, lengthened again and so on. How does the period T of these vibrations depend on the density ϱ, the surface tension σ and the radius r of the drop?

239. A jet of liquid flows through a horizontal pipe in the side wall of a vessel (Fig. 7). The pipe is of elliptic cross-section, with the major axis horizontal. The jet has the shape of a chain, the links of which are in turn compressed then flattened in the horizontal direction. Explain this phenomenon. How does the length l of the link in the initial part of the jet depend on the density ϱ, the surface tension σ, the distance h from the base of the pipe to the level of the liquid and the acceleration g due to gravity, if the pipe cross-section remains fixed?

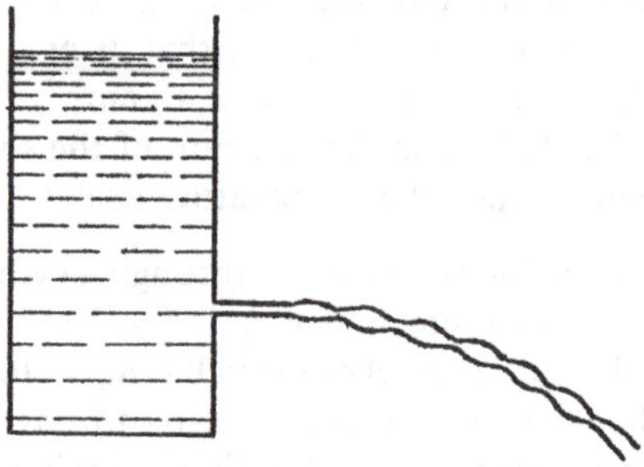

FIG. 7

240. A beaker is filled with water to a height of 10 cm. Capillary tubes, closed at one end and filled with air, lie at the bottom. When the water boils, vapour bubbles form at the open ends of the capillaries, the diameter of the bubbles at the instant when they break off being 0·2 mm. What is the temperature at the bottom of the vessel whilst boiling occurs, if the atmospheric pressure is 760 mm Hg? The surface tension of boiling water is 57 dyne cm^{-1}, and the pressure of water vapour close to 100° increases by 2·7 cm Hg for a temperature rise of 1°.

241. Find the shape of a soap film, the edge of which is fixed to two identical rings of radius R, spaced a distance $2h$ apart. The centres of the rings lie on a straight line perpendicular to their planes. The planes of the rings are not closed by films.

242. A cylindrical soap bubble is formed between two circular rings of the same radius, whilst soap films, which will evidently be spherical, are also stretched over the bases of the rings. Find the ratio of the radii of the cylindrical to the spherical parts of the films.

243. Solve Problem 241 on the assumption that soap films are stretched over the planes of the rings, as well as over the lateral surface.

244. In Problem 242 the air pressure inside the bubble is gradually changed, with the result that the straight generators of the cylindrical surface become bent. Show that, if the bending is small, the generator takes a sinusoidal form, its period being equal to the circumference $2\pi r$ of the base of the undisturbed cylindrical film. Use this result to show that, on increasing the air pressure inside the bubble, when its length is less than πr, the bubble bulges, and on decreasing the pressure it contracts. But if the bubble length is greater than πr, but less than $2\pi r$, increase of the internal pressure causes the lateral surface of the film to become concave, and decrease to become convex.

Hint. The result of the previous problem may be used.

245. It was shown by D. I. Mendeleev that the surface tension of a liquid is zero at the critical temperature. How can this be proved?

246. Show that, if two vessels are filled with liquid and have a common atmosphere of saturated vapour (for instance, they may be covered by the same bell-jar), the liquid levels at thermal equilibrium will be the same, provided capillary forces are neglected.

247. Find the pressure p of the saturated vapour over the meniscus in a capillary tube if the meniscus radius is r and the pressure of the saturated vapour over a plane surface is p_0.

Hint. Consider the conditions for equilibrium between the liquid and vapour over the meniscus and over a plane surface.

248. Find the stationary flow of vapour from a spherical drop of liquid of radius a during vaporisation (or condensation of vapour into the drop). The coefficient of diffusion of the vapour into air is D, the vapour density remote from the drop is $\varrho_{v\infty}$, the density of the saturated vapour is ϱ_{v_s}. Find also the vapour density ϱ as a function of the distance r from the centre of the drop. Neglect the dependence of the saturated vapour pressure on the curvature of the liquid surface.

249. By using the analogy between the equations of stationary diffusion and electrostatics, find the stationary flow of vapour from a liquid drop of arbitrary shape. The remaining conditions are the same as in the previous problem.

250. Find the time τ_{vap} of vaporisation of a water drop of initial radius a in air with relative humidity f and temperature $t = 20°$. Consider two cases: (1) $f = 40$ per cent, $a = 1$ mm, (2) $f = 99$ per cent, $a = 1\ \mu$. The pressure of saturated water vapour at $t = 20°$ is equal to $p_s = 17{\cdot}5$ mm Hg; $D = 0{\cdot}22\ \text{cm}^2/\text{sec}$.

Hint. Regard the vaporisation process as stationary. This is permissible if the vapour density is much less than the liquid density ϱ_l.

251. Find the time τ_{vap} of vaporisation of a spherical drop of liquid of radius a into an atmosphere saturated with vapour of the liquid, taking into account the dependence of the saturated vapour pressure on the surface curvature (see Problem 247). The surface tension of the liquid (water) is $\sigma = 73\ \text{dyne}\,\text{cm}^{-1}$, the temperature $t = 20°$. Consider two cases: (1) $a = 100\ \mu$, (2) $a = 1\ \mu$.

252. Find the osmotic pressure p_{osm} of a 5 per cent solution of cane sugar ($C_{12}H_{22}O_{11}$) in water at 18°.

253. At what temperature t is the osmotic pressure of a 2 per cent solution of salt in water equal to 18 atm? Take the degree of dissociation of the salt as 75 per cent.

254. The osmotic pressure of a solution of 36 g glucose in 2·24 litres water at 27° is 1·1 atm. Find the molecular weight μ of glucose.

255. What is the osmotic pressure p_{osm} of an electrolyte, the degree of dissociation of which is α, if a molecule of the electrolyte splits up on dissociation into n ions?

256. Find the osmotic pressure p_{osm} of a 1 per cent solution of sodium nitrate ($NaNO_3$) in water at 27°. Assume that the sodium nitrate is completely dissociated.

257. A solution and the pure solvent in communicating vessels are separated by a semi-permeable membrane, and the vessels are covered by a bell jar. Write down the conditions for equilibrium of the solution and solvent in the solvent vapour and derive from this the relationship between the osmotic pressure p_{osm} and the difference $(p_l - p_0)$ between the pressures of the saturated vapour over the solution and over the solvent.

258. The saturated vapour pressure is less over a solution than over a pure solvent. Express the difference between these pressures in terms of the ratio k of the total number of moles of dissolved substance to the number of moles of solvent.

259. What is the water vapour pressure p_l over a sugar solution if the number of moles of sugar is 5 per cent of the total number of moles of solvent. The temperature of the solution is 20°. The pressure of saturated water vapour at 20° is 17·535 mm Hg.

260. Find the variation with time of the dimensions of a water drop if m g of common salt are dissolved in it. The drop is in an atmosphere saturated with water vapour. The solution is assumed to be dilute.

261. What is the boiling-point T_b of a solution of 100 g ordinary salt in 1 litre water? Assume that the salt is completely dissociated. The latent heat of vaporisation of water is $q = 539$ cal g^{-1}. The external pressure is 760 mm Hg.

262. One gram of cane sugar (molecular weight 342) is dissolved in 100 cm^3 water. Find the boiling-point of this solution at standard atmospheric pressure. The density of water at 100° is equal to 0·96 g cm^{-3}, the latent heat of vaporisation is 539 cal g^{-1}.

263. Find the freezing-point of the solution of the previous problem at atmospheric pressure. The latent heat of melting is $q = 80$ cal g^{-1}.

264. Sugar in aqueous solution raises the boiling-point at standard atmospheric pressure by $\Delta T = 0·05°$. Find the freezing-point t of the solution at the same pressure. The heat of melting of ice is $q_1 = 80$ cal g^{-1}, the heat of vaporisation of water is $q_2 = 539$ cal g^{-1}.

265. Dissolving $m = 1$ g iodine in $M = 285$ g ethyl ether raises the boiling-point of the latter by $\Delta T = 0·032°$. What is the number of atoms n in a molecule of iodine in solution? The atomic weight of iodine is $A = 127$, the boiling-point of ethyl ether is $T = 307·8$ °K, the heat of vaporisation is $q = 81·5$ cal g^{-1}.

§ 6. Kinetic Theory of Matter

266. How many molecules of nitrogen does a vessel of 1 litre capacity contain, if the temperature of the nitrogen is 27° and the pressure is 10^{-6} mm Hg?

267. What is the pressure of the gas mixture in a 2·5-litre flask, if it contains 10^{15} molecules oxygen, 4×10^{15} molecules nitrogen and $3{\cdot}3 \times 10^{-7}$ g argon? The temperature of the mixture is 150°.

268. Use kinetic theory to show that, when a piston is displaced quasi-statically in a cylinder filled with an ideal monatomic gas, the pressure and volume of the gas are connected by

$$pV^{5/3} = \text{const.}$$

The cylinder walls and piston are impermeable to heat.

Hint. Consider the collision of a molecule on the moving piston and use the fact that the molecule speed is much greater than the piston speed.

269. Solve the previous problem for a diatomic gas. Show that in this case the pressure p and volume V are connected by

$$pV^{7/5} = const.$$

Hint. Use the theorem on the uniform distribution of the kinetic energy over the various degrees of freedom.

270. Starting from the Maxwell distribution, find the mean square x-component of a gas molecule velocity. Find from this the mean kinetic energy per degree of freedom of the translational motion of gas molecules.

271. What is the pressure dependence of the mean velocity of the molecules of an ideal monatomic gas when it contracts or expands adiabatically?

272. Find the ratio of the number n_1 of molecules of hydrogen whose velocities lie between the limits 3000 and 3010 m sec^{-1} to the number n_2 of molecules having velocities between 1500 and 1510 m sec^{-1}, if the temperature of the hydrogen is 300°.

273. Find the most probable (v_m), the mean ($\bar{v}$) and the root mean square ($\sqrt{\bar{v}^2}$) velocities of chlorine molecules at 227°.

274. At what temperature is the root mean square velocity of hydrogen molecules equal to the root mean square velocity of nitrogen molecules at 100°?

275. Show that, if the most probable velocity is taken as unit velocity for gas molecules, the number of molecules, the absolute values of the velocities of which lie between v and $(v + dv)$ is independent of the temperature.

276. Express the number z of molecules colliding per second with 1 cm^2 of the walls of the vessel in terms of the mean velocity of the motion of the gas molecules, if the velocity distribution function is isotropic (i.e. depends only on the absolute value of the velocity but not on its direction). Consider the particular case of a Maxwell distribution.

277. Find the total kinetic energy E of the molecules of a monatomic gas, colliding with 1 cm^2 of wall in unit time. Solve the problem first in the general form for an isotropic distribution function, then apply the result to the particular case of a Maxwell distribution.

278. A tap of very small cross-section S is opened in a vessel of volume V from which all the air has been pumped out. How long (time τ) does it take the pressure inside the vessel to become half the atmospheric pressure? Assume that the filling process is so slow that, in spite of the non-equilibrium character of the process, it is possible to speak of a pressure and temperature of the air inside the vessel. Assume that the temperature of the air in the vessel is equal to the external temperature.

279. (1) How long does it take the air pressure in a thin-walled evacuated vessel, in the wall of which there is an aperture of cross-section $S = 10^{-6}$ cm^2, to increase from $p_1 = 10^{-4}$ to $p_2 = 10^{-2}$ mm Hg, if the pressure of the outside air is $p_0 = 760$ mm Hg and the temperature is 20°? The volume of the vessel is $V = 1$ l. (2) How long does it take the pressure in the vessel to become half the atmospheric pressure?

280. A vessel is divided by a partition into two equal parts, each of volume V. One part contains nitrogen, and the other oxygen, both at the same pressure p and temperature T. The gases are strongly rarefied (the mean free path is large compared with the vessel dimensions). At the instant $t = 0$ a small hole of area S is made in the aperture. Find the pressures in the two halves of the vessel as a function of time (the gas temperature is assumed constant throughout the process). Express the result in terms of the mean velocities $\bar{v}_N$ and $\bar{v}_O$ of the nitrogen and oxygen molecules.

281. A vessel is pumped out to high vacuum, then a hole made in one of its walls. A parallel beam of molecules having the same velocity v is directed towards the hole. The molecules of the beam, on entering the vessel, collide with its walls and are reflected from them, whilst they also collide with one another, as a result of which a Maxwell velocity distribution is established in the vessel. Find the equilibrium ratio of the gas densities in the beam and the vessel after thermal equilibrium has been established between the vessel walls and the gas filling it.

282. In a saturated water vapour atmosphere (no air) at a temperature $t = 20°$ a water drop of radius $r = 2$ mm with the same temperature is suddenly introduced. Determine the instantaneous rate of evaporation per unit surface area of the drop at the initial instant (that is, the number of molecules lost by the drop per unit time and unit area through evaporation). The saturated water vapour pressure at 20° is $p = 17{\cdot}54$ mm Hg. The surface tension of water at this temperature is $\sigma = 72{\cdot}7\,\text{dyne cm}^{-1}$. (Compare Problems 250 and 251).

283. The ratio of the molecular weights of two different gases can be measured from their effusion velocities, i.e. the velocities of their flow from a vessel with a very small orifice. Show that the time required for a given volume of gas to flow from the vessel is proportional to the square root of the molecular weight.

284. The mean free path for hydrogen at atmospheric pressure is $\Lambda = 1{\cdot}28 \times 10^{-5}$ cm. Find the kinetic diameter d of a hydrogen molecule.

285. The coefficient of internal friction for nitrogen at 0° is $\eta = 16{\cdot}8 \times 10^{-5}\,\text{g cm}^{-1}\,\text{sec}^{-1}$. Find the mean free path Λ of nitrogen molecules under these conditions.

286. What is the number z of collisions per second of neon molecules at 600°K and 1 mm Hg if the kinetic diameter of a neon molecule is $d = 2{\cdot}04 \times 10^{-8}$ cm?

287. Find the pressure p of hydrogen in a round litre flask, in which the mean free path of a molecule is greater than the dimensions of the vessel. The kinetic diameter of hydrogen is $2{\cdot}2 \times 10^{-8}$ cm, and its temperature 300°K.

288. An ideal gas is heated at constant pressure. What is the variation with temperature of the mean free path Λ and the number z of collisions of its molecules per second?

289. An ideal gas is compressed isothermically. Find Λ and z as functions of the pressure.

290. An ideal gas is compressed adiabatically. Find Λ and z as functions of the pressure.

291. To determine the coefficient of internal friction of carbon dioxide a round 1 litre flask is filled with the gas at a pressure $p_1 = 1600$ mm Hg. A tap is then opened, allowing the carbon dioxide to flow from the flask through a capillary of length $l = 10$ cm and diameter $d = 0{\cdot}1$ mm. The pressure in the flask falls to $p_3 = 1350$ mm Hg in $\tau = 22$ min. Calculate from these data the viscosity and kinetic diameter d of carbon dioxide molecules. The external atmospheric pressure is $p_2 = 735$ mm Hg. The process can be regarded as isothermal and occurring at 15°.

292. To measure the thermal conductivity of nitrogen, the space between two long coaxial cylinders, radii $r_1 = 0{\cdot}5$ cm, $r_2 = 2$ cm, is filled with the gas. The inner cylinder is heated uniformly by a spiral carrying a current $i = 0{\cdot}1$ amp. The spiral resistance per unit length of the cylinder is $R = 0{\cdot}1$ ohm. The outer cylinder is maintained at $t_2 = 0°$. In steady-state conditions the temperature of the inner cylinder is $t_1 = 93°$. Find the kinetic diameter d of nitrogen molecules. A small gas pressure (of the order of 10 mm) is used in such experiments, so that convection can be neglected.

293. Determine the angle of rotation φ of a disc suspended from an elastic thread when a second similar disc rotates at a distance $h = 1$ cm below it with angular velocity $\omega = 50$ radian sec^{-1}. The radius of each disc is $R = 10$ cm, the modulus of torsion of the thread is $f = 100$ dyne cm rad^{-1}, the coefficient of internal friction of air is $\eta = 1{\cdot}8 \times 10^{-4}$ g sec^{-1} cm^{-1}. Neglect edge effects. Regard the motion of the air between the discs as laminar.

294. Solve the previous problem on the assumption that the discs are situated in a strongly rarefied atmosphere at pressure $p = 10^{-4}$ mm Hg, when the mean free path of the air molecules is large compared with the distance between the discs. To simplify the calculation, assume that all the molecules move with the same absolute value of the velocity, equal to the mean velocity $v = 450\ \text{m} \cdot \text{sec}^{-1}$ of the air molecules.

295. The thermal conductivity of a gas is known to be independent of its pressure. Explain why the air is pumped out from the space between the double walls of a Dewar flask in order to create as high a vacuum as possible in the space.

296. Estimate the mass M of liquid air evaporating per hour from a badly evacuated Dewar flask, if the pressure (at room temperature $T_0 = 293\ ^\circ\text{K}$) of the air between the walls is $p = 10^{-3}$ mm Hg. The surface area of the flask is $S = 600\ \text{cm}^2$, the heat of vaporisation of liquid air is $q = 48{\cdot}4\ \text{cal g}^{-1}$, and its temperature is $T = 93\ ^\circ\text{K}$. The gap between the walls is small compared with the free path.

Hint. Assume for simplicity that the air molecules, alternately striking the cold and the hot walls, are each time reflected from them with mean translational kinetic energies corresponding to the wall temperatures. Neglect the difference between the mean and the root mean square velocities of the molecules, and use the formula for the root mean square velocity.

297. Estimate the order of magnitude of the velocity of the motion of a plane disc in strongly rarefied air when one side of the disc is heated to $T_1 = 310\ ^\circ\text{K}$ and the other to $T_2 = 300\ ^\circ\text{K}$. The air temperature is $T = 300\ ^\circ\text{K}$.

298. Two vessels of the same volume are connected by pipes. The diameter of one of the pipes is very large, and of the other very small compared to the mean free path of the gas molecules contained in the vessel. The first vessel is held at constant temperature $T_1 = 800\ ^\circ\text{K}$, the second at constant temperature $T_2 = 200\ ^\circ\text{K}$. In which direction does the gas flow through the narrow pipe if the wide pipe is closed by a tap? What mass m of the gas flows in this case from one vessel to the other, if the total mass of gas in the two vessels is M?

299. Find the kinetic energy E of the molecules of 5 litres hydrogen at a pressure of $3\ \text{kg cm}^{-2}$.

300. A mixture of equal weights of hydrogen and helium at 0° is placed in a cylindrical vessel of $1\ \text{m}^3$ volume, closed at the top by a weightless piston which moves without friction. The atmospheric pressure is 740 mm Hg. What is the quantity of heat required to heat the mixture to 200°?

301. Calculate the specific heat at constant pressure of a gas of the following molar composition:

$$20\% \text{ He} - 30\% \text{ H}_2 - 50\% \text{ CH}_4$$

(The molar composition indicates the relative numbers of moles of the given components to the total number of moles in the mixture.)

302. What is the change in $\gamma = c_p/c_v$ for nitrogen if, under the action of some reagent, a certain fraction of the molecules dissociates into atoms? The ratio of the number of dissociated molecules to the total number of molecules is α.

303. Show that, at sufficiently high temperature, the atomic specific heat of a solid must be equal to $c_v = 3R \approx 6$ cal mol^{-1} deg^{-1}.

304. Find the molecular specific heat at constant volume of solid compounds of the type XY and XY_2, assuming the validity of classical statistics.

305. Find the specific heat at constant volume of hydrogen, heated to a very high temperature of the order of several keV.

306. When an atom (uranium) bomb explodes a temperature of the order $T \approx 10$ keV is reached at its centre. Taking as a guide $\varrho = 20$ g cm^{-3} as the density of the uranium at the bomb centre, find the pressure inside the bomb at this temperature. Compare this pressure with the pressure at the Earth's centre, calculated on the assumption that the Earth's density is constant and equal to $\varrho_{\text{Earth}} = 5{\cdot}5$ g cm^{-3}. Neglect the pressure of the light radiation. (Compare with Problem 362.)

307. According to an early theory (Helmholtz, 1854; Lord Kelvin, 1861), the solar radiation is maintained by the heat from contraction of the Sun. Assuming that the Sun is a homogeneous sphere, the density of the material of which is the same whatever the distance from the centre, calculate the amount of heat Q released if the Sun's radius diminishes from R_1 to R_2. How long will the heat released last, if we assume that the intensity of the solar radiation is constant in time and the Sun's radius diminishes by $\frac{1}{10}$ its initial value ($R_2 = 0{\cdot}9\, R_1$)? The mass of the Sun is $M = 2 \times 10^{33}$ g, its mean radius is $R_1 = 6{\cdot}95 \times 10^{10}$ cm, the gravitational constant $\gamma = 6{\cdot}67 \times 10^{-8}$ cm^{3}g^{-1}sec^{-2}, the solar constant $A = 1{\cdot}39 \times 10^6$ ergcm^{-2}sec^{-1}, the mean distance of the Earth from the Sun is $1{\cdot}5 \times 10^{13}$ cm. Estimate also the relative rise in the Sun's temperature if the compression were to occur suddenly. The specific heat of the Sun's material can be estimated roughly by assuming that the Sun consists wholly of hydrogen (this gives a high value for the specific heat. According to modern data the mass of the sun consists of approximately 70–80 per cent hydrogen).

308. According to classical theory the molar specific heat of hydrogen is $c_v = 5R/2$. What sort of deviation from this value must be expected at sufficiently low temperatures?

309. Calculate the mean energy $\bar{E}$ of a mole of monatomic gas consisting of molecules having two discrete energy levels: ε_1 and $\varepsilon_2 > \varepsilon_1$. Show that the specific heat of such a gas is $3R/2$ at very low temperatures. Neglect rotation of the molecules.

310. A mirror is suspended from a quartz thread, the modulus of torsion of which is D, and is illuminated so that rotations of it produced by collisions with surrounding gas molecules can be recorded on a scale. The rest position corresponds to $\varphi = 0$ (φ is the angle of rotation). What are the changes in the mean square of the angular velocity $\overline{\dot{\varphi}^2}$ and the mean square of the angular deflection $\overline{\varphi^2}$ if the moment of inertia of the mirror, the length of the thread and its diameter are increased by the factors α, β, γ respectively? What value is obtained for Avogadro's number N from measurements at temperature $T = 287$°K, if $D = 9{\cdot}43 \times 10^{-9}$ dyne cm, $\overline{\varphi^2} = 4{\cdot}18 \times 10^{-6}$?

311. By regarding the mirror suspended on a quartz thread (see the previous problem) as a harmonic oscillator performing undamped vibrations, find $\overline{\dot{\varphi}^2}$ and $\overline{\varphi^2}$ in the quantum case. Write down the condition for the classical expressions to be applicable. Find the quantum corrections, by using the data of the previous problem. Take $I \approx 0{\cdot}01$ gcm^2 for the moment of inertia of the mirror.

312. Perrin determined Avogradro's number by finding the height distribution of spherical gamboge particles suspended in water. He found that the ratio α of the number of particles in layers spaced at a distance $l = 30\ \mu$ apart was equal to $2{\cdot}08$. The density of the particles was $\varrho = 1{\cdot}194$ gcm^{-3}. The density of water is

$\varrho_0 = 1\ \text{gcm}^{-3}$. The particle radius was $r = 0{\cdot}212\ \mu$. Calculate Avogadro's number N on the basis of these data. The water temperature $t = 18°$.

313. The molecular weights of colloidal particles may be determined by studying the distribution of their concentration in the field of the centrifugal force produced by a centrifuge. Find the molecular weight μ of the colloidal particles, given that the ratio of their concentrations at points distances r_2, r_1 from the axis of the centrifuge is α. The density of the particles is ϱ, the density of the solvent ϱ_0. The angular velocity of the centrifuge is ω.

314. At thermodynamic equilibrium the temperature of a gas situated in a gravitational field is constant with respect to height. From the molecular–kinetic viewpoint it seems at first sight that the gas temperature must decrease with the height, since a molecule travelling upwards will be slowed down by the gravitational field, and one travelling downwards accelerated. Give a qualitative molecular–kinetic explanation of the constancy of the gas temperature with height.

315. An ideally elastic sphere moves upwards and downwards in a gravitational field, the action of the field being in accordance with the law of elastic collisions. Find the connection between its time-averaged kinetic and potential energies. Use the result to establish the connection between the average kinetic and potential energies of a molecule of air in the earth's gravitational field. Use this result to obtain a formula for the difference $c_p - c_v$ between the molar specific heats.

316. A vertical cylindrical vessel of height H contains 1 mole of an ideal gas. Find the specific heat c of the gas, taking account of the presence of the gravitational field and assuming that $\mu g H \ll RT$, where μ is the molecular weight of the gas. Neglect the expansion of the vessel on heating.

317. A cylindrical heat-insulated vessel containing an ideal gas is suspended from a thread. Due to the action of gravity the gas density at the bottom of the vessel is greater than at the top. The thread breaks and the vessel falls. Does the gas temperature alter after thermodynamic equilibrium has been established during the descent?

318. Find the density distribution of the gas molecules in a cylinder of radius R and length l, rotating in a gravitational field about its axis with angular velocity ω. The cylinder axis is vertical.

319. A liquid contains identical Brownian particles, the concentration of which depends on the z co-ordinate only. Equalisation of the concentration occurs as a result of diffusion. Express the diffusion coefficient D of the Brownian particles in terms of the mean square displacement of a particle in the z direction in time τ.

320. The mobility B of a Brownian (or any other) particle is defined as the coefficient of proportionality between the velocity u its steady-state motion under the action of a constant force f and the magnitude of the force itself: $u = Bf$. A suspension of identical Brownian particles in a liquid is situated in a gravitational field. Write down the expression for the total flux of the particles due to diffusion and the action of gravity. In the stationary state the total flux must be zero. At the same time the stationary height distribution of the particles is given by Boltzmann's formula (the barometric formula). Starting from these ideas, establish the connexion between the mobility and the diffusion coefficient.

321. Use the results of the two previous problems to find the connexion between the mean square displacement $\overline{\Delta z^2}$ of a Brownian particle in any given direction during time τ with the mobility of the particle. What form does the connexion take for a spherical particle of radius a? (According to Stokes, $B^{-1} = 6\pi\eta a$, where η is the viscosity of the liquid.)

322. Find the root mean square horizontal displacement per minute of gamboge grains in water at 20°, given that their radius is $0{\cdot}5\,\mu$, and the viscosity of water is $0{\cdot}01$ g cm^{-1} sec^{-1}.

323. According to Einstein and Smoluchowski, Avogradro's number N can be determinedby observing the Brownian motion of gamboge particles and measuring the root mean square displacement in a fixed direction. Find N, given that the root mean square displacement in 5 min of particles of radius $a = 0{\cdot}385\,\mu$ in glycerine at 20° is $1{\cdot}5\,\mu$. The viscosity of glycerine is $\eta = 1{\cdot}49$ g cm^{-1} sec^{-1}.

324. When measuring the charge on an electron by Millikan's method, the Brownian movement of oil drops is observed. By observing this movement, it is possible to determine Avogradro's number as well as the charge on an electron. Let v_1 be the steady-state rate of fall of the drop in a gravitational field in the absence of an electric field. When an electric field E is present, the drop rises upwards with a steady-state speed v_2. It is well known that the charge e on the drop can be calculated from these observations. Let $\overline{(\Delta x)^2}$ be the mean square of the particle displacement in time τ in the (horizontal) x direction.

Assuming that the steady-state velocity of the particle is proportional to the applied force, find an expression for Ne, where N is Avogadro's number.

325. During observation of the Brownian movement of an oil drop in a Millikan condenser (see the previous problem), it was found that $\overline{(\Delta x)^2} = 1{\cdot}05 \times 10^{-5}$ cm^2, $\tau = 10$ sec, $v_1 + v_2 = 0{\cdot}0268$ cm sec^{-1}, $T = 300\,°$K. The voltage across the condenser plates is $V = 940$ V, the distance between them is $d = 0{\cdot}7$ cm. Calculate Avogadro's number from these data. The charge on the drop measured by experiment proved to be equal to the charge on an electron $e = 4{\cdot}8 \times 10^{-10}$ e.s.u.

326. Cosmic rays move randomly in the Galactic as a result of being deviated by the interstellar magnetic fields. The process resembles diffusion. Find the time τ required for a particle to travel a distance of the order of the Galactic dimensions $R \approx 5 \times 10^{22}$ cm, if the effective mean free path is $l \approx 100$ parsec $\approx 3 \times 10^{20}$ cm.

327. Find the wavelength at which sound starts to be strongly damped when propagated in a monatomic gas.

328. Find the order of magnitude of the effective cross-section for collisions of electrons with ions of a plasma heated to a temperature T. The collisions occur with a transfer of momentum, accompanied by strong deflexions of the electrons.

329. Starting from the result of the previous problem, obtain an approximate expression for the electric conductivity λ and the specific resistance ϱ of a hydrogen or deuterium plasma, heated to an absolute temperature T. Find the plasma conductivity as a function of the density and temperature.

330. At what temperature is the theoretical conductivity of a hydrogen or deuterium plasma equal to the conductivity of copper at room temperature? The conductivity of copper is $5{\cdot}14 \times 10^{17}$ sec^{-1} $= 5{\cdot}72 \times 10^5$ ohm^{-1} cm^{-1}.

331. Obtain an approximate expression for the thermal conductivity $\varkappa$ of a hydrogen or deuterium plasma, heated to an absolute temperature T. Find the thermal conductivity of the plasma as a function of its density and temperature.

§ 7. HEAT RADIATION

332. An infinitely long plane-parallel layer of isotropic material of thickness l is at the same temperature T throughout. Find the intensity of the heat radiation from the layer in different directions, neglecting reflexion of the radiation at its boundaries, and scattering inside the layer. (Reflexion at the boundaries will not occur in practice if the refractive index changes smoothly close to the boundaries.) The coefficient of absorption of the material (per unit length of ray) is α.

333. Solve the previous problem on the assumption that reflexion occurs at the boundaries but neglecting scattering.

334. Find the radiation from an infinitely thick layer of material, neglecting scattering inside the layer. Verify that an infinitely thick layer of any material radiates in all directions like an absolutely black body, provided reflexion at its boundaries and scattering inside the layer can be neglected.

335. A light "rectifier"*, which transmits radiation from left to right but not in the reverse direction, contains a plane-parallel

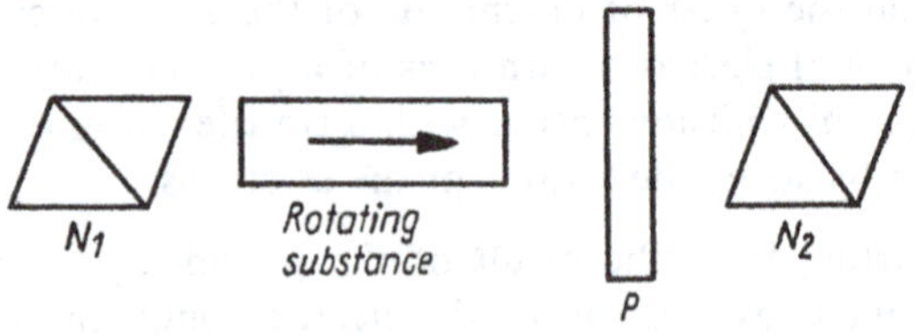

FIG. 8

plate P (Fig. 8) made of a dichroic crystal, heated to a temperature T. The plate P passes all the light of a certain polarisation and

* Such a "rectifier" is of practical interest at radio wavelengths.

completely absorbs light polarised in the perpendicular plane (we neglect reflexion at the plate surface). The plate is orientated in such a way that it entirely absorbs the light passed by the Nicol prism N_2. Find the intensity of the heat radiation from the plate leaving the system from left to right and from right to left.

336. Show that, if radiant energy involved no pressure, it would be possible to construct a *perpetuum mobile* of the second kind.

337. Show that the Carnot cycle corresponding to the radiation of an absolutely black body has an efficiency $\eta = (T_1 - T_2)/T_1$, where T_1 and T_2 are the radiation temperatures on the isothermal parts of the cycle ($T_1 > T_2$).

338. Find the entropy of black radiation.

339. A body A is in equilibrium with its radiation and is enclosed in a cylinder with ideally reflecting walls and closed by an ideally reflecting piston B (Fig. 9), which can be displaced in the cylinder without friction. By considering the Carnot cycle for such a system, find the temperature dependence of the spatial density U of the equilibrium radiation.

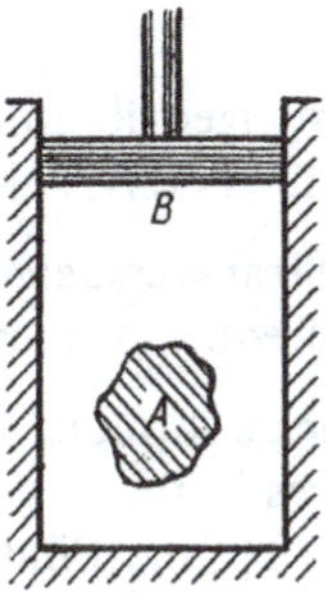

FIG. 9

340. Find the specific heat c_v per unit volume of black radiation in a closed cavity, the volume of which is held constant on heating.

341. Find the equation for an adiabatic process performed with equilibrium radiation.

342. On the average, about 2 cal radiant energy is incident per minute per square centimetre of the Earth's surface. The distance of the Earth from the Sun is 150 million km, the Sun's diameter is 1·39 million km, the Sun's temperature is 6000 °K. Regarding the

Sun as an absolutely black body, find the constant σ in the Stefan–Boltzmann law, connecting the energy radiated from 1 cm^2 of the surface of a black body per second with the absolute temperature.

343. One kilogram of water, heated to 50°, is poured into a black thin-walled metal vessel of cubical shape. Find the time t required for the vessel to cool to 10°, if it is placed in a black cavity, the wall temperature of which is held at about 0 °K, and the water fills the entire volume of the vessel.

344. Find the steady-state temperature T of a black plate which is mounted *in vacuo* perpendicular to the Sun's rays (the flux of light energy is 2 cal cm^{-2} min^{-1}).

345. Establish the connexion between the energy density U of isotropic radiation, its intensity I and the luminosity S.

346. Find the number of eigenvibrations of a string of length z in the frequency interval $(\nu, \nu + d\nu)$. Assume that the string can only vibrate in one plane.

347. Find the number of eigenvibrations of a square membrane of side z in the frequency interval $(\nu, \nu + d\nu)$.

348. Find the number of transverse eigenvibrations of a parallelepiped of volume V in the frequency interval $(\nu, \nu + d\nu)$.

349. According to Planck's formula, the radiation density of a black body with frequencies in the interval $(\nu, \nu + d\nu)$ is equal to $U_\nu d\nu = (8\pi h\nu^3/c^3)\,[e^{h\nu/kT} - 1]^{-1}\,d\nu$. Find approximate expressions for U_ν, when $h\nu \gg kT$ and $h\nu \ll kT$.

350. Use Planck's formula (see the previous problem) to find the constants in the Stefan–Boltzmann and Wien laws: $S = \sigma T^4$ and $\lambda_{max} T = \alpha$, i.e. express them in terms of the constants h, k and c.

351. Find the temperature T of the sun by regarding it as an absolutely black body, and using the fact that the maximum intensity of the solar spectrum lies in the green region ($\lambda = 5 \times 10^{-5}$ cm).

352. Find the wavelength corresponding to maximum intensity in the spectrum of an absolutely black body, the temperature of which is 10^6 degrees.

353. The ratio of the total radiating capacity of a given body to the radiating capacity of a black body at the same temperature is ϵ_T.

Find the connection between the true and the radiation temperatures.

Note. The radiation temperature T_r is the temperature of a black body, the total radiating capacity of which is equal to the radiating capacity of the given body at the temperature T.

354. Is it possible for the radiation temperature to be higher than the true temperature?

355. Neglecting thermal conductivity losses, calculate the power W of the electric current required to heat a filament of length 20 cm and diameter 1 mm to 3500°K. Assume that the filament radiation is according to the Stefan–Boltzmann law ($\sigma = 5{\cdot}7 \times 10^{-5}$ erg cm^{-2} sec^{-1} deg^{-4}).

356. $\epsilon_T \approx 0{\cdot}35$ for tungsten at $T = 3500$°K (see Problem 353). Find T_r and W for a tungsten filament under the conditions of the previous problem.

357. The brightness temperature of a body is the temperature of a black body at which the lattter has a brightness equal to the brightness of the given body at the given wavelength. Find the brightness temperature of a grey body as a function of the wavelength (a grey body is one for which the radiative capacity over the part ofthe spectrum in question is independent of the wavelength).

358. Wien obtained the following empirical formula for the energy distribution in the spectrum of a black body:

$$E(\lambda, T) = C_1 \lambda^{-5} e^{-\frac{C_2}{\lambda T}},$$

where C_1, C_2 are constants. Obtain from this formula Wien's displacement law, and, taking the present accepted value of 1·43880 cm deg for C_2, find the constant in the displacement law.

359. By comparing Wien's formula with Planck's, find the temperature up to which Wien's formula can be used within the limits of the visual spectrum (7500 Å $< \lambda <$ 4000 Å) with an error not exceeding 1 per cent.

360. What formula would be obtained for the black body radiation density U_ν if there were no induced emission of light?

361. A gas constists of molecules or atoms having two non-degenerate energy levels E_1 and E_2 ($E_1 < E_2$). The gas is in a state of thermodynamic equilibrium. Taking induced emission into account, express the absorption coefficient $\varkappa(T)$ at a gas temperature T in terms of its value $\varkappa_0$ at $T = 0$. Consider the two limiting cases: (1) $kT \gg h\nu = E_2 - E_1$; (2) $kT \ll h\nu = E_2 - E_1$.

362. Find the light pressure at the centre of an atom (uranium) bomb at the instant of explosion, on the assumption that the radiation is that of a black body. Take the data from Problem 306.

363. Determine the effective temperature, within the range of applicability of the Rayleigh–Jeans law, of the radiation of an infinitely long plane-parallel layer of isotropic material of thickness l and temperature T, neglecting reflexion of the radiation at the boundaries of the layer, and scattering inside the layer. Confine the discussion to the radiation in a direction normal to the layer. The coefficient of absorption of the material (per unit length of ray) is α.

364. The corona is the source of the Sun's radio radiation in the metre band. Find the flux S of the radio radiation from the Sun to the Earth in a band 1 Mc/s wide on the assumption that the radiation is thermal. The effective temperature of the corona radiation is $T \approx 10^6$ deg.

365. Let a medium consist of particles which can be at either of two energy levels E_1, E_2 ($E_2 > E_1$). (For instance, they could be particles with spin $\frac{1}{2}$ in a magnetic field.) The concentrations of the particles at levels 1 and 2 are N_1, N_2 respectively. A radio wave of frequency $\nu = (E_2 - E_1)/h$ is incident on the system. What will be the law of variation of its intensity I? Is amplification of the wave possible, and under what conditions?

CHAPTER II

ATOMIC AND NUCLEAR PHYSICS

§ 8. STRUCTURE OF THE ATOM AND SPECTRA

366. Find the frequency of vibration of the electron in J.J. Thomson's model of the atom with one electron. In this model the atom is a sphere with a charge $+e$ distributed uniformly over the sphere; inside the sphere a point charge $-e$ (the electron) moves.

367. How many spectral lines can be radiated by Thomson's model of the atom with one electron? What must be the radius of the atom if it radiates the wavelength $\lambda = 5000$ Å?

368. If a gas consists of Thomson atoms with one electron and no account is taken of the rotation of the atoms, what is the molar specific heat of the gas according to classical theory?

369. Show that, when an α-particle collides with a nucleus whose

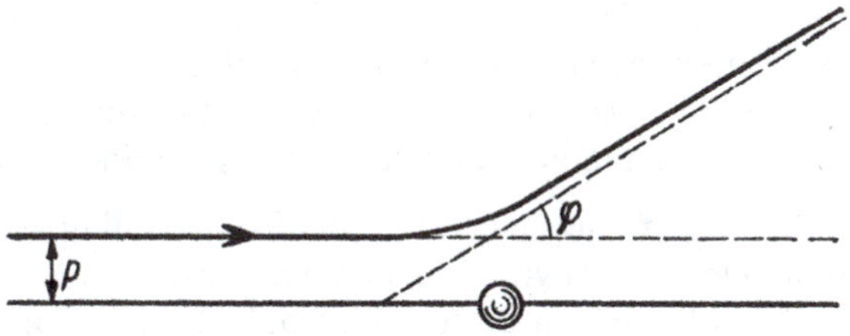

FIG. 10

charge is Ze, the impact parameter p is connected with the angle of deflection φ (Fig. 10) by

$$\cot\frac{\varphi}{2} = \frac{mpv^2}{2Ze^2},$$

where m is the mass of the α-particle and v is its velocity.

370. Use the result from the previous problem to find the effective scattering cross-section of α-particles in the angular interval φ to $\varphi + d\varphi$.

Note. The effective cross-section is the ratio of the scattered flux to the density of the incident flux of α-particles.

371. What is the number Δn of α-particles scattered in the interval of angles between 44° and 46° if $n = 10^4$ α-particles with 1 MeV energies are deflected from a copper plate 0·005 mm thick?

372. Find the ratio of the electrostatic and gravitational self-energies of a uniformly charged, gravitating sphere. What is this ratio for an electron and a proton?

373. An electron performs damped nearly-harmonic vibrations with a frequency $\nu = 10^{15}$ sec^{-1}. How long does it take (time Δt) to lose 0·9 of its initial energy?

Hint. It is shown in electrodynamics that the energy loss of a vibrating electron as a result of radiation is given by

$$\frac{dW}{dt} = -\frac{2}{3}\frac{e^2}{c^3}\dot{v}^2$$

(W is the energy and $\boldsymbol{v}$ the velocity of the electron).

374. How long (time Δt) would it take an electron, revolving about a proton in a circle of radius $a_0 = 0{\cdot}53$ Å to strike the nucleus as a result of radiation losses, if the classical theory were valid? Assume that, in spite of the approach of the electron to the nucleus, its acceleration is always approximately equal to the acceleration in its uniform motion about a circle of corresponding radius.

375. What is the frequency of the radiation according to classical theory of an electron moving in a circle at a rate of ν revolutions per second? In which of the Bohr orbits would the radiation be more intense: in the first or second?

376. Use Bohr's theory to find the radius a_0 of the first orbit of an electron and its velocity v in it.

377. What is the electric field-strength of the nucleus for the first and fourth Bohr orbits of the hydrogen atom?

378. Calculate the force F of attraction between an electron in the first orbit of a hydrogen atom and the nucleus. What is the ratio of this force to the force of gravitation between the electron and proton at the same distance?

379. Show that the frequency radiated on transition from the $(n+1)$-st to the nth Bohr orbit tends to the frequency of revolution of an electron in the nth orbit as n tends to infinity.

380. Find the wavelength of the first three lines of the Balmer series. Rydberg's constant for H is $R = 109{,}677{\cdot}58\ \text{cm}^{-1}$.

381. Find the wavelength of the lines of the Lyman, Paschen, Brackett and Pfund series.*

382. Find the wavelength corresponding to the limit of the Balmer series.

383. Find the least number of levels of a hydrogen atom, between which transitions are possible, accompanied by radiation of radio waves of wavelengths 1 cm, 10 cm, 1 m and 10 m.

384. Find the energy E of a hydrogen atom in the ground state, and calculate the ionisation potential V_i of the atom.

385. Express the ionisation potential of hydrogen in cal mol^{-1}.

386. The first excitation potentials of lithium (Li) and sodium (Na) are 1·84 and 2·1 V respectively. At what temperature is the mean kinetic energy of the particles equal to the excitation energy?

387. What are the relative numbers of hydrogen atoms in the ground state and in the first, second and third excited states at 2000 °K?

388. Evaluate the first excitation potential of hydrogen.

389. Find an expression for the frequencies of the line absorption spectrum of atomic hydrogen.

390. Will a hydrogen atom absorb radiation of frequency $\nu = 2Rc$? (R is Rydberg's constant, c is the velocity of light).

* All these series are covered by the Balmer–Ritz formula

$$\nu = R(1/m^2 - 1/n^2).$$

$m = 1,\ n = 2, 3, 4, \ldots$	Lyman series
$m = 2,\ n = 3, 4, 5, \ldots$	Balmer series
$m = 3,\ n = 4, 5, 6, \ldots$	Paschen series
$m = 4,\ n = 5, 6, 7, \ldots$	Brackett series
$m = 5,\ n = 6, 7, 8, \ldots$	Pfund series

391. What spectral lines appear when atomic hydrogen is excited by electrons with energies of 12·5 eV?

392. What lines appear if the electron energy in the previous problem is 14 eV?

393. A recombination process amounts to transition of an electron from a free state to one of the orbits of the ionised atom. Recombination may be accompanied by luminescence. What special features distinguish a recombination spectrum from the spectrum obtained by thermal excitation and impact excitation?

394. Find the ionisation potential of He^{+} and Li^{++} ions.

395. Find the wavelength of the resonance line of He^{+}.

396. What is the expression for Rydberg's constant R_∞ for an infinitely heavy nucleus in terms of fundamental constants?

397. Find an expression for the energy of the terms of a hydrogen-like atom (charge on the nucleus Ze), taking into account the finiteness of the mass of the nucleus.

398. Rydberg's constants for hydrogen and helium are respectively $R_H = 109{,}677{\cdot}6\ \text{cm}^{-1}$ and $R_{He} = 109{,}722{\cdot}3\ \text{cm}^{-1}$. Find the ratios m_H/m and m_{He}/m_H, where m_H and m_{He} are the masses of the proton and α-particle; m is the mass of the electron.

399. Find the difference in wavelength between the H_α and D_α lines (the first line of the Balmer series for deuterium). Find also the difference $H_\gamma - D_\gamma$.

400. What is the voltage difference between the ionisation potentials of deuterium (D) and of hydrogen (H)? Express the difference between the ionisation energies of hydrogen and deuterium in calories per mole.

401. Determine the orbits such that transition between them in the case of a helium ion He^{+} is accompanied by radiation close to H_α.

402. What is the difference between the wavelength of the H_α line and the wavelength of the He^{+} spectrum line corrsponding to it? (See the previous problem.)

403. According to modern data, the Rydberg constants for hydrogen and deuterium are respectively

$$R_H = (109{,}677{\cdot}576 \pm 0{\cdot}012)\ \text{cm}^{-1};$$
$$R_D = (109{,}707{\cdot}419 \pm 0{\cdot}012)\ \text{cm}^{-1},$$

and the atomic masses:

$$H = 1{\cdot}008142 \pm 0{\cdot}000003 \quad \text{(physical scale)}$$

$$D = 2{\cdot}014735 \pm 0{\cdot}000006 \quad \text{(physical scale)}.$$

The Faraday constant is

$$F = Ne = (2{\cdot}89366 \pm 0{\cdot}00003) \times 10^4 \text{ e.s.u. mol}^{-1}$$

$$= (9652{\cdot}19 \pm 0{\cdot}11) \text{ e.m.u. mol}^{-1} \quad \text{(physical scale)}.$$

Use these data to find e/m for an electron.

404. Close artificial Earth's satellites move with velocities of the order $V = 8 \text{ km sec}^{-1}$. Could an hydrogen (H), nitrogen (N) or oxygen (O) atom, elastically reflected from a satellite, ionise an atom of the same type in the atmosphere? The ionisation potentials of hydrogen, nitrogen and oxygen are respectively 13·60; 14·47; 15·56 eV.

405. What is the orbital magnetic moment of a hydrogen atom in the ground state according to Bohr's theory?

Hint. The magnetic moment of a current is $\mu = IS/c$, where I is the current, S is the surface area round which the current flows, and c is the velocity of light.

406. What is the ratio of the orbital moment μ of an electron in the nth circular Bohr orbit to its angular momentum l?

407. Show that the answer to the previous problem is also correct for elliptic orbits.

408. Find the energy of the magnetic interaction of two hydrogen atoms 3×10^{-6} cm apart. Assume that the electrons in the atoms move in the first Bohr orbits and that the planes of the orbits of the two atoms are parallel. Neglect electron spin.

409. What is the initial angular velocity ω with which a cylinder rotates, suspended in a magnetic field of field-strength H oersteds directed parallel to its axis, when the direction of the field is reversed? Assume that the cylinder is magnetised to saturation. (The angular momentum of an electron in an atom is equal to l.)

410. Find the ratio of the magnetic moment of an electron in an atom to its angular momentum, given the value of ω (see the previous problem) and the magnetic moment of the cylinder in the field.

411. What value of ω is to be expected in the simplified Einstein–de Haas experiment (Problem 409), if the length of the cylinder is 1 cm, its mass 1 g, its material iron, and if its assumed that the angular momentum of each atom is equal to the angular momentum of an electron in the first Bohr orbit?

412. What are the angular momentum l and the magnetic moment μ of an electron? What is the ratio of these two magnitudes?

413. Find the possible multiplicities of H, He, Li, Mg, Fe, Hg, U and Cl atoms.

414. What are the possible multiplicities of Sr^+, Li^+, Ca^+, C^{++} and O^{++++}?

415. What is the highest multiplicity of an atom of group III?

416. What is the number of levels into which the term with $l = 3$ splits in a magnetic field in the normal Zeeman effect? What is the energy difference between neighbouring levels?

417. What is the number of components into which the spectral line, connected with the transition $l = 3 \rightarrow l = 2$ splits in a magnetic field in the normal Zeeman effect?

418. Calculate the splitting of the level $n = 2, l = 1$ of hydrogen due to the magnetic interaction of the spin with the orbit.

419. Find the doublet splitting of the first line of the Lyman series; notice that the state $n = 1$ does not split, whilst the state $n = 2$ splits into the number calculated in the previous problem.

Note. The calculated splitting is not equal to the observed one, since no account is taken in the calculation of relativistic corrections and apart from that, the calculation itself is too crude.

420. Show that, if account is taken of the magnetic interaction of the spin with the orbit, the intervals between components of one multiplet (in the frequency scale) have integral ratios to one another. What are the integers?

Hint. The energy of the interaction of the spin with the orbit is proportional to $\cos(\widehat{\boldsymbol{l} \cdot \boldsymbol{s}})$, where $\boldsymbol{l}$ is the orbital and $\boldsymbol{s}$ the spin angular momentum.

421. Into how many components does the term with internal quantum number j split in a weak magnetic field?

422. Into how many components does a beam of hydrogen atoms split in a Stern–Gerlach experiment?

423. Find the term splitting of an atom of the alkali metal group when placed in a weak magnetic field. Regard the spin and orbital angular momenta as having the same direction.

424. How many components are produced when the sodium (Na) line corresponding to the transition

$$\left\{\begin{matrix} l = 3 \rightarrow l = 2, \\ j = 3\frac{1}{2} \rightarrow j = 2\frac{1}{2} \end{matrix}\right\}$$

splits in a weak magnetic field?

425. For the sodium (Na) line of the previous problem, find the number of components of the anomalous Zeeman effect which are polarised along the magnetic field.

426. What is the maximum possible number of electrons possessing a given principal quantum number n?

427. Show that the total angular momentum of a closed shell is zero.

428. What is the maximum possible number of electrons possessing given values of the principal and azimuthal quantum numbers?

429. How many terms are obtained when the ground state level of a hydrogen atom splits due to interaction of the magnetic moments of the electron and proton (hyperfine splitting)? What is the order of the energy difference ΔE between the sublevels of the hyperfine structure?

430. What is the order of magnitude of the wavelength of the radiation corresponding to transition between sublevels of the hyperfine structure of the ground state level of hydrogen (see the previous problem with $r = 2 \times 10^{-9}$ cm)?

431. A vessel filled with mercury (Hg) vapour at low pressure absorbs per sec 10^{16} quanta of resonance radiation of Hg from a mercury lamp. The life of an mercury atom in the excited $2\,^3P$ state is $\approx 10^{-7}$ sec. How many excited mercury atoms are to be found simultaneously in the vessel?

432. What proportion of sodium (Na) atoms is excited to emit of the D line ($\lambda = 5890$ Å) in the flame of a Bunsen burner (2000 °K).

433. Experiment shows that, for sodium vapour in the Bunsen flame ($T = 2000\,°K$), $n = 2000$ quanta ($\lambda = 5890$ Å) are emitted per second per atom. Find the average life t of an excited sodium atom.

434. What is the distance r from which the naked eye can see the light from a laser, generating 10 kW in the continuous operation at a frequency $\nu = 4 \times 10^{15}\ \text{sec}^{-1}$, if a parabolic mirror of diameter $D = 5$ m is used for forming the beam.

The eye sees a source if 60 quanta per second are incident on the pupil (pupil diameter $d = 5$ mm) at a frequency in the green part of the spectrum.

435. A ruby laser radiates energy $E = 10$ joules in a $T = 0{\cdot}5\,\mu$sec pulse in the form of an almost parallel beam of light of cross-section $S = 1\ \text{cm}^2$. The laser operating wavelength is $\lambda = 6943$ Å, the line width is $\Delta\lambda = 0{\cdot}01$ Å.

Determine from the spectral density of the radiated energy the effective temperature T_{eff} in the laser beam: (1) Close to the laser without focusing; (2) With the maximum possible narrowing of the beam in the focus.

436. A ruby laser radiates a $T = 0{\cdot}5\ \mu$sec pulse of energy $E = 1$ joule at $\lambda = 6943$ Å in the form of an almost parallel pencil with cross-sectional area $S = 1\ \text{cm}^2$. Find: (1) The light pressure p on an area close to the laser and perpendicular to the beam; (2) The light pressure p on an area perpendicular to the beam with maximum possible concentration of the beam (in the region $\sim \lambda^2$); (3) The electric field strength E in the region of maximum possible concentration of the beam.

Note. Assume that the radiation is uniform during the pulse.

437. A particle with a charge e and mass m moves round a circle of radius r with velocity v_0. Suppose that, when the velocity of the particle changes, the motion still takes place round the same circle (under the action of forces that ensure a sufficiently small change in the orbit radius; for example, motion along a "groove"). Show that, as a result of switching on of a magnetic field of intensity H, the angular velocity of the particle changes by $\omega_L = -eH/2mc$ (this statement amounts to Larmor's theorem applied to the case in question).

438. Consider a particle moving round a circle in the presence of a magnetic field and show that the quantisation rule $mvr = hn/2\pi$ does not apply in this example.

Hint. Consider the process of switching on the field (see the previous problem) and show that, if $mvr = hn/2\pi$, the magnetic flux $\Phi = \pi r^2 H$ proves to be quantised, which is untrue in the general case, as is clear from simple physical considerations.

439. Using Bohr's quantisation rule (see the previous problem), show that the magnetic flux through an aperture in a large, hollow, superconducting cylinder is $\Phi = nhc/|e^*| = nhc/2e$ (here $|e^*|$ is the absolute value of the charge of the superconducting current carriers; these carriers are bound pairs of electrons, so that $|e^*| = 2e$, where e is the absolute value of the charge on the electron).

Hint. If the magnetic flux through a circle of radius r is Φ, the momentum of a particle with charge e^* is $p = mv + |e^*|\,\Phi/2\pi cr$ (assuming $e^* < 0$).

§ 9. X-Rays

440. The fact that X-rays are transverse waves was first proved by Barkla with the following experiment. A beam of X-rays is scattered by the body A (Fig. 11). The scattered radiation is incident on the body B and is again scattered. The transverse character is

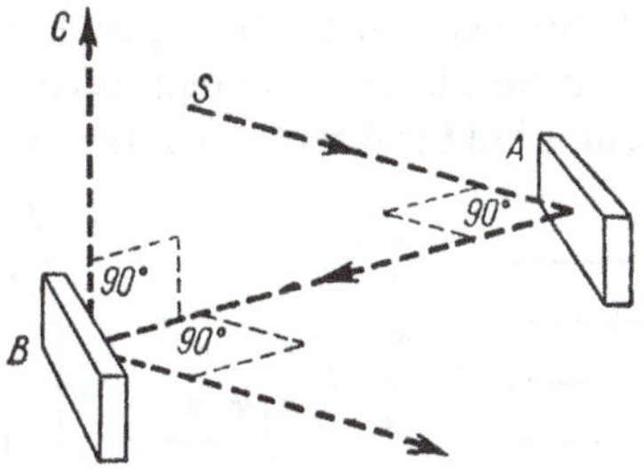

Fig. 11

proved by the fact that the intensity of the second scattered radiation in the direction BC is zero. Explain the underlying idea. Why are the bodies A and B made of material of small atomic weight? (The bodies were made of carbon in Barkla's experiment.)

441. Calculate approximately the frequency and wavelength of the K_α-line of molybdenum (Mo), and the energy of a quantum corresponding to this line.

442. Find approximately the minimum voltage V on an X-ray tube at which lines of the K_α series of molybdenum (Mo), copper (Cu) and iron (Fe) start to appear.

443. Find the edge of the absorption *K*-band of molybdenum (Mo), copper (Cu) and iron (Fe).

444. Can the K_α-radiation of iron (Fe) lead to secondary γ-radiation of chromium (Cr) and cobalt (Co)?

445. How many nickel (Ni) lines are excited by the *K*-radiation of cobalt (Co)?

446. The wavelength of the K_α-line of one element is known to be 0·788 Å, and of another 0·713 Å. Do the elements belong to the same row in the periodic table? What are the elements?

447. What is the first element at which the *L*-series appears?

448. Find the voltage on an X-ray tube, given that there is no wavelength less than 0·206 Å in the continuous spectrum radiated by it.

449. The sphere of an electroscope is irradiated by X-rays. The electroscope leaves cease to separate when the sphere potential is 8 kV. Find the wavelength λ of the incident radiation.

450. What is the maximum velocity v of electrons ejected from lead by the characteristic radiation of iron?

451. A linear lattice (chain of scattering centres) of period a is placed in the path of a parallel beam of light perpendicularly to the direction of the beam. Find the directions at the diffraction maxima

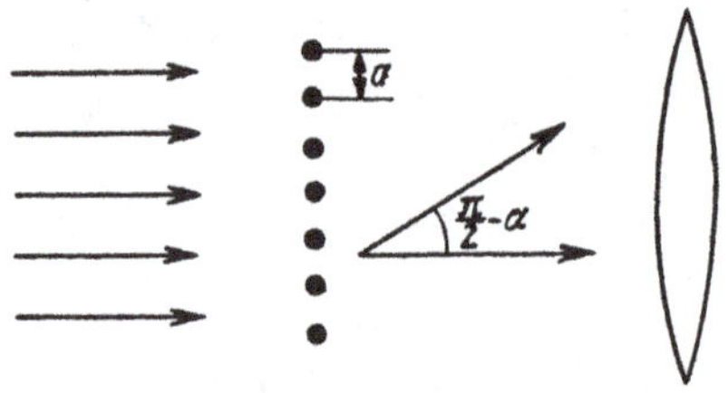

FIG. 12

and the diffraction pattern in the focal plane of a lens mounted perpendicularly to the incident beam (Fig. 12).

452. (1) What change occurs in the diffraction conditions at the chain if the light is incident at an angle α_0 to it (α_0 is the angle between the light beam and the chain)? (2) If the chain is of length L, what is the condition, in the case $\alpha_0 = \pi/2$, for the diffraction pattern to be observable without a lens on a screen mounted perpendicularly to the incident beam?

453. In the case of diffraction from a linear lattice, what pattern will be observed on a screen mounted perpendicularly to the direction of the chain, if the light is normally incident on the lattice?

454. Given a plane rectangular point diffraction lattice of periods a and b, find the diffraction pattern on a remote screen whose plane is parallel to the plane of the lattice. What are the maxima when the light is normally incident?

455. An X-ray beam is incident on a three-dimensional rectangular point lattice, its direction being parallel to one rib of the parallelepiped forming the cell of the lattice. Find the directions at the diffraction maxima and the conditions under which these maxima can be observed.

456. Find the directions for the diffraction maxima when a X-ray beam is incident from an arbitrary direction on a three-dimensional cubical lattice of constant a.

What condition must be satisfied by the wavelength λ in order for the maxima to be observed?

457. Use the conditions obtained in solving the previous problem to find the angle 2ϑ between the incident and diffracted beams for a cubical lattice.

458. Show that, in a crystal of cubical structure, the distance between the planes with indices khl is equal to

$$d = \frac{a}{\sqrt{h^2 + k^2 + l^2}}.$$

Hint. The Bragg condition is a consequence of the results obtained in Problems 456 and 457, since $a/\sqrt{n_1^2 + n_2^2 + n_3^2} = d/n$, where n is a divisor of n_1, n_2, n_3.

459. Is X-ray diffraction possible at an optical diffraction grating with a constant of 1 micron, and if so, under what conditions?

460. A sample consisting of fine crystals is placed in the path of a monochromatic X-ray beam (the Debye–Scherrer method). What sort of diffraction pattern is observed on a screen perpendicular to the incident beam? How is the distance z from the point of maximum intensity on the screen to the central spot related to the distance R from the sample to the screen (Fig. 13)?

461. How many atoms are there per elementary cell in crystals with simple cubic, body-centred cubic and face-centred cubic cells?

462. Find the lattice constants of iron (body-centred cubic) and sodium chloride (NaCl) (regarded for simplicity as a simple cubic lattice, i.e. the difference between the sodium and chlorine atoms is neglected), given that the density $\varrho_{NaCl} = 2{\cdot}164\ \text{g cm}^{-3}$ and $\varrho_{Fe_\alpha} = 7{\cdot}86\ \text{g cm}^{-3}$.

463. Find the wavelength of the L_α line for W, if a fourth order spectrum is observed when it is incident on a sodium chloride (NaCl) crystal at an angle 31°32′ to the reflecting plane (001).

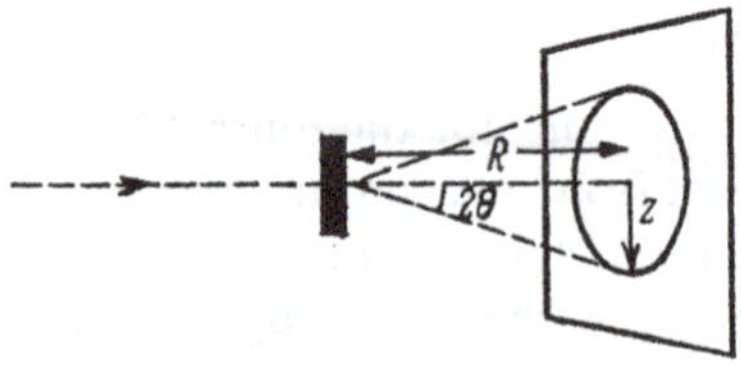

FIG. 13

464. Find the lattice constant of sylvinite (KCl) if the K_α-line of iron is reflected from the (001) face at an angle 18°3′ in the second order.

465. Find the material of the anticathode if the smallest glancing angle of radiation incident on the (001) plane of the sodium chloride (NaCl) crystal, at which a maximum is observed, is 17°. The tube voltage is large enough for the K-series of the element to be excited. Take only the K_α-line into account.

§ 10. THE QUANTUM NATURE OF LIGHT. THE WAVE PROPERTIES OF PARTICLES

466. Find the mass of a photon of visual light ($\lambda = 5000$ Å).

467. What is the wavelength of a photon if its mass is equal to the rest mass of an electron?

468. Find the momentum of a photon of visual light ($\lambda = 5000$ Å). Compare it with the momentum of a hydrogen molecule at room temperature. The mass of the hydrogen molecule is $M = 3{\cdot}35 \times 10^{-24}$ g.

469. At what wavelength is the momentum of a photon equal to the momentum of a hydrogen molecule at room temperature? (See the previous problem.)

470. Compare the energy of a photon ($\lambda = 5000$ Å) with the kinetic energy of the translational motion of a hydrogen molecule at room temperature.

471. The average wavelength of the radiation of an incandescent lamp with metallic filament is 12,000 Å. Find the number of photons emitted by a 200 W lamp per unit time.

472. Express the energy E of a light quantum in terms of its momentum and mass.

473. Show that a free electron cannot emit light quanta, since the assumption that it can implies that the laws of conservation of momentum and conservation of energy are not fulfilled simultaneously.

474. Use the quantum aspect of light to derive the formula for the Doppler effect, on the assumption that the light source moves with a non-relativistic velocity.

475. Do the same for a source which moves with a relativistic velocity.

476. In the previous problem, consider the nature of the dependence of the frequency ν on the angle Θ as $\beta \to 1$. Estimate the angle Θ, starting from which the radiated frequency is small compared with the frequency radiated at the angle $\Theta = 0$.

477. When a charged particle moves rapidly in a region of space filled by isotropic electromagnetic radiation (for instance, light from the Sun and stars), the particle loses energy as a result of the interaction with the radiation (assuming that the energy of the particle is greater than the energy of the photons which make up the radiation). Assuming that the particle is ultrarelativistic (its energy $E_0 \gg mc^2$) and that it collides head-on with the photon, find the particle energy change $E_0 - E = \Delta E$ and the energy of recoil $\hbar\omega$ of the photon. Assume that the energy $\hbar\omega_0$ of the photons (before collision) is small compared with $\hbar\omega$. Analyse the result. What is the energy $\hbar\omega$, if the particle is an electron with energy $E_0 = 2{\cdot}5 \times 10^9$ eV and $\hbar\omega_0 = 1$ eV.

478. An electron with energy $E_0 \gg mc^2$ is scattered by a photon with energy $\hbar\omega_0 \ll mc^2$. Under what circumstances does the energy of the photon satisfy the condition $\hbar\omega \ll mc^2$ in a co-ordinate system in which the electron is at rest?

479. What energy losses are sustained by an ultra-relativistic electron as a result of its "friction" in a radiation field (they are usually called "Compton losses"; see Problem 478). Assume that $E \ll (mc^2)^2/4h\omega_0$. Take account of glancing collisions by dividing the losses by 4.

480. An electron with energy $E_0 = 10^{10}$ eV starts to move at the instant $t_0 = 0$ in a field of black-body radiation with energy density $W_{ph} = 1$ eV cm^{-3} and the temperature of the Sun. What will be the energy of the electron after 10^6 and 10^8 years?

481. An electron with initial energy $E_0 = 10^{10}$ eV moves from the galactic space in the direction of the Sun's centre. What energy does the electron lose on the way to the photosphere as a result of "Compton" losses?

482. The effect of a medium on the propagation of light can be taken into account by introducing a refractive index n. If we avoid going into details about the mechanism of the phenomena, we can introduce the same concept for describing the quantum properties of light in a medium. We obtain agreement with experiment by supposing that the quantum momentum is $p = h\nu n/c$, and the quantum energy $E = h\nu$ (instead of $p = h\nu/c$ and $E = h\nu$ *in vacuo*). Use these relationships to derive an expression for the Doppler effect when a source moves in a medium with a non-relativistic velocity.

483. Do the same for sources moving with relativistic velocities. Investigate specially the case when the source velocity exceeds the phase velocity of the emitted light in the medium.

484. Investigate the nature of the dependence in the previous problem of the frequency of the emitted light on the angle Θ as $\beta \to 1$ for two cases: (a) $n > 1$, (b) $n < 1$.

485. Use the result obtained from Problem 483 to find the condition under which Cherenkov radiation is obtained, and the connexion between the direction of this radiation and its frequency ν.

486. An electron moves in a dispersive medium with continuously increasing velocity. At what frequency does Cherenkov radiation begin? Neglect absorption.

487. An electron moves in a medium without dispersion with continuously increasing velocity. At what frequency does Cherenkov radiation begin?

488. A particle moves in a medium parallel to the axis of a narrow cylindrical channel. What are the sectional dimensions of the channel if the radiation intensity in the Cherenkov and Doppler effects is of the same order as when the motion occurs in a continuous medium?

489. A particle moves uniformly in a medium in which, by radiating a photon, it can transmit energy $l\hbar\omega_0$ and momentum $l\hbar\boldsymbol{k}_0$, where $l = 0, \pm 1, \pm 2$, etc. (Such a situation is obtained for instance if the particle moves in a medium, the dielectric constant of which varies according to the law $\varepsilon = \varepsilon_0 + \varepsilon_1 \cos[\omega_0 t - (\boldsymbol{k}_0 \cdot \boldsymbol{r})]$, $\varepsilon_0 \gg |\varepsilon_1|$.) Find the frequency ω of the wave which is radiated under these conditions at an angle Θ to the direction of the particle velocity $\boldsymbol{v}$.

490. Are there conditions (and if so, what) under which it may be expected that Cherenkov radiation will occur when electromagnetic waves are propagated in a medium?

491. An X-ray quantum (frequency ω_0, wave vector $\boldsymbol{k}_0$) is propagated in a medium, and forms as a result of scattering an X-ray quantum and a soft (optical) photon of frequency Ω and wave vector $\boldsymbol{K}$ (such Raman scattering is only possible when there is an interaction between radiations of different frequencies, i.e. it is a non-linear effect). Find the angle at which the soft quantum is emitted.

492. For an extraordinary wave in a uni-axial crystal (refractive index $n^2 = \varepsilon_\perp \varepsilon_\parallel (\varepsilon_\perp \sin^2\vartheta + \varepsilon_\parallel \cos^2\vartheta)^{-1}$; $\varepsilon_\perp > 0$; $\varepsilon_\parallel < 0$), find the conditions for excitation of:

(1) Cherenkov radiation for a charge moving with constant velocity v along the optical axis of the crystal;

(2) (a) the normal Doppler radiation of frequency ω,

(b) the anomalous Doppler radiation of frequency ω (both (a) and (b) for a particle oscillating in an external field of frequency Ω and moving with constant velocity v along the optical axis of the crystal).

(3) Find the conditions under which anomalous Doppler radiation exists but Cherenkov radiation is absent, for a charge moving with the same velocity as the oscillator.

493. An atom moves along the axis of a narrow channel in a non-dispersive medium with a super-velocity of light. It is initially in its ground state. What will be the energy level of the atom after traversing a very long path?

494. Find the wavelength change in the Compton effect, if the observation is carried out perpendicularly to the direction of the primary radiation beam.

495. Find the angle between the direction of motion of a recoil electron and the direction of the primary quantum, if the quantum is scattered at a right-angle ($\varphi = \pi/2$).

496. What is the energy acquired by the recoil electron under the conditions of the previous problem?

497. Find the maximum wavelength change when light is scattered by protons.

498. What is the change in wavelength of the light radiated by a hydrogen atom as a result of recoil sustained by the nucleus (proton) from the incident light quantum? (See also Problems 658 and 659.)

499. According to classical electromagnetic theory of light, the light energy flux from a source is propagated continuously in all directions. According to this theory, how long does it take an individual atom of a tantalum cathode to collect enough energy for release of a photoelectron to be possible, if the cathode is 10 m from a 25 W lamp? The work function of tantalum is about 4 eV. Assume that the photoelectron receives all the energy stored in the tantalum atom, the diameter of which can be taken as about 3 Å.

500. Assuming that electromagnetic energy is propagated in accordance with classical theory and not in the form of quanta, find the time required for a copper atom to accumulate the energy needed for release of a photoelectron of the *K*-shell under the action of hard X-rays. Assume that the atom absorbs all the incident energy. The atom cross-section is $\sigma = 10^{-15}$ cm^2. The X-ray flux is $S = 2 \times 10^3$ erg cm^{-2} sec^{-1} (the value of S corresponds to the radiation obtainable from modern X-ray tubes). The *K*-series of copper (Cu) is excited by electrons with energies not less than 8·86 keV.

501. Light quanta possess mass as well as inertia. It follows from this that, when the spectral lines radiated by heavy bodies (stars) are observed on the Earth, there must be a red-shift. Find the gravitational frequency shift in the general form (when light is propagated between points 1 and 2 in a gravitational field) when the light from stars is observed on the Earth. (See also Problem 663.)

502. Calculate the red shift of the *D*-lines of sodium (Na) emitted on the sun. The mass of the Sun is $M = 1{\cdot}99 \times 10^{33}$ g, its radius $R = 696{,}000$ km.

503. Under certain conditions a star can pass to the neutron state, i.e. become a neutron star, consisting practically of neutrons only. Regarding the mass of a neutron star as equal to the Sun's mass ($M_0 = 2 \times 10^{33}$ g), and the average distance between neutrons as 3×10^{-13} cm, find approximately the gravitational shift in the wavelength of the radiation emitted from the surface of the star. Regard the density of the star as constant throughout its volume.

504. Find the deflexion of a light ray when it passes close to the sun, using classical non-relativistic theory.

Hint. See Problems 501 and 502.

505. The theory of liquids and solids introduces the concept of sound quanta (phonons), which are the analogues of photons. Use the analogy to express the energy E and momentum p of a phonon in terms of the frequency ν_{ac} and velocity of propagation v_{ac} of acoustic waves.

506. Obtain the formula for the fine structure of the Rayleigh scattering lines by starting from the concepts of phonons and photons.

507. Find the de Broglie wavelength corresponding to an electron with energy 1, 10^4 or 10^5 eV. Neglect any corrections connected with the theory of relativity.

508. Find the de Broglie wavelength for electrons with energies 10^5, 10^{10} and 10^{16} eV, taking into account the dependence of the mass of the electron on the velocity.

509. Find the de Broglie wavelengths λ_1 and λ_2 of hydrogen and mercury atoms with energies of 1 and 10^6 eV, and the wavelength λ_3 for these atoms when moving with the average thermal velocity at 0°.

510. Find an expression for the refractive index of electronic waves in terms of the work function $U_0 = eV_0$ (V_0 is the internal potential of the crystal).

511. Show that the refraction law $\sin\varphi/\sin\varphi' = \mu$ holds when an electronic wave is refracted.

Hint. Only the normal component of the electron velocity changes on penetrating into the crystal.

512. What modification is required to the Bragg formula when account is taken of wave refraction at the crystal surface? Assume that the reflecting plane is parallel to the surface.

513. Find the internal potential of silver, if $\vartheta = 28°$ for electronic waves ($V = 100$ V) when undergoing fourth order reflexion from the (001) face. The lattice constant for silver is $a = 4{\cdot}0776$ Å.

514. What is the effect on the Laue condition for diffraction of electronic waves in a spatial lattice, when account is taken of refraction? Confine the discussion to a crystal of cubic structure and assume that the (001) plane is parallel to the crystal surface.

515. Starting from the requirement that the group velocity of the de Broglie waves be equal to the velocity of the particle motion, and using Rayleigh's formula, connecting the phase and group velocities, determine the phase velocity w of these waves, and find the connexion between the energy E of the particle and the frequency ν.

516. Find the change in the momentum of an electron, introduced

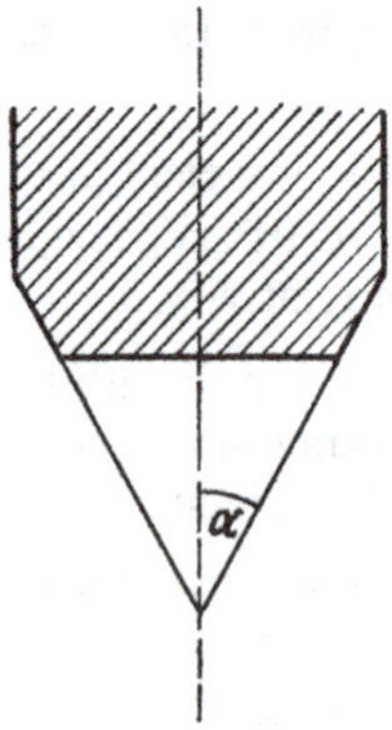

FIG. 14

by measuring its co-ordinates with the aid of a microscope (aperture α) (Fig. 14).

517. Find the connexion between Δp_x (see the previous problem) and the error in determining the co-ordinates of an electron with the aid of a microscope.

518. Taking the wave properties of the electron into account, find the connexion between the errors Δp_x and Δx when measuring the momentum and co-ordinates of an electron, if Δx is determined by the width d of the slit through which the electron beam passes (Fig. 15).

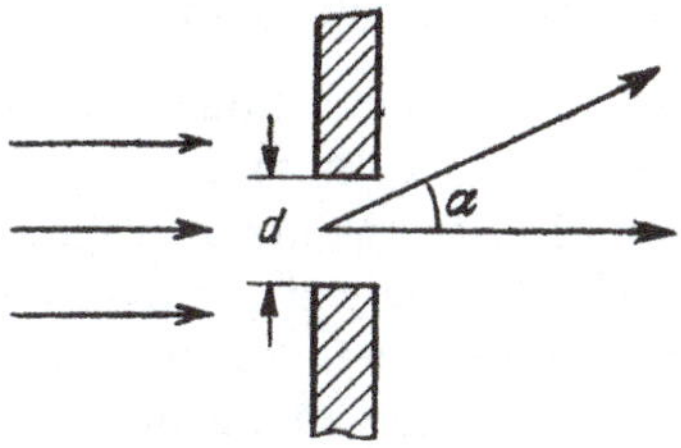

FIG. 15

519. The position of the centre of a sphere of mass 1 g and the position of an electron are known to an accuracy of 0·01 cm. Find the least error with which the velocity of the sphere and the electron velocity can be determined.

520. Estimate the error in measuring the velocity of the electron of a hydrogen atom.

521. Find the order of magnitude of the radius and energy of a hydrogen atom in the ground state by using the Heisenberg principle. Estimate by the same method the size and energy of the ground state of a diatomic molecule, which can be regarded approximately as a linear oscillator with natural frequency ω_0 and reduced mass μ.

522. The ideas of a plasma can be applied within limits to the solid state. What is the plasma frequency ν in metals with one free electron per atom? What is to be expected from the quantum point of view as regards the possible values of the energy of the plasma waves? Find the frequency ν and energy loss E on excitation of plasma waves in copper (atomic weight $A = 63{\cdot}57$, density $\varrho = 8{\cdot}9\ \text{g cm}^{-3}$).

§ 11. Nuclear Physics

523. How much water is needed to fill a 10-litre cloud chamber with saturated vapour at 23°? (See Table I, page 234.)

524. Find the temperature t_2 in a cloud chamber immediately after its rapid expansion. The chamber is filled with a mixture of air and water vapour, for which $\gamma = c_p/c_v = 1{\cdot}4$. The wall temperature is $t_1 = 20°$, the expansion coefficient is $k = V_2/V_1 = 1{\cdot}25$ (V_1 is the initial, V_2 the final volume of the chamber).

525. The supersaturation S in a cloud chamber is defined as the ratio of the vapour density ϱ_1 immediately after expansion (but prior to condensation) to the saturated vapour density ϱ_2 at the temperature T_2 also immediately after expansion. Find the expression for the supersaturation as a function of the partial pressures p_1 and p_2 of the vapour before and after expansion, the expansion coefficient $k = V_2/V_1$ and the specific heat ratio $\gamma = c_p/c_v$ of the mixture.

526. If γ_g and γ_v are the specific heat ratios c_p/c_v for the gas and vapour in a cloud chamber, the coefficient γ for the mixture can be determined from the formula

$$\frac{1}{\gamma - 1} = \frac{1}{\gamma_g - 1}\,\frac{p_g}{p} + \frac{1}{\gamma_v - 1}\,\frac{p_v}{p},$$

where p_g and p_v are the partial pressures of the gas and vapour, and $p = p_g + p_v$. The cloud chamber operates with a mixture of air and water vapour. Find its supersaturation for (1) $p = 20$ cm Hg, (2) $p = 1140$ cm Hg. The initial temperature of the chamber is 25°; the expansion coefficient $k = 1{\cdot}2$; $\gamma_{air} = 1{\cdot}4$; $\gamma_{H_2O} = 1{\cdot}3$. Find the supersaturation at the same pressures when alcohol is used instead of water vapour.

527. When the expansion coefficient (in the vapour–air system) exceeds 1·37, a thick fog appears throughout the cloud chamber even in the absence of an ionising source, which then settles down. Find the supersaturation corresponding to this expansion if the initial temperature is $t_1 = 20°$, and $\gamma = 1{\cdot}374$.

528. In the case of a liquid water bubble chamber, determine the radius of the bubble which is in a state of unstable equilibrium (the

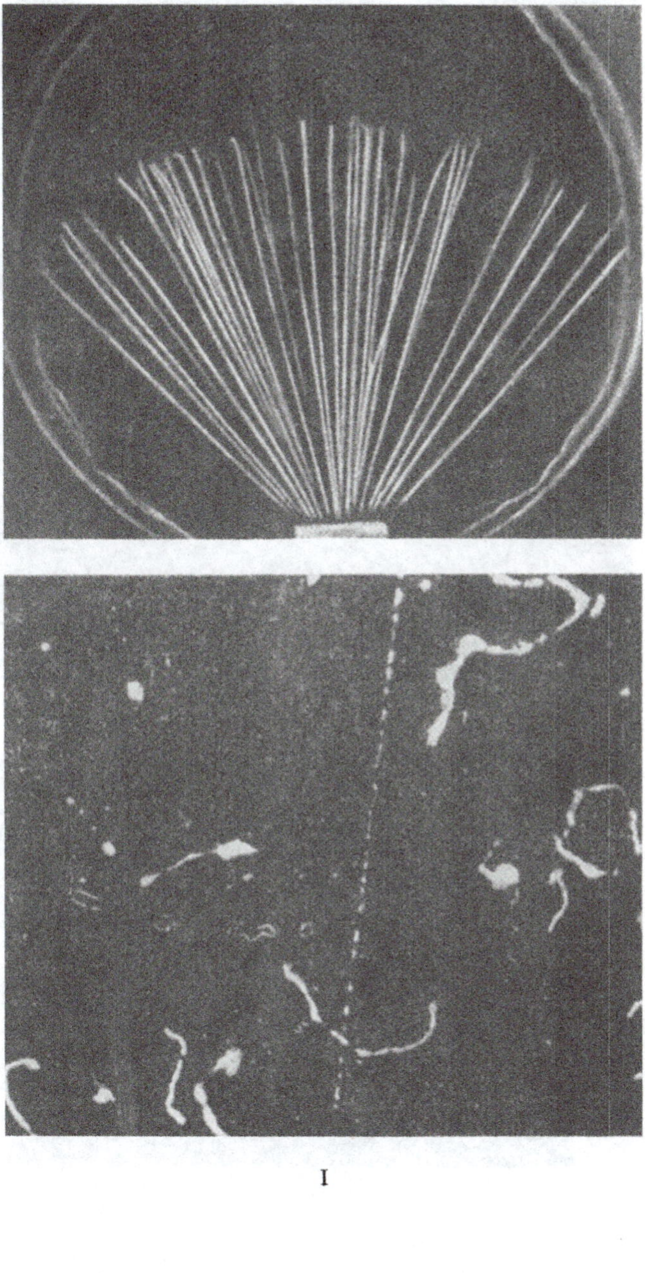

I

III

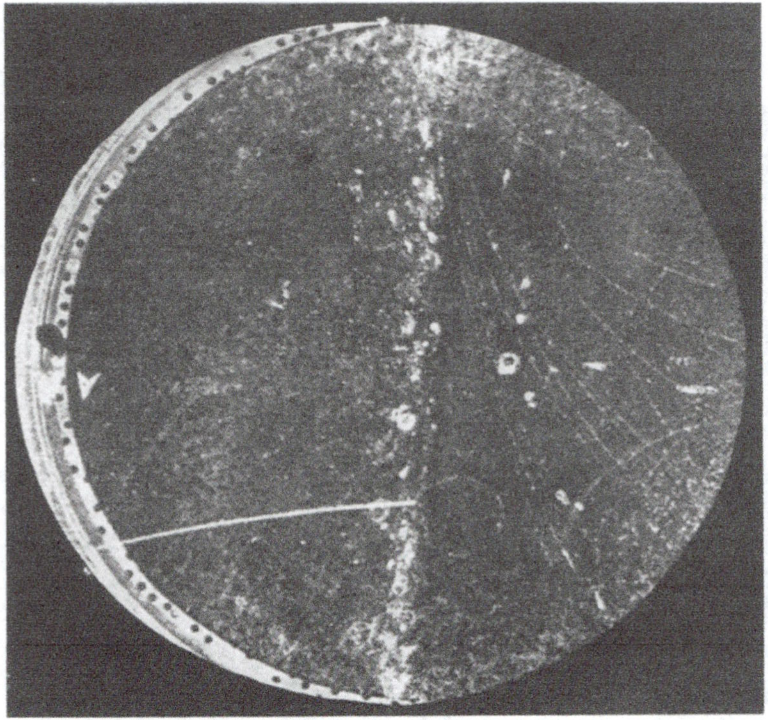

II

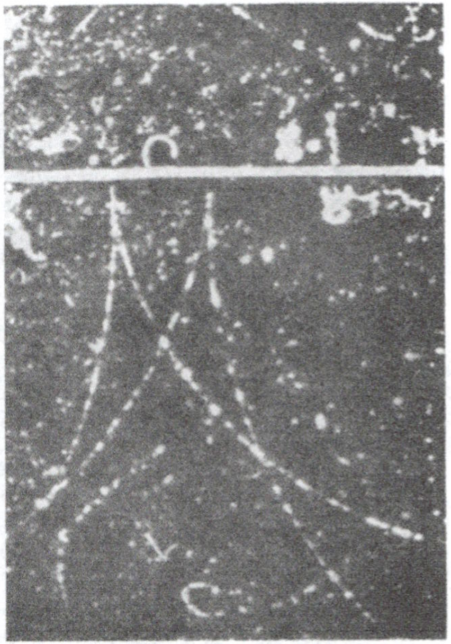

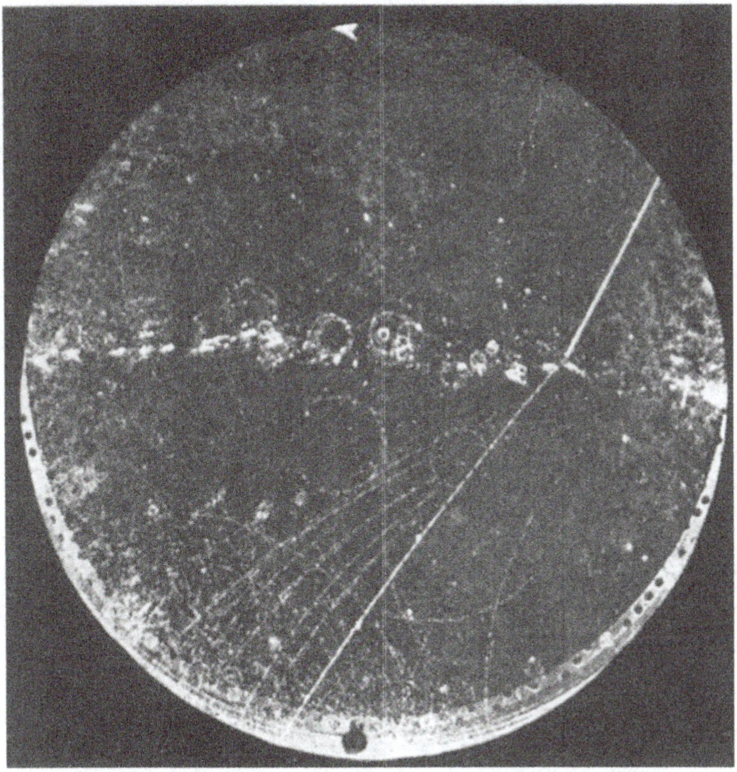

IV

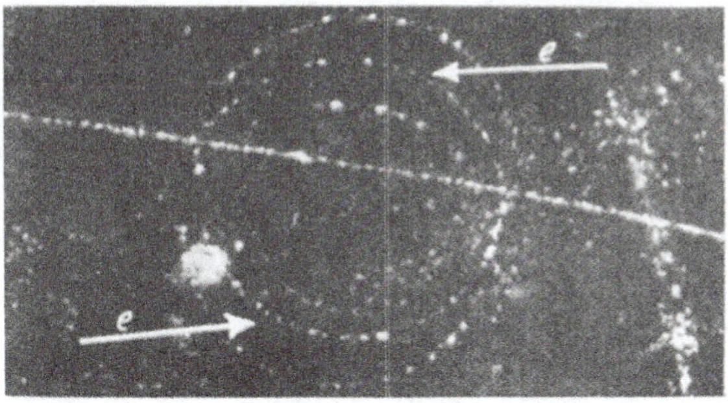

V

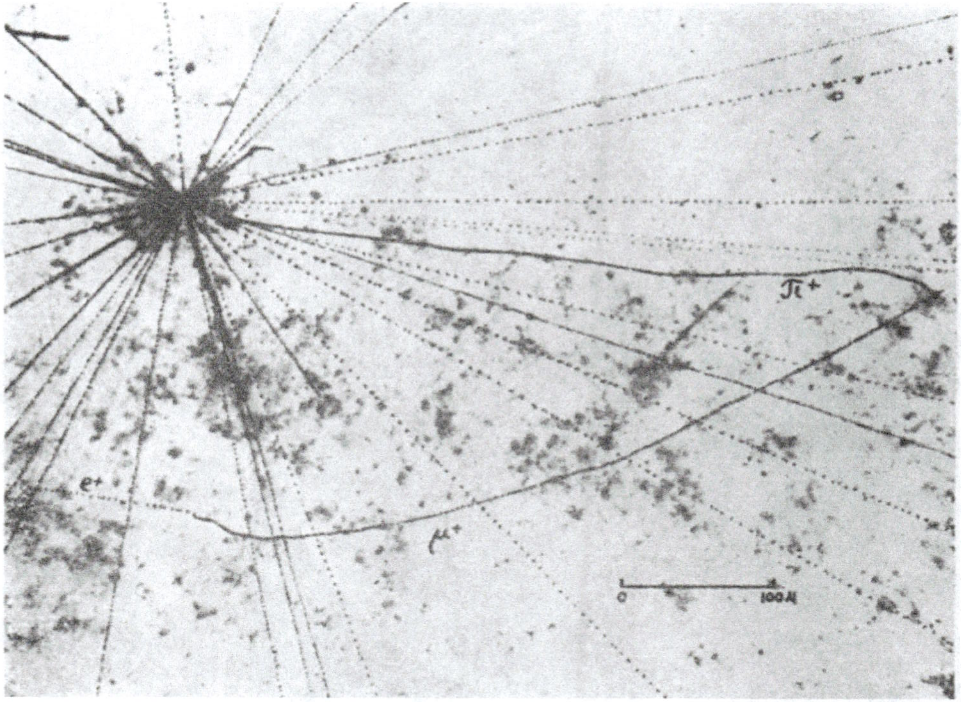

VI

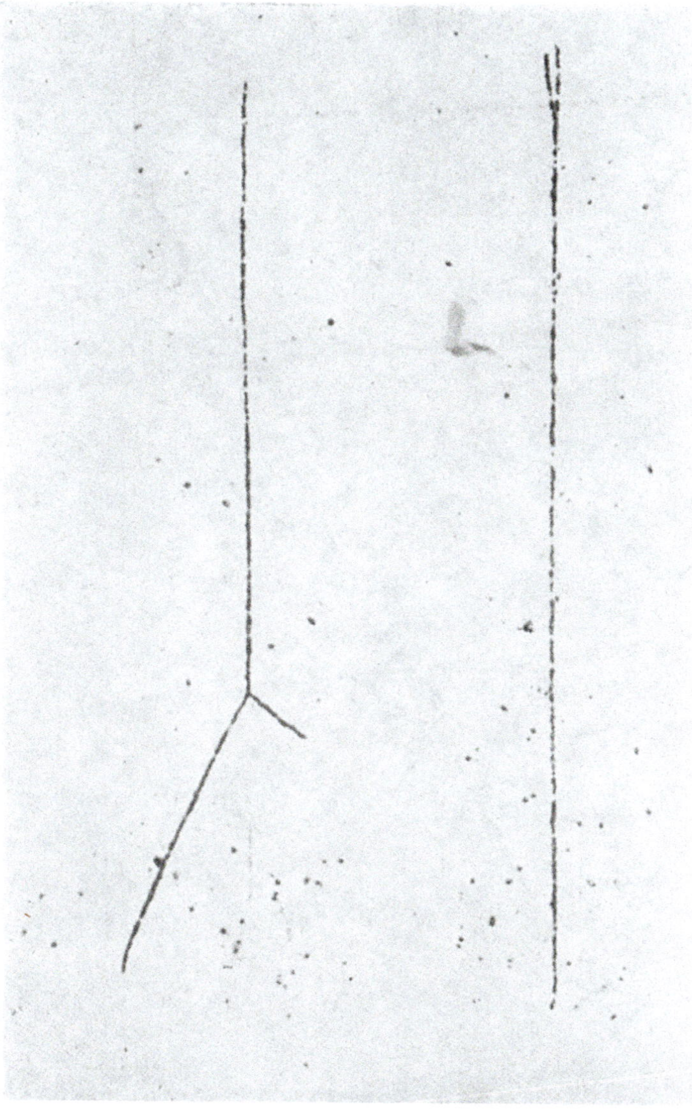

VII

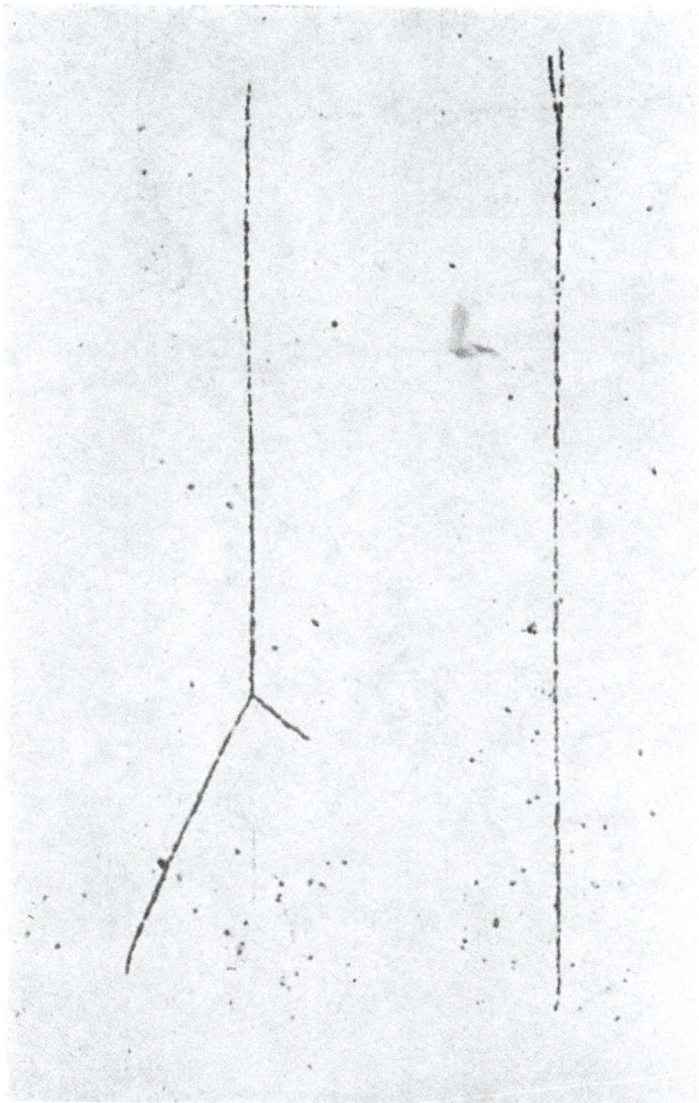

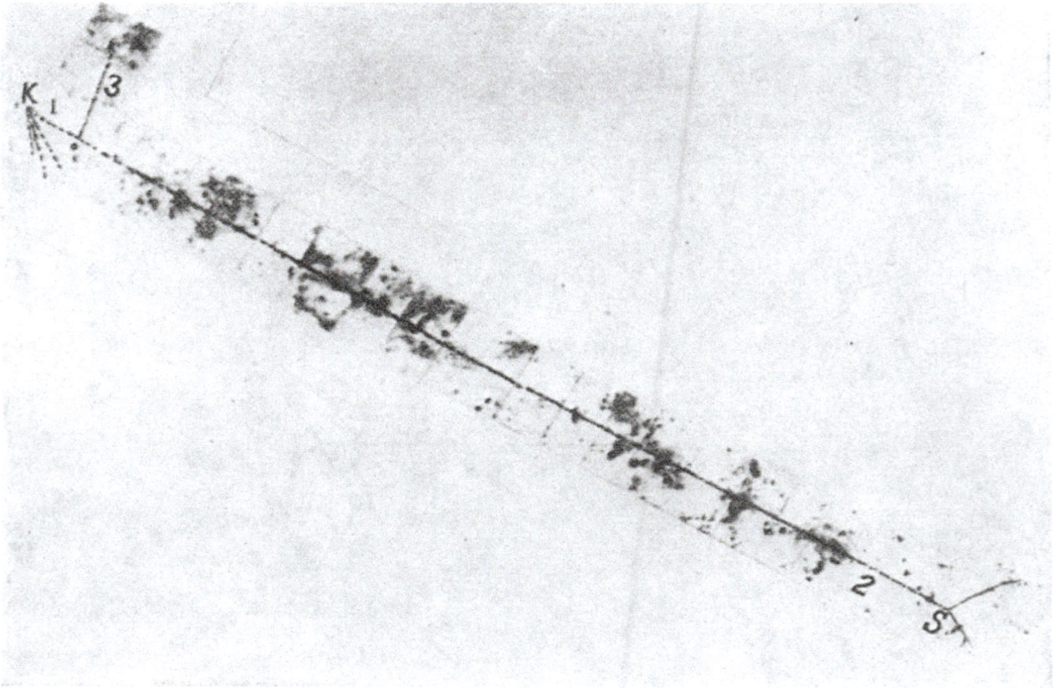

VIII

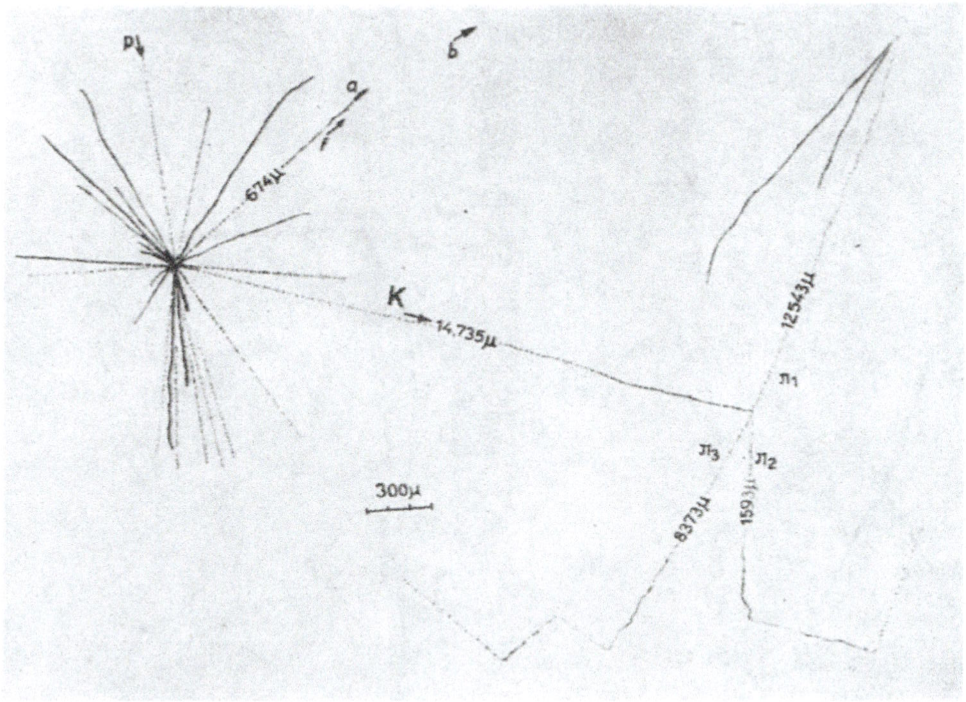

XI

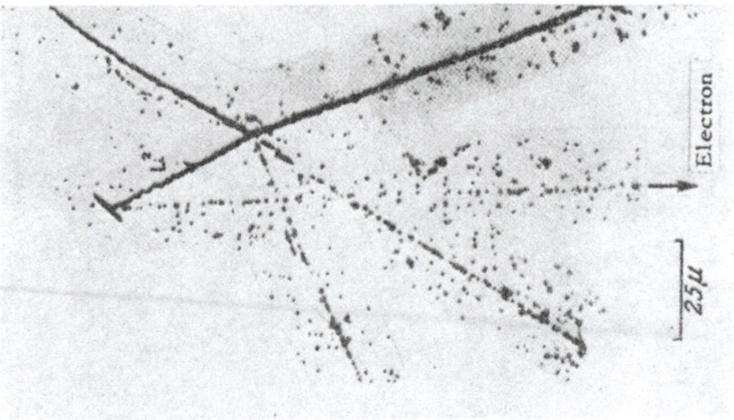

IX

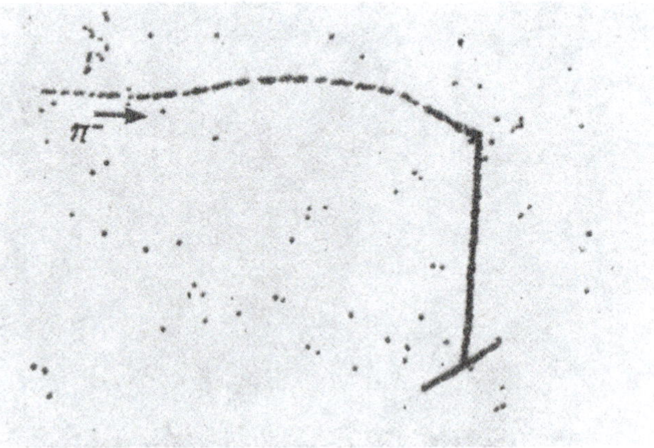

X

so-called critical radius R_{cr}), if the surface tension of liquid water is $\sigma = 0{\cdot}97$ dyne cm^{-1}, the liquid pressure is $p_1 = 1$ kg cm^{-2}, the liquid water saturated vapour pressure at the chamber temperature (27°K) is $p_v = 6$ kg cm^{-2}.

529. According to modern theory, the formation of bubbles along the track of a charged particle in a bubble chamber is due to δ-electrons with energies sufficient for the formation of a bubble of critical radius, but not large enough for their range to exceed the critical radius. Find the minimum energy in a propane bubble chamber at $T = 328$°K and pressure $p_1 = 5$ kg cm^{-2}. The surface tension of propane is $\sigma = 4{\cdot}46$ dyne cm^{-1}, the corresponding saturated vapour pressure is $p_v = 15$ kg cm^{-2}, the molar heat of vaporisation of propane is $q = 3{\cdot}9$ cal mol^{-1}. Neglect the work of expanding the bubbles.

530. Sharp breaks are sometimes observed at the end of straight tracks due to the collision of α-particles with the nuclei of atoms. Usually one out of a 100 α-particle tracks has a break. About 3×10^5 cloud droplets are formed along the track of an α-particle, of which about one third result from the primary transmission of energy to the electron of an atom. Find the probability of collision of an α-particle with a nucleus.

531. In comparison with α-particles (see the previous problem), β-particles form much thinner tracks in a cloud chamber (about 50 ions per centimetre length). The tracks of β-particles show discontinuities. The tracks of slow β-particles are unusually twisting. Determine from Photograph I the tracks of the α-particles, and of the fast and slow β-particles.

532. Photograph II was taken in a cloud chamber situated in a magnetic field. Lead foil was subjected to trans-irradiation by γ-rays with energy 17 MeV. Determine the particles observed in the chamber, and the direction of travel of the γ-quanta.

533. Photographs III and IV are of a cloud chamber filled with helium and operating in the γ-radiation beam of a synchrotron with energy not greater than 150 MeV. Determine the particles whose tracks are recorded on these photographs.

534. Photograph V was obtained in a cloud chamber in a magnetic field of 18,000 oersted. The tracks marked by arrows are caused by electrons. What sort of particle produces the central track?

535. A cloud chamber is used in an attempt to discover double β-decay in Ca^{48}. A fairly thin specimen of calcium weighing 5 g, enriched 85 per cent by the isotope Ca^{48}, is mounted in the chamber in such a way that events occurring during the 0·15 sec period of the photograph can be recorded. The geometrical efficiency of the device is 3/4. Find how many photographs have to be taken in order to verify that the half-period of this decay process exceeds 10^{19} years.

536. A propane bubble chamber is mounted in the bremsstrahlung beam of a betatron in order to study the photofission of carbon into three α-particles. Determine the cross-section σ of the process, if the beam of γ-rays passes along the diameter $D = 20$ cm of the chamber, the beam cross-section in the chamber is $S = 3\ \text{mm}^2$, the density of propane (C_3H_8) is $\varrho = 0{\cdot}33\ \text{gcm}^{-3}$, the number of effective quanta in the acceleration pulse is $f = 3 \times 10^4$, the number of photographs taken $K = 9300$, the number of recorded cases of photofission $n = 1000$.

537. Find the energy E of an electron if the radius of curvature ϱ of its track in a cloud chamber situated in a magnetic field $H = 10{,}000$ oersted, is 2 m.

538. Find the kinetic and total energies of a proton from the curvature of its track in a cloud chamber, situated in a magnetic field $H = 10{,}000$ oersted, if the measured sag of a segment with a chord $a = 20$ cm is $h = 2{\cdot}5$ mm.

539. If the mass of a particle carrying a single charge substantially exceeds the mass of an electron, and its energy is not very large, (less than 10^{12} eV for a proton and less than 10^{10} eV for a meson), the ionisation loss $(-dE/dx)_{\text{ion}}$ is independent of the mass and is a function of only the velocity of the particle:

$$(-dE/dx)_{\text{ion}} = f[\beta/(1-\beta^2)^{1/2}].$$

The values of f are given at the end of the book in Table II (page 234).

Measurement of the track of a meson in a cloud chamber in a magnetic field showed that $Hr = 0{\cdot}6 \times 10^5$ oersted cm, where H is the field-strength and r the radius of curvature of the track. The meson produces 780 ion pairs per centimetre of air. Find the mass of a meson, if an energy of 32 eV is required for the production of an ion pair.

Find the mass of a meson for the following data also: $(-dE/dx)$ of 10^3 electron Volts per centimetre of air. (1) 12·5; (2) 7·5; (3) 15·0; (4) 25.

$H \cdot r$ oersted cm: (1) 1·1; (2) 1·47; (3) 0·96; (4) 0·55.

Hint. Use Table II (page 234) to solve the problem graphically.

540. The range of a particle is

$$R = \int \frac{dE}{\left(-\dfrac{dE}{dx}\right)_{\text{ion}}} = \int \frac{dE}{f\left(\dfrac{\beta^2}{(1-\beta^2)^{1/2}}\right)} = \frac{M}{m} g\left(\frac{\beta}{(1-\beta^2)^{1/2}}\right),$$

where M is the mass of the particle, m is the mass of an electron (see the previous problem). The function g is given in Table III (page 235) at the end of the book. By measuring the range R and track curvature r in a cloud chamber, find the mass of the particle for the following data:

$Hr \times 10^4$ oersted cm (1) 5·5; (2) 5·5; (3) 3·87; (4) 1·74.
R centimetres in air (1) 18; (2) 4; (3) 6·5; (4) 770.

Hint. Solve the problem graphically by using Table III.

541. To measure the mass of a particle, a cloud chamber is partitioned by a lead sheet. The track curvature in a magnetic field is measured before and after passage through the lead sheet. The quantity $[(Hr)_1 - (Hr)_2]/\Delta x = d(Hr)/dx$ is calculated, where the indices 1 and 2 refer to the product (Hr) obtained before and after passage through the sheet. The results are set down in the following table:

(Hr) average $\times 10^5$ oersted · cm (1) 2·20; (2) 3·27; (3) 6·15.
$d(Hr)/dx \times 15^5$ oersted (1) 2·67; (2) 0·67; (3) 0·522.

Use Table V (page 235) for the function $d(Hr)/dx = \beta f/e$ (see Problem 539) to find the mass of the particle.

542. When ionising particles pass through a photographic emulsion they act on the silver bromide crystals in such a way that, after developing, they form a series of black grains of silver halide along the track of the particle. The grain density depends on the type of emulsion and the method of developing, and increases as the specific energy loss of the particle increases. At velocities $v \ll c$, we have approximately:

$$-\frac{dE}{dx} \approx \frac{4\pi Z^2 e^2 N}{mv^2},$$

where Ze is the charge on the particle, v is its velocity, N is the number of atoms per cubic centimetres, m is the mass of an electron.

(a) How is the direction of the particle motion determined from its track in the emulsion?

(b) How are the specific energy losses of protons, deuterons and α-particles related, given equal velocities, or alternatively, equal energies?

(c) Protons, deuterons and α-particles have the same $100\,\mu$ range in an emulsion. What are their relative specific energy losses at the start of the path? (Use Table IV, page 235.)

543. The range of a charged particle in a substance is given as a function of its velocity by

$$R = \frac{M}{mZ^2}\, g(v),$$

where M is the mass of the particle, Z is its charge, expressed in elementary charges, v is the velocity of the particle, m is the mass of an electron, $g(v)$ is a function which depends neither on the charge nor the mass (see Problem 540 and Table IV).

(a) The tracks of protons, deuterons and tritons in an emulsion have the same number of grains over equal pieces of track. How are the residual ranges and energies of these particles related?

(b) The range–energy relationship is known for protons (Table IV). Find the range–energy relationship for tritons in the same substance.

(c) The dependence of the number N of grains (over a section τ) on the range R, and $E = f(R)$, are known for protons. How can the energy of deuterons and tritons be determined when their tracks do not terminate in the emulsion?

544. A charged particle undergoes multiple scattering on its passage through a substance. The mean value of the projection (on the plane of the photographic plate) of the multiple scattering angle over the section τ is $\bar{\Phi} = KZ\sqrt{\tau}/pv$, where K is a scattering constant, usually determined experimentally, Z is the charge on the particle (expressed in elementary charges), p and v are the momentum and velocity of the particle. By measuring $\bar{\Phi}$ for a known particle, we can determine its energy. If the particle energy is known, we can find its mass from a knowledge of $\bar{\Phi}$.

Several tracks of unknown particles are recorded in photographic emulsions. How can the ratios of the masses of these particles be found, if their tracks terminate in the emulsion? (Use the method of scattering and the method based on grain counting.)

545. What tests can be used to distinguish the tracks of slow π^- and π^+ mesons, terminating in the emulsion?

546. Nuclear emulsions contain the light elements hydrogen, carbon, nitrogen, oxygen and the heavy elements silver, bromine (with about 0·6 per cent sulphur and iodine content). When investigating the interaction of particles with such nuclei, emulsions can be used as targets, which are simultaneously detectors of the charged products of the reaction.

Photograph VII illustrates the case of the decay of a light nucleus by a γ-quantum into three identical particles. Determine the type of nucleus and the reaction process.

In a similar star, two tracks 1 and 2 are established in an emulsion, their ranges being $R_1 = R_2 = 15{\cdot}3\ \mu$, whilst the angle between them is $\alpha = 75°$. Track 3 leaves the emulsion.

(a) Find the energy of the third particle and the energy of the γ-quantum producing the decay. Neglect the momentum of the γ-quantum, on the assumption that all three tracks are co-planar.

(b) Suppose that the reaction proceeds in two stages: particle 3 is first emitted and an intermediate nucleus is formed, then the intermediate nucleus splits up into particles 1 and 2. What is the intermediate nucleus and what is its excitation energy?

547. The microphotograph (Photograph VIII) shows a three-pronged star, formed as a result of the interaction of a γ-quantum with deuterium, with which the photographic emulsion was filled. The energy of the γ-quantum cannot exceed 250 MeV. As is clear from the photograph, particle 1 has formed a star at the end of its range (at the point K), and particle 2 has undergone elastic scattering at the point S.

(a) Determine the reaction corresponding to the star in question.

(b) What sort of nucleus has produced the scattering of particle 2, if it is known from the measurements that the angle between the tracks before and after scattering is 90°? (Would such an angle be observed between the tracks if the scattering of particle 2 took place at deuterium and the range of the deuterium after scattering proved to be twice the range of particle 2?)

548. In a star (Photograph IX), recorded on electron-sensitive plates, a dense track is observed, belonging to Li^8 and ending in two α-particles, which branch in opposite directions (a hammer or T track). At the end of the Li^8 range an electron track is also observed.

(a) What process has occurred at the end of the Li^8 nucleus range? What other nucleus could yield a similar track in the emulsion?

(b) Determine the maximum energy of the electron, if $E_{\alpha_1} = E_{\alpha_2} = 1{\cdot}5$ MeV.

549. By using photographic emulsions which are insensitive to electrons, the absorption of slow π^--mesons by Be^9 nuclei in the emulsion was observed. Photograph X illustrates one of the cases of absorption of a π^--meson by beryllium, accompanied by nuclear splitting. At the end of the meson track, only a T track is observed (see the previous problem). What reaction has occurred? Determine the energy of the decay products.

550. Photographic emulsions are often used as neutron detectors. Neutrons can be recorded from the proton recoil or from the characteristic reactions occurring when the neutrons react with elements specially introduced into the emulsion.

(a) In the case of slow neutrons, the reaction with B^{10} and Li^6 nuclei, introduced into the emulsion, can be used. The following reactions are expected:

$$Li_3^6 + n^1 \rightarrow He_2^4 + H_1^3; \quad B_5^{10} + n^1 \rightarrow Li_3^7 + He_2^4.$$

Find the total length of the α-particle and triton tracks in the first reaction and the energy of the α-particle and of the Li^7 nucleus in the second reaction. (Consider the case when the Li^7 nucleus is formed in the first excited state with excitation energy $\approx 0{\cdot}5$ MeV.)

(b) Fast neutrons are usually detected from proton recoil. What scattering characteristics must be measured in order to determine the neutron energy? (The direction of the neutron flux is usually known in the experiment.)

551. Photograph XI shows the microprojection of a star taken on an electron-sensitive pellicle stack. The star is induced by the cosmic particle P. The nuclear fission produces a K-meson, which splits up at the end of its travel into three π-mesons. The two π-mesons π_2 and π_3 give a μ-e-disintegration at the end of the range. One π-meson π_1 passes 14,130 μ through the emulsion, is absorbed by the nucleus and yields a star. The energies of the mesons π_2 and π_3 were found from the ranges ($R_{\pi_2} = 6050 \pm 250$ μ, $R_{\pi_3} = 10{,}700 \pm 200$ μ): $E_{\pi_3} = 17{\cdot}06 \pm 0{\cdot}85$ MeV, $E_{\pi_1} = 23{\cdot}61 \pm 0{\cdot}84$ MeV. The energy of π_1 is obtained by the scattering method: $R_{\pi_1} = 30{\cdot}8 \pm 6$ MeV. Find the charge and mass of the K-meson.

552. The cosmic ray meson flux density at sea-level is 1 meson $\text{cm}^{-2}\,\text{min}^{-1}$, and each meson produces 85 ion pairs per centimetre of path in air at normal atmospheric pressure. Calculate the current produced by mesons in a cylindrical ionisation chamber, radius 20 cm, height 30 cm, filled with air at 5 atm pressure. The chamber is mounted vertically. Assume that ionisation is only produced by mesons, incident vertically on the chamber.

553. Find the number of cosmic particles passing through an ionisation chamber of 8 cm diameter, if the collector potential increment is 0·2 V. The chamber is filled with air at 1 atm pressure. The collector capacity is 10 pF. On the average one cosmic particle produces 60 ion pairs per centimetre path in air. The particles are incident perpendicular to the chamber axis.

554. Find the mean free path of electrons in the operating volume of a chamber (the so-called "effective" depth of the chamber) if the angular distribution of the electrons incident on the chamber is isotropic. The geometrical depth of the chamber is d.

555. A small gas cavity in the body of a material does not distort the angular and energy distributions of the secondary electrons produced in the material by γ-radiation. The ionisation I_g produced by the secondary electrons per cubic centimetre of the gas cavity is connected with the ionisation I_m produced per cubic centimetre of the material by $I_g = I_m/\varrho$, where ϱ is the ratio of the stopping-powers of the material and the gas. Find the number of ion pairs produced per second in the operating volume of an ionisation chamber of depth 1 cm and area 25 cm^2, if the radiation incident on the chamber is from a radioactive source Co^{60} of intensity

1·5 curie, at 1 m from the chamber. The chamber walls are of aluminium, of a thickness exceeding the range of the secondary electrons of maximum energy. The coefficient of absorption of γ-radiation in aluminium is $0{\cdot}195\ \text{cm}^{-1}$. The mean energy of the γ-radiation is 1·7 MeV; the energy of formation of one ion pair in the gas of the chamber is 33·5 eV.

Hint. If the secondary electron range is less than the thickness of the front wall of the chamber, the energies lost per unit volume by the γ-radiation and the secondary electrons are equal. The ratio $\varrho \approx 0{\cdot}88\, n(Z)/n(\text{gas})$, where n is the number of electrons per cubic centimetre. The chamber is filled with air.

556. When using ionisation chambers in work on electron accelerators it has to be borne in mind that the ion recombination in the chamber is determined in this case not by the average intensity, but by the intensity in the pulse, the length of which is usually of the order 10^{-5} sec. The degree to which the saturation state is attained in a plane-parallel ionisation chamber is now determined by the equation $I/I_{\text{sat}} = (1/u) \ln (1 + u)$, where $u = 2{\cdot}09 \times 10^9 \alpha d^2 r / V(k_1 + k_2)$, α is the coefficient of ion recombination, k_1 and k_2 are the mobilities of the positive and negative ions, r is the intensity in r-units of the γ-radiation in the pulse, d and V are the distance and potential difference between the chamber electrodes. Use this formula to find the maximum intensity that can be measured with the aid of an ionisation chamber in which the spacing between the electrodes is 1 cm and the field-strength is $3000\ \text{V cm}^{-1}$, on condition that the ionisation current must be not less than 98 per cent of the saturation current. 25 pulses of γ-radiation pass per second through the chamber, $\alpha = 1{\cdot}6 \times 10^{-6}$; $k_1 = 1{\cdot}3\ \text{cm sec}^{-1}$; $k_2 = 1{\cdot}8\ \text{cm sec}^{-1}$.

557. Calorimetric methods are often used for determining the γ-radiation intensity from strong radioactive sources and electron accelerators. A calorimeter suitable for these purposes consists of a lead cylinder mounted in an evacuated vessel on supports of negligible thermal conductivity (e.g. lucite). The cylinder dimensions must be such that the measured radiation is completely absorbed. Find how long it takes the calorimeter temperature to change by 5°, if its specific heat is $22\ \text{cal deg}^{-1}$, and a Co^{60} source of intensity 2 curies is placed inside the cylinder. Co^{60} releases an energy of 2·6 MeV in one disintegration.

558. A polonium compound of intensity 0·1 curie is placed in a calorimeter of specific heat 1 cal deg^{-1}. Find the temperature rise per hour, given that polonium radiates α-particles with an energy 5·3 MeV.

559. Determine the number of "effective" γ-quanta in one pulse of a synchrotron, if the temperature rise in an hour of the calorimeter cylinder is 0·016°. The cylinder diameter is 11 cm, its length 20 cm, and the synchrotron pulse frequency 50 sec^{-1}. The maximum energy of the γ-quanta spectrum is 200 MeV. The density of lead (or the cylinder) is 11·4 g cm^{-3}, and its specific heat is 0·031 cal g^{-1} deg^{-1}.

Note. The number of "effective" γ-quanta is usually defined as the ratio U/W, where U is the energy flux in the γ-quanta beam, W is the maximum energy of their spectrum.

560. The number of photons formed when a charged particle passes through a scintillation counter can be found from the formula $p = EC/E_p$, where p is the number of photons, E is the energy lost by the particle in the crystal, E_p is the mean energy of the spectrum of the radiated photons, and C is the counter efficiency. For anthracene $C = 0{\cdot}04$, and the mean wavelength of the radiation spectrum is 4450 Å. Find the energy involved when one photon is formed.

561. Find the number of photons in a light pulse produced in a phosphor crystal NaI(Tl) by a relativistic proton, if the energy lost by the proton in the crystal is 2 MeV, and the efficiency and mean wavelength of the radiation spectrum are respectively 0·084 and 4100 Å.

562. Scintillation counters are used for recording X-rays and γ-rays as well as for recording charged particles. Find the efficiency of the scintillation counter recording of γ-quanta, if the efficiency for recording charged particles is 100 per cent (d is the thickness of the counter, μ is the coefficient of absorption of the γ-quanta).

563. Due to the relatively high density $\varrho = 3{\cdot}67$ g cm^{-3} and to the relatively high atomic number of iodine ($Z = 53$), NaI(Tl) crystals are specially suitable for recording X- and γ-rays. What is the intensity N_γ of a beam of γ-quanta if 240 light pulses are produced per minute in an NaI(Tl) crystal $d = 2$ cm thick? The coefficient of absorption of photons in the crystal is 0·126 cm^{-1}.

564. A photomultiplier is used to record the light pulse in a scintillation counter. Find the size of the voltage pulse V at the multiplier output if $n = 500$ electrons are knocked out from the photocathode during a regular light pulse in the crystal. The multiplication coefficient of the multiplier is $M = 2 \times 10^6$ and the anode–earth capacity is $C = 10$ pF.

565. Find the voltage pulse amplitude of the photomultiplier output when fast electrons pass through an anthracene crystal, given that each electron loses 2·5 MeV in the process, and about 70 per cent of the photons formed in the crystal are incident on the photocathode. The multiplier efficiency is $C_m = 0{\cdot}05$. The remaining characteristics of the multiplier and crystal are given in Problems 560 and 564.

566. Pulses of amplitude $V \geqslant 10$ V are recorded at a photomultiplier output. Find the minimum energy of a proton detected by the circuit if the photomultiplier efficiency is 0·07; the multiplication coefficient is $M = 10^7$, the anode–earth capacity is 8 pF, and stilbene is used as the phosphor (the mean wavelength of the radiation spectrum is $\lambda = 4100$ Å, the efficiency $C = 0{\cdot}024$). About 65 per cent of the total number of photons formed during a light pulse is incident on the photocathode.

567. During one discharge 10^8 electrons pass through a Geiger–Müller counter. Calculate the mean current through the counter if there are 600 discharges per minute.

568. Find the threshold V of the proportional region of a counter filled with argon at a pressure $p = 60$ mmHg. On reaching the threshold the electric field-strength close to the filament becomes such that an electron acquires over its free path an energy sufficient for impact ionisation. The counter radius is $r_k = 1$ cm, the filament radius $r_a = 0{\cdot}005$ cm. The mean range of an electron in argon at a pressure of 1 mmHg is $\lambda_0 = 6{\cdot}8 \times 10^{-2}$ cm; the ionisation potential of argon is $V_a = 15{\cdot}8$ V.

569. Find the voltage pulse amplitude from a proportional counter when (a) an α-particle with energy 3·5 MeV, and (b) a fast electron, passes through it. The counter has a diameter $d = 2{\cdot}2$ cm and is filled with argon at a pressure of 100 mmHg. The specific ionisation by fast electrons in argon is 70 ion pairs per centimetre at a pressure of 1 atm. The range of an α-particle in argon is 1·9 cm.

The mean energy of formation of an ion pair is 25·4 eV. The counter gas amplification coefficient is $A = 10^4$. The filament capacity is 15 pF.

Hint. The mean path traversed by an α-particle in a counter is 1·7 cm; the mean path traversed by an electron is given by $l = \pi d/4$.

570. The resolving time of a counter is defined as the time it needs to return to the working state after a response. The resolving time of a scintillation counter is determined by the de-excitation time. Let N be the true number of particles passing through the counter per second, and n the number of responses per second obtained experimentally from the counter. Find the counter resolving time τ.

571. The characteristic of a Geiger–Müller counter is found by using two radioactive sources of unknown intensity. Each source can be covered by a screen. When the first and the second source are covered in turn, n_1 and n_2 responses per second are recorded by the counter. When both sources are uncovered, n_{12} responses per second are obtained. Find the counter resolving time, if $n_1 = 100$, $n_2 = 155$, $n_{12} = 248$.

572. A counter responds 1000 times per second. Its resolving time is 2×10^{-4} sec. Find the true frequency of the event investigated.

573. The de-excitation time of stilbene is approximately $\tau = 7 \times 10^{-9}$ sec. The photomultiplier resolving time is $1{\cdot}5 \times 10^{-9}$ sec. Find the number of pulses n of the multiplier output, if the density of the electrons incident on the stilbene is $N = 5 \times 10^7$ electron sec^{-1}.

574. The resolving time of a counter is $\tau_1 = 3 \times 10^{-5}$ sec, and of the recording device, $\tau_2 = 2{\cdot}5 \times 10^{-4}$ sec ($\tau_2 > \tau_1$!) Find the number of recorded particles if the number of particles incident on the counter is $N = 5 \times 10^3$ sec^{-1}.

575. Two identical counters are connected in a coincidence circuit, i.e. the only events recorded are those when ionising particles pass simultaneously through both counters. Let the resolving time of the counters be τ, the average number of particles passing through the first counter n_1, and through the second n_2. Find the number of random coincidences.

576. Two coincidence-connected scintillation counters are placed in a beam of statistically distributed particles (e.g. in a beam of photons from an electron accelerator target). Find the mean intensity of the beam if the number of responses of the coincidence circuit is 2×10^4 pulses per second, and the resolving time of the circuit is 10^{-8} sec. The scintillation counter recording efficiency is 100 per cent.

577. The cosmic radiation noise in a counter of average size is 40 pulses per minute. A very weak radioactive source gives 5 pulses per minute. How many responses are required from the counter in order to find the radioactive source intensity to 10 per cent accuracy?

578. The background of a Geiger–Müller counter is 92 responses per minute. When a radioactive source is present the counter responds 260 times per minute. How should be measurement be carried out if the relative error is not to exceed 4 per cent?

579. Coincidence circuits are often used nowadays for reducing the effect of background when counting relatively infrequent events. Let the number of particles recorded per second be 50, and the number of background pulses be 10^5. To reduce the effect of the background on the results of measurements, two scintillation counters with a resolving time of 10^{-8} sec are connected in a coincidence circuit, the arrangement of the counters being such that particles which are to be recorded pass through both. The particles that produce the background are recorded as random coincidences. Find the relative shortening of the measurement time if the experimental error is not to exceed 10 per cent.

580. What is the least radiation frequency ν capable of positron–electron pair production? What is the energy ε of a quantum of this radiation?

581. (a) What is the maximum kinetic energy E_{max} of a positron pair formed by a γ-quantum with energy $E = 150$ MeV? (b) What is the maximum energy E_{max} of the bremsstrahlung of an electron with energy $E = 80$ MeV?

582. What are the velocities of a positron, proton and α-particle having energy 1 MeV?

583. What velocity V is acquired by an RaB nucleus, resulting from the decay of RaA, if the energy of the α-particles radiated during the decay is 4·7 MeV?

584. Find the energy carried away in an hour by α-particles resulting from decay of 1 g radium, if the velocity of Ra α-particles is $1{\cdot}51 \times 10^9$ cm sec^{-1}, and the half life is 1550 years for radium. Take no account of the decay products.

585. A radium drug weighing 1 g is enclosed in an envelope opaque to α-particles. How much heat Q is released in an hour in the drug and envelope?

Hint. Take into account the nuclear recoil.

586. A betatron is a device for obtaining high energy charged particles. A vacuum chamber in which a particle can rotate freely in a circle is mounted between the poles of an electromagnet, the excitation current of which can be varied in time in accordance with a given law. The acceleration is achieved by the rotational electric field produced by the variation of the magnetic field. Show that, if the magnetic flux $\Phi(R)$ through the particle orbit at each instant is twice $\pi R^2 H(R)$, where R is the orbit radius, and $H(R)$ is the magnetic field in the orbit, then the orbit radius will be constant. Show that, if $\Phi(R) > 2\pi R^2 H(R)$, the orbit radius will increase, whilst if $\Phi(R) < 2\pi R^2 H(R)$, the radius will decrease. Assume for the proof that the magnetic field depends only on the radius R, and that the orbits are circles whose centres lie on the axis of symmetry.

587. Prove that the charged particle orbits in the previous problem will be stable in a radial direction if the magnetic field decreases from the periphery in accordance with the law $1/R^n$, where $n < 1$. Prove the more general assertion that the motion in a radial direction is stable if $-(R/H)\,\partial H/\partial R < 1$, where $H(R)$ is any magnetic field with an axis of symmetry.

588. Show that, in a magnetic field with axial symmetry (as in a betatron, see Problem 586), motion round circles with their centres on the axis of symmetry of the field will be stable in a vertical direction (i.e. in the direction of the axis of symmetry), if the magnetic field diminishes from the periphery, and will be unstable if the field increases from the periphery.

589. In a betatron, the position of the equilibrium orbit R_0, satisfying the condition $\Phi(R_0) = 2\pi R_0^2 H(R_0)$ (see Problem 586), corresponds to a minimum of the rotational electrical field $\mathscr{E}_\Phi$. Prove this property and show that it can be used for finding the equilibrium orbit in a betatron.

590. When an electron moves round a circle it radiates electromagnetic waves and loses energy $(4\pi e^2/3R)(E/m_0c^2)^4$ in one complete revolution, where R is the orbit radius, E is the energy of the electron, m_0 is the rest mass of the electron. Calculate the energy loss of an electron per revolution in a betatron at 100 MeV at the end of the acceleration process, if the orbit radius is 80 cm. Find for what energy the radiation loss per revolution is equal to the energy acquired from the rotational electric field, if $dH(t)/dt = 2\times10^6$ oersted $\sec^{-1}$ ($H(t)$ is the field at the electron orbit).

591. In a cyclotron ions are whirled round in a magnetic field and are accelerated in the gap between two accelerating electrodes, called dees (Fig. 16). For resonance acceleration the frequency of ion

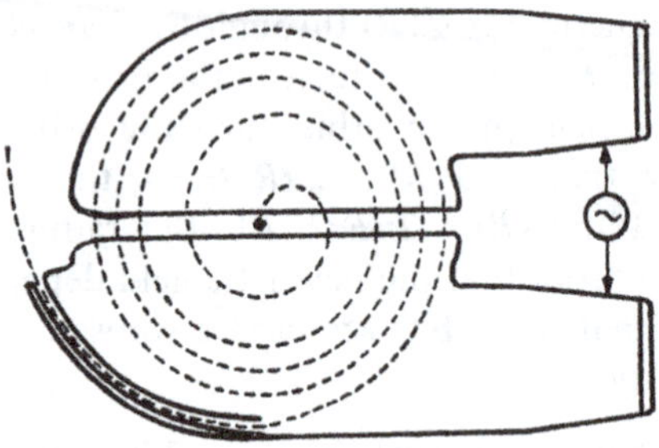

FIG. 16

rotation and the electric field frequency must coincide. The ion rotation frequency does not remain constant, however, since the mass of the ion increases in accordance with the Einstein equation $m = m_0/\sqrt{1-(v^2/c^2)}$. Detuning therefore occurs in a cyclotron, and the ions cannot attain a very high energy. The maximum energy is obviously obtained if the detuning, i.e. the difference between the frequency of rotation and the accelerating field frequency, is a minimum. Suppose that the cyclotron magnet produces a constant field of 15,000 gauss and the magnet radius is 65 cm. It is proposed to accelerate protons in the cyclotron. How must the accelerating field frequency be chosen so as to obtain a minimum average detuning in the cyclotron?

592. To prevent detuning in a cyclotron (see the previous problem) a slow variation of the accelerating field frequency was proposed. This type of accelerator is called a phasotron (or synchrocyclotron). What should be the law of variation and the percentage frequency change of the accelerating field when accelerating deuterons up to 200 MeV? The magnetic field is 15,000 oersted. On the average a deuteron acquires an energy of 15,000 eV per revolution.

593. To prevent detuning in an accelerator of the cyclotron type (see Problem 591), the magnetic field can be varied with time. The frequency of rotation of the particle now remains constant. Such an accelerator is called a synchrotron. Find the variation in the radius in a synchrotron in a magnetic field which is spatially uniform and varies in time according to $H(t) = H_0 \sin \Omega t$. The electric accelerating field frequency is ω_0, and the intrinsic energy of the accelerated particle is E_0.

594. The magnetic field in a 72 MeV synchrotron varies sinusoidally at 50 c/s. The magnetic field-strength is 8000 oersted. Up to 2 MeV the electrons are accelerated in the betatron mode in an orbit of radius 29·4 cm. An accelerating electric field of frequency $\omega_0 = 10^8$ sec^{-1} is then switched on. The central core which produces the initial acceleration in the betatron mode becomes saturated, and acceleration proceeds by virtue of the electric field of the accelerating dee gaps, i.e. in the synchrotron mode. Find: (1) the orbit radius variation during the synchrotron mode; (2) the instant corresponding to passage from the betatron to the synchrotron mode; (3) the electron trajectory length in the betatron and synchrotron modes, if the particles have an initial energy of 13,600 eV when they start to accelerate in the betatron mode.

595. A coincidence method (see Problem 575) is sometimes employed in investigations into accelerators. In a betatron or phasotron the beam leaves in short pulses, the frequency of these pulses being equal to the accelerator magnetic field frequency in the case of a betatron and synchrotron, and to the number of cycles of high frequency modulation in the case of a phasotron.

Determine the number of random coincidences per second for two counters placed near a betatron operating with a magnetic field feed frequency of f c/s. The coincidence circuit resolving time is τ sec, the number of pulses per sec in each counter is N_1 and N_2, the γ-ray beam pulse length is t sec. The resolving time T of the counter itself is much greater than τ and the γ-ray pulse length. Consider the following cases: (1) $t = 2\tau$; (2) $t > 2\tau$; (3) $t < 2\tau$.

596. If the accelerating electric field frequency and the magnetic field are both varied simultaneously in an accelerator of the cyclotron type, it is termed a synchrophasotron or proton synchrotron. Find the connexion between the magnetic field $H(t)$ and the circular frequency $\omega_0(t)$ of the electric field, such that acceleration proceeds in an orbit of constant radius $R = R_0$.

597. Determine the mean energy acquired by a proton per revolution in a synchrophasotron. The orbit radius is 4·5 m. The magnetic field increases proportionally to the time up to 15,000 oersted after 1 sec. The calculation can neglect the effect of the rotational electric field. Find the maximum energy which is attained in this accelerator, and the length of path traversed by a proton, if the initial energy is 4 MeV.

598. Determine the law of variation of the frequency in the 10,000 MeV synchrophasotron (see Problem 596) of the Dubna Institute for Nuclear Studies. The proton trajectory consists of four arcs each of radius 28 m and length 44 m, joined by straight intervals of 8 m. The initial energy of the protons is 9 MeV. The magnetic field increases linearly in time from 0 to 13,000 oersted after 3·3 sec and drops as the orbit radius increases according to the law $\sim R^{-2/3}$. Find also: (a) the magnetic field at the start of the acceleration process, (b) the change in the trajectory if the accelerating field frequency deviates by 0·2 per cent from the correct law (at the start of the acceleration process).

599. A relativistic particle of mass m radiates electromagnetic waves when it moves in a uniform magnetic field, with the result that it loses the following energy per unit time (for $E \gg mc^2$):

$$-\frac{dE}{dt} = \frac{2c}{3}\left(\frac{e^2}{mc^2}\right)^2 H_\perp^2 \left(\frac{E}{mc^2}\right)^2 = 0{\cdot}98 \cdot 10^{-3} H_\perp^2 \left(\frac{E}{mc^2}\right)^2 \text{eVsec}^{-1},$$

where $H_\perp$ is the magnetic field-strength perpendicular to the particle trajectory, and E is the total energy of the particle. Find the radiation energy-loss at the end of the acceleration process in the synchrophasotron described in the previous problem.

600. When accelerating *in vacuo*, a relativistic charged particle radiates electromagnetic waves, mainly in the direction of its velocity, in a cone of angle $\vartheta \sim mc^2/E = \sqrt{1 - v^2/c^2}$, where m is the rest mass of the particle and E is its total energy.

(a). What is the nature of the magnetic bremsstrahlung (synchrotron radiation) of a superrelativistic electron ($E/mc^2 \gg 1$) when it moves in a magnetic field $\boldsymbol{H}$?

(b). What is the frequency spectrum of the radiation and where is its maximum when the motion is round a circle (i.e. when $\boldsymbol{v} \perp \boldsymbol{H}$)?

601. What wavelength is radiated by electrons with energies 10^9 and $3 \cdot 10^{14}$ eV, forming part of cosmic radiation, when they move in the interstellar magnetic fields (field-strength $H \sim 3 \times 10^{-6}$ gauss).

602. What is the polarisation of magnetic bremsstrahlung?

603. A linear particle accelerator has the following construction. An ion beam passes inside collinear tubes of different lengths. Acceleration takes place in the gaps between the tubes (Fig. 17). The tubes are connected alternately to opposite terminals of a generator, so that at any given instant the potential difference in the even gaps is $V_0 \cos \Omega t$ and in the odd gaps, $-V_0 \cos \Omega t$. If the ions enter the accelerator with initial energy W_{init} and the total length

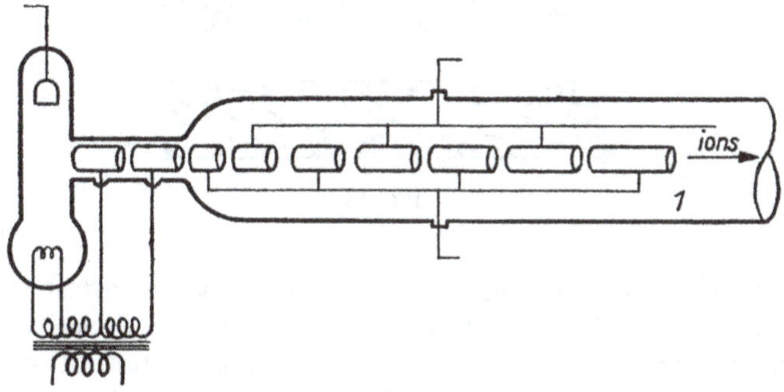

FIG. 17

of the gaps is 25 per cent the length of the tubes, calculate the total tube length required. Consider the 40 MeV linear proton accelerator: $W_{\text{init}} = 4$ MeV, $\Omega = 12{\cdot}56 \times 10^8$ sec^{-1}. The proton acquires 1 MeV on passing through each accelerator gap.

604. In modern linear accelerators (see Problem 603) the tubes are not connected to the generator terminals. Instead, they are mounted in a resonator in which an in-phase electric field is excited, directed along the tubes. What modification is needed in this case to the tube lengths, as compared with the old type of accelerator considered in Problem 603?

605. The most popular of the modern types of linear accelerator is the travelling wave type. Imagine an electromagnetic field propagated along the z axis, the electric field axial component being E_z. Let a charged particle move along the same axis. If the particle velocity differs substantially from the wave velocity, the particle will encounter different phases of the electric field E_z as it moves along, and will be slowed down as well as accelerated, so that on the whole there is no gain in energy. When, however, the wave phase velocity is equal or close to the particle velocity, the particle may be in roughly the same phase as the wave for a long time, and will be accelerated. A wave of suitable type can be obtained in a waveguide (a hollow pipe) by mounting inside it diaphragms with apertures on the axis (Fig. 18). The phase velocity of the wave depends on the spacings between the apertures.

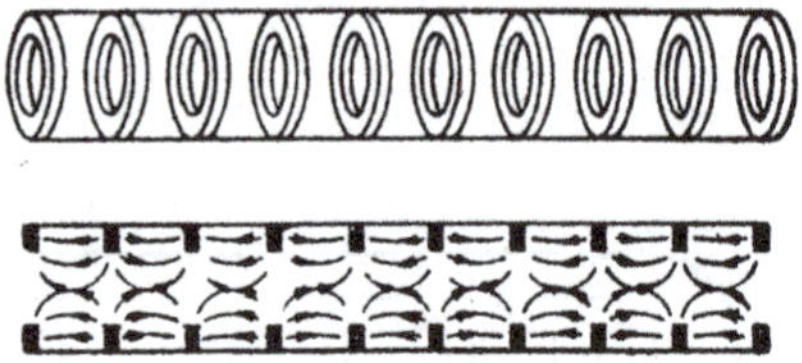

FIG. 18

Find the phase velocity as a function of the distance from the input aperture of the accelerator. What must be the relative variation in the phase velocity for resonance acceleration of protons and electrons from 4 to 1000 MeV?

606. Use the general theorem of electrostatics to the effect that stable equilibrium of electrostatic systems is impossible to prove the absence of stability in linear travelling wave accelerators in at least one of two directions: either in the direction of the tube axis or in the perpendicular direction.

607. In linear travelling wave electron accelerators the wave propagation velocity is sometimes chosen constant, equal to the velocity of light. Suppose that the electrons enter with energy 4 MeV and start to move in the wave crest of field-strength

$\mathscr{E}_0 = 20$ kV cm^{-1}. The wavelength is 1 m. When the acceleration is up to 100 MeV, what is the distance of the electrons behind the wave? Assume for simplicity that the field-strength in the wave has a rectangular instead of sinusoidal time variation, i.e. the field-strength always has one of two values: $\mathscr{E} = \pm\mathscr{E}_0$.

608. A "strong-focusing" method can be used to increase the focusing forces in accelerators and thereby ensure the motion of the charged particles along a given trajectory in the magnetic field. The magnet used for this purpose consists of $2N$ sectors of equal size; in the first half of the set of sectors the magnetic field increases in accordance with R^n, and in the second half set it decreases in accordance with $R^{-n} (n > 0)$, where R is the distance from the centre of the magnet to the point in question. Sectors with different characteristics are arranged alternately. The magnetic field is thus

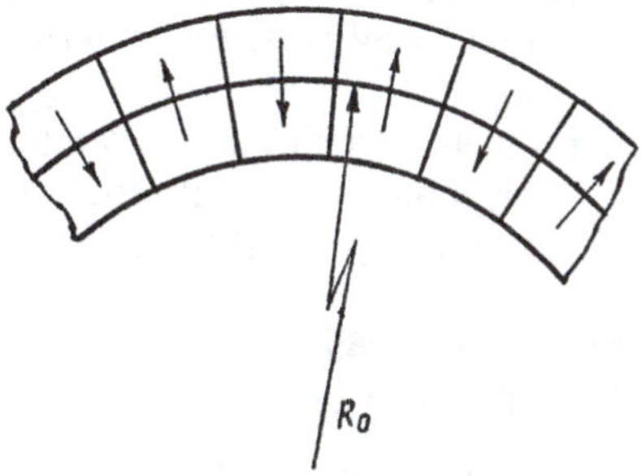

FIG. 19

independent of the azimuth on some circle of radius R_0 (see Fig. 19, which shows the arrangement of the sectors). The arrows indicate the direction of the increase of the magnetic field, perpendicular to the plane of the radius). Consider the motion of a particle at small deviations from the circular orbit of radius R_0, and find the stability condition for the motion, assuming $n \gg 1$.

609. An isochronous cyclotron is one in which the particle revolution period round a closed orbit is independent of the particle energy. Show that it is possible to construct an isochronous cyclotron by using several magnetic sectors separated by gaps in which there is no magnetic field. The total length L along the orbit of these gaps increases from the magnet centre in accordance with the formula

$$L = 2\pi R\left\{\frac{\omega T_0}{\sqrt{1+(eH_0R/E_0)^2}} - 1\right\},$$

where R is the radius of curvature of the orbit of a particle, of charge e and rest energy E_0, in a magnetic field of intensity H_0 in the sectors, and T_0 is the given constant period of revolution.

610. Find the dependence of the length of the "gaps" in an isochronous cyclotron (see Problem 609) on the radius R of the orbit in the sectors, if a small magnetic field is present in the "gaps".

Hint. The magnetic field in the gaps must be assumed uniform and equal to xH_0, where $x < 1$, and H_0 is the magnetic field in the sectors.

611. In counter beam accelerators more efficient use is made of the particle energy, since the laboratory system is at the same time a centre-of-mass system and new particles of zero velocity can be created.

The effective energy of a counter beam accelerator is the particle energy in the system when one beam is at rest.

Calculate the effective energy of the following counter beam accelerators:

(1) 100 and 1000 MeV electron accelerators,

(2) 10 and 100 GeV proton accelerators.

612. Modern lasers enable powerful directional coherent light beams to be produced with a specific number of photons in focus exceeding the specific density of the electrons in a solid. A ruby laser radiates red light of wavelength approximately 6940 Å (the photon energy ~ 1·78 eV). The laser light is focussed by an electron beam in a 6000 MeV accelerator, travelling towards the light beam. (This is equivalent to the Compton effect for electrons at rest.) What is the energy of the photons in the coordinate system in which the electrons are at rest? What is the electric field-strength in this system, if it is equal to 1 MV cm^{-1} in the laboratory?

613. For carrying out experiments on counter beams, it is desirable to produce a magnetic field of such a configuration that particles of one sign can be rotated round similar orbits but in different directions, so that they often meet each other at nodal points. How can such a magnetic field be produced?

614. Show that a charged particle will undergo resonance acceleration through the action of a plane electromagnetic wave, propagated in the z direction and in a uniform constant magnetic field having only a component along the z axis, if the following resonance condition is satisfied:

$$eH_0/\gamma_0 m_0 c = \omega\left(1 - \frac{\dot{z}_0}{c}\right),$$

where $\dot{z}_0$ is the initial velocity component along the z axis, ω is the wave frequency, m_0 is the rest mass, $\gamma_0 m_0$ is the total initial mass, i.e. $\gamma_0 = 1/\sqrt{1 - v_0^2/c^2}$, and v_0 is the initial velocity.

615. For an absolute determination of the cross-section of the reaction

$${}_1D^2 + {}_1D^2 \rightarrow {}_1H^3 + {}_1H^1 + 4{\cdot}0 \text{ MeV}$$

in the energy interval 15–100 keV, a "thick" target of heavy ice is used (in which the deuterons are completely braked and stopped). The charge carried to the target by the deuterons is measured by a current integrator (a condenser which charges to a certain voltage then automatically discharges). The number of protons is determined by a counter with a known effective solid angle $\Omega = 4\pi/1000$. The angular proton distribution is taken to be given by

$$n(\vartheta) = n(90°)\,[1 + A\cos^2\vartheta].$$

The quantity A depends on the deuteron energy (A is of the order 0·2–0·4).

(a) Find the angle ϑ_0 of the counter so that the total proton output can be calculated from the number of responses without knowing A.

(b) Let $N(E)$ be the total proton output per microcoulomb of deuteron beam, where E is the kinetic energy.

$$N(E) = 2{\cdot}53 \times 10^2 \quad \text{for} \quad E = 15{\cdot}4 \text{ keV},$$

$$N(E) = 4{\cdot}78 \times 10^5 \quad \text{for} \quad E = 105{\cdot}6 \text{ keV}.$$

Very roughly,

$$N(E) = 4{\cdot}2 \times 10^7\, e^{-\frac{46}{\sqrt{E}}} \ \mu\text{curie}^{-1} \quad (E \text{ in keV}).$$

The deuteron ionisation loss curve in heavy water is known and can be roughly approximated by

$$\left(-\frac{dE}{dx}\right)_{\text{ion}} = 2{\cdot}5 \times 10^{19}\, ME$$

(M is the number of D_2O molecules per cubic centimetre).

Find the effective reaction cross-section as a function of the energy.

616. A hydrogen threshold neutron detector consists of an ionised chamber filled with hydrogen at such a pressure that the proton recoil range is much less than the chamber dimensions. The pulses are amplified and counted when they exceed a certain level. Find the detector sensitivity curve for neutron energies $E > E_0$ (E_0 is the threshold) for the following conditions:

(a) the neutron scattering in hydrogen is isotropic in a proton and neutron centre of gravity system;

(b) the scattering cross section $\sigma(E)$ is proportional to $E^{-1/2}$.

617. A fission chamber is an ionisation chamber in which there is a thin layer of uranium for recording neutrons. The ionisation is produced by the fission fragments. If it is desired to record only fast neutrons and to exclude the effects of U^{235} fission, the chamber is surrounded by a layer of cadmium. The residual background in the chamber is produced by α-particles resulting from α-decay of the uranium. Determine which is the greater: the total ionisation from the α-particles or from the fragments, using the following data:

(1) The chamber is at a distance $R = 10$ cm from the neutron source of intensity 1 millicurie (corresponding to $n = 3{\cdot}7 \times 10^7$ disintegrations per second). The fission cross-section for fast neutrons is taken to be $\sigma = 0{\cdot}5$ barn, and the energy transferred by the fission is $E = 80$ MeV.

The uranium layer thickness is much less than the range of the fragments in the uranium (several micron), in order to know the absolute sensitivity of the chamber.

(2) The half-life of uranium is $\tau = 4{\cdot}5 \times 10^9$ years, the energy of the α-particles is $E_\alpha = 4{\cdot}2$ MeV.

618. The reaction $Li^7(p, n)\, Be^7$ is a convenient source of neutrons of known energy in the interval 0·2–1·5 MeV and higher. The neutron energy can be varied by varying the energy of the primary protons and the angle of observation. (a) Knowing the mass of the Li^7, Be^7 and H^1 atoms, and of a neutron, in atomic units (see Table VI, page 236), find the energy release in the reaction $Li^7(p, n)\,Be^7$. (b) What is the minimum proton energy at which this reaction is possible?

619. Use Table VI (on page 236) to find the binding energy of Li^6.

620. Find the binding energy of a helium nucleus (α-particle).

621. It is proposed to use deuterium as the nuclear fuel in a controlled thermonuclear reaction. Particular importance attaches to the following primary nuclear reactions, which proceed with roughly the same probability:

$$\text{(a) } D^2 + D^2 \rightarrow H^3 + p + Q_a;$$

$$\text{(b) } D^2 + D^2 \rightarrow He^3 + n + Q_b.$$

Evaluate the energies Q_b and Q_b of these reactions.

622. The following secondary reactions can occur in a thermonuclear reactor using deuterium fuel:

$$\text{(a) } He^3 + D^2 \rightarrow He^4 + p + Q_a;$$

$$\text{(b) } H^3 + D^2 \rightarrow He^4 + n + Q_b.$$

Evaluate the energies Q_b and Q_b of these reactions.

623. Heavy water (D_2O) is known to be contained in small amounts in water, roughly in the proportion of 1 molecule heavy water to 6000 molecules ordinary water. How much energy is released when all the deuterium contained in 1 litre of water is burned in a thermonuclear reactor? How much petrol is equivalent in energy to 1 litre of water, if 13 kWh energy is released when 1 kg petrol is burnt?

624. How many thermonuclear reactions will occur per cubic centimetre per second, if the reaction cross section is $\sigma(v)$, where v is the relative velocity of the reacting deuterons, and N is the number of deuterons per cubic centimetre?

625. How much power is produced by thermonuclear reactions per cubic centimetre, if $N = 10^{15}\ \text{cm}^{-3}$, $\overline{\sigma v} = 10^{-17}\ \text{cm}^3\,\text{sec}^{-1}$ (the value of $\overline{\sigma v}$ is taken at a deuterium temperature of roughly $T = 40$ keV $\approx 4{\cdot}6 \times 10^8\,°$K).

Note. The notation of Problem 624 is used here. Take account of the energy of the primary reactions only in the calculations (see Problem 621).

626. It is proposed to use magnetic field pressure for thermal insulation of a hot ionised deuterium gas (plasma) from the walls of a thermonuclear reactor. Calculate the pressure of a magnetic field $H = 20{,}000$ oersted on the plasma on the assumption that no field exists inside the plasma.

627. How many calories are released when 1g of helium is formed from protons and neutrons?

628. Find the atomic weight of deuterium, given that the binding energy of a deuteron is 2·19 MeV. Find also the atomic weight of a deuteron and the atomic weight of an electron (the atomic weight of the O^{16} nucleus is taken as 16).

629. Relatively slow protons with energies of a few hundred kilo electron volts or even less can cause the fission of lithium:

$$Li^7 + H^1 \rightarrow 2He^4.$$

What is the energy of the two α-particles?

630. The distintegration of a deuteron into a proton and neutron by the action of ThC′ γ-rays, having an energy of 2·62 MeV, can be observed experimentally. Find the energy and direction of release of the neutron and proton, neglecting the γ-quantum momentum. (See Problem 628.)

631. Heat amounting to 10,000 cal was released in an intense reaction. What was the change in mass of the reagents?

632. What is the increase in grams in the mass of 1 kg water when it is heated to 100°?

633. What is the difference between the mass of a hydrogen atom and the total mass of a proton and electron?

634. What is the mass reduction per second of the Sun due to radiation energy losses?

Hint. The necessary data can be found in Problem 342.

635*. Find the decay constant of a substance, given that its β-radiation intensity drops 10 per cent per hour. The decay product is not radioactive.

636*. Find the decay constant of radium, if its half-life is $T = 1550$ years.

637*. How many radium atoms disintegrate per second per gram of radium? Assume that the decay constant λ is known (Problem 636).

638*. Find the half-value period of a radioactive element from the following measurements:

Time in hours	0	0·5	1·0	1·5	2·0	2.5	
No. of counts per min	2345	1195	654	390	263	197	
Time in hours	3·0	3·5	4	6	8	10	12
No. of counts per min	165	144	130	98	78	61	48

Hint. Draw the graph with time as abscissa and the natural logarithm of the number of responses per min as ordinate, and analyse the shape of the graph.

639*. An RaD preparation in equilibrium with its decay products emits 10^5 α-particles per second. How many atoms of RaD, RaE and Po are contained in the preparation? How many RaD and RaE β-particles does the preparation emit per second?

640*. Determine the volume of radon (at normal temperature and pressure) in equilibrium with 1 g radium (radon or radium emanation is the gaseous product of radium decay).

641*. Find the amount of helium in cubic millimetres released by the decay of 1 g radium during a year. Assume that the helium is at 0° and standard pressure.

642. A scintillation counter shows that roughly $1{\cdot}15 \times 10^4$ α-particles per second are released by the decay of 1 g UI. Find the decay constant of UI (uranium I).

* General hints on Problems 635–648, which are marked by asterisks, will be found in the answer section (p. 226).

643*. U^{234} (or UII) is the decay product of the basic uranium isotope U^{238} (or UI). Find the half-value period of U^{234}, if its content in natural uranium is 0·006 per cent. The half-value period of U^{238} should be taken from the solution of Problem 642.

644*. The half-value period of radioactive phosphorus P^{32} is 15 days. Find the activity of a P^{32} compound 10, 30, 90 days after its preparation, if the initial activity is 100 millicurie.

645*. Find the half-value period of UI, given that the number of radium atoms in equilibrium with n uranium atoms is $n \times 3{\cdot}45 \times 10^{-7}$. The decay constant of radium is also given (see Problem 636).

646*. Find the atomic number and weight of the ionium produced from uranium as a result of two α-transitions and two β-transitions. Of what element is ionium an isotope?

647*. Certain uranium ores contain pure uranium lead as an impurity (A = 206). Assuming that all the lead has been derived from decay of uranium and its products, the age of the ore can be determined. Take the lead content of 1 g ore to be 0·2 g.

648*. A sample of iodine I^{127} is irradiated by a neutron beam with a flux such that 10^7 atoms of radioactive iodine I^{128} (half life 25 min) are formed per second. Find the number of I^{128} atoms and the activity of the sample 1, 10, 25 and 50 min after the start of the irradiation. What is the maximum number of I^{128} atoms and the activity of the sample after long-term irradiation (i.e. irradiation to saturation)?

649. In recent years new particles have been discovered with a very short life, less than 10^{-20} sec. It is impossible in this case to record the tracks of charged particles or measure the distance from the point of formation to the point of decay of neutral particles. Only the disintegration products can be recorded. How can the process

$$\tilde{p} + p \rightarrow \pi^+ + \pi^- + \omega \rightarrow 2\pi^+ + 2\pi^- + \pi^0$$

be differentiated experimentally from the process

$$\tilde{p} + p \rightarrow 2\pi^+ + 2\pi^- + \pi^0,$$

where p, $\tilde{p}$ are the proton and antiproton, π^+, π^-, π^0 are π-mesons, ω is the new short-lived particle which disintegrates into $\pi^+ + \pi^- + \pi^0$.

650. In addition to the laws of conservation of energy, momentum and angular momentum, particle production and disintegration are governed by the following three exact laws of conservation:

1. The law of conservation of charge.

2. The law of conservation of baryon charge (the baryon charge is equal to 1 for nucleons (n, p) and hyperons ($\Lambda\Sigma\Xi$); to -1 for antinucleons ($\tilde{\text{n}}$, $\tilde{\text{p}}$) and antihyperons ($\tilde{\Lambda}\tilde{\Sigma}\tilde{\Xi}$); and to zero for all other particles).

3. The law of conservation of lepton charge (the lepton charge is equal to 1 for the electron or a negative μ-meson and neutrino (e^-, μ^-, ν) and equal to -1 for a positron, positive μ-meson and antineutrino (e^+, μ^-, $\tilde{\nu}$) and equal to zero for all other particles).

Determine which of the following reactions are forbidden:

1. $n \to p^1 + e^- + \tilde{\nu}$,
2. $2p \to 2n + 2e^+$,
3. $\mu^- \to e^- + \nu + \tilde{\nu}$,
4. $K^+ \to \pi^- + 2e^+$,
5. $\pi^- + p \to \Lambda^0 + K^0$,
6. $K^- + n \to \Lambda^0 + \pi^-$,
7. $\pi^+ + n \to \Lambda^0 + K^+$,
8. $\pi^+ + n \to K^+ + K^0$.

651. Reactions of the type $\mu^+ \to e^- + \gamma^-$, $\mu^- \to 2e^- + e^+$, cannot be obtained experimentally (although the laws of conservation (see the previous problem) are not broken). It has therefore been suggested that two neutrinos exist, an electronic neutrino ν_e and a μ-mesonic neutrino ν_μ, and two lepton charges l_e and l_μ: $l_e = 1$ for e^-, ν_e and $l_e = -1$ for e^+, $\tilde{\nu}_e$ and $l_e = 0$ for all other particles and $l_\mu = 1$ for μ^-, ν_μ, while $l_\mu = -1$ for μ^+, $\tilde{\nu}_\mu$ and $l_\mu = 0$ for all particles, including (e^+, e^-, ν_e, $\tilde{\nu}_e$). Support has recently (1962) been found for this suggestion. Consider the following reactions from this point of view and state which of those are forbidden:

1. $\pi^- \to \mu^- + \tilde{\nu}_\mu$
2. $\pi^- \to \mu + \tilde{\nu}_e$
3. $\mu^- \to e^- + \nu_e + \tilde{\nu}_e$
4. $\mu^- \to e^- + \tilde{\nu}_e + \nu_\mu$
5. $\tilde{\nu}_\mu + p \to n + \mu^+$
6. $\tilde{\nu}_\mu + p \to n + e^+$
7. $\tilde{\nu}_e + p \to n + \mu^+$
8. $\tilde{\nu}_e + p \to n + e^+$
9. $\mu^- \to e^- + \gamma$.

652. The interaction and disintegration of particles occurs as a result of strong, electromagnetic or weak interactions. The probability of weak interaction processes is roughly 10^{12} times less than that of strong interaction processes.

Strong and electromagnetic interaction can only occur between baryons and mesons, with conservation of the new quantum number S (strangeness):

$S = 0$ for nucleons, antinucleons, π-mesons (p, n, $\tilde{\text{p}}$, $\tilde{\text{n}}$, π^+, π^-)

$S = -1$ for Λ, Σ^+, Σ^-, Σ^0, K^-, $\tilde{K}^0$ (K-mesons, Σ-hyperons, Λ-particles)

$S = -2$ for Ξ^-, Ξ^0 (cascade hyperons)

$S = +1$ for $\tilde{\Lambda}$, $\tilde{\Sigma}^+$, $\tilde{\Sigma}^-$, $\tilde{\Sigma}^0$, K^+, K^0

$S = +2$ for $\tilde{\Xi}^-$, $\tilde{\Xi}^0$

(the tilde indicates the antiparticle).

When S is changed by 1 the probability of the process is diminished 10^{10} to 10^{12} times (the reaction time is increased to 10^{-8} to 10^{-10} sec), and when S changes by 2 the reaction is not observed in practice (it is evidently 10^{20} to 10^{24} times less probable than in the case of strong interaction).

Discover which of the following reactions are permissible with regard to S, and which are not (in the latter case they proceed after 10^{-8} to 10^{-10} sec or are not observed in practice).

1. $\pi^- + \text{p} \to \Lambda + K^0$
2. $\pi^- + \text{p} \to \Lambda + \pi^0$
3. $\Lambda \to \text{p} + \pi^-$
4. $\Xi^- \to \Lambda + \pi^-$
5. $\Xi^- \to 2\pi^- + \text{p}$
6. $\pi^+ + \tilde{\text{p}} \to \tilde{\Sigma}^- + K^-$
7. $\pi^+ + \tilde{\text{p}} \to \tilde{\Sigma}^- + \pi^-$
8. $\pi^+ + \text{n} \to \Lambda^0 + K^+$
9. $K^- + \text{p} \to \Sigma^- + \pi^+$
10. $\text{p} + \tilde{\Sigma}^- \to K^+ + \pi^+$
11. $\text{p} + \tilde{\Sigma}^- \to \pi^+ + \pi^+$
12. $\pi^- + \text{p} \to \tilde{\Xi}^- + \Xi^- + \text{n}$
13. $\pi^- + \text{p} \to \Sigma^+ + K^-$
14. $\pi^- + \text{p} \to \Xi^- + K^+ + K^0$.

653. Determine the π-meson production threshold when a nucleon, γ-quantum and electron of energy W interact with a nucleon at rest ($m_\pi c^2 \approx 140$ MeV).

654. Prove the impossibility of annihilation of an electron and positron with the emission of one γ-quantum:

$$e^+ + e^- \to \gamma,$$

and of the disintegration of the γ-quantum in flight:

$$\gamma \to e^+ + e^-.$$

655. An ultrarelativistic proton moves in a magnetic field. Can it radiate π^+, π^- and π^0 mesons, electrons and positrons?

656. Find the γ-ray flux (number of photons $cm^{-2}\cdot sec\cdot steradian$) at the limit of the solar system in directions from the centre, anti-centre and pole of the Galaxy which is produced in the Galaxy as a result of π^0-meson disintegration. The π^0-meson formation cross-section when cosmic rays act on protons of the interstellar gas is $\sigma = 2 = 10^{-26} cm^2$. Regard the cosmic ray flux in the Galaxy as isotropic and equal to $I_{cr} = 0{\cdot}2$ particles $cm^{-2}\cdot sec\cdot steradian$. The number of protons $N(L)$ in the interstellar medium on a line of sight directed from the solar system to the centre, pole and anti-centre of the Galaxy are respectively roughly $6 \times 10^{22} cm^{-2}$, $10^{21} cm^{-2}$ and $10^{22} cm^{-2}$.

657. The cosmic ray flux I_{cr} in the metagalactic is unknown. It may possibly be determined by measuring the intensity I_γ for the γ-rays from disintegration of π^0-mesons of the metagalactic (see the previous problem). Express I_{cr} in terms of I_γ, taking the gas concentration as $n = 10^{-5} cm^{-3}$ and taking account of the expansion of the Metagalaxy.

Hint. The speed of recession of the galaxies and gas at a distance R from us is equal to $u = hR$, where Hubble's constant is now taken as $h = 100$ km $sec^{-1}\cdot$megaparsec (the law $u = hR$ is only suitable up to $u \ll c = 3 \times 10^{10} cm\,sec^{-1}$, but it can be used approximately for $u < 0{\cdot}5\,c$).

658. A free atomic nucleus of mass M at rest undergoes a transition from an excited state to the ground state with the emission of a γ-quantum. Find the γ-quantum energy and the recoil energy R, if the excitation energy was E_{12}. Evaluate the recoil energy of the Ir^{191} nucleus, if $E_{12} = 129$ keV. Compare the solution of this problem with the solution of Problem 498.

659. A free atomic nucleus of mass M at rest undergoes a transition to an excited state with excitation energy E_{12} with the absorption of a γ-quantum. Determine the energy of the γ-quantum and the nuclear recoil energy R.

660. Find the energy difference between the emission and absorption lines of γ-quanta for free nuclei. Compare this difference with the natural (Γ) and Doppler width of the lines (the Doppler width is $E_{12}\sqrt{2kT/Mc^2}$). Find the temperature T_0 at which the Doppler width is equal to the difference between the emission and absorption lines, using the data in the table below. Explain the difficulty of observing resonance absorption of γ-quanta for free nuclei.

TABLE OF NUCLEI

	E_{12} in keV	Mc^2 in GeV	Γ/E_{12}
Tu^{169}	8·4	157·3	10^{-11}
Fe^{57}	14·4	53	3×10^{-13}
Dy^{161}	26	149·9	6×10^{-13}
Ir^{193}	73	179·7	10^{-12}
Au^{197}	77	183·4	3×10^{-12}
Er^{166}	80·6	154·5	3×10^{-12}
Zn^{67}	93	60·3	5×10^{-16}
W^{182}	100	169·4	4×10^{-12}
Hf^{177}	113	164·8	10^{-11}
Ir^{191}	129	177·8	4×10^{-11}
Re^{187}	187	174·1	3×10^{-10}

661. The Mössbauer effect amounts to the fact that γ-quanta emission and absorption processes can exist in crystals without nuclear recoil. In this case the law of conservation of momentum is fulfilled by the transfer of momentum to the entire crystal. Since the crystal mass is very large, it follows from this that the emission and absorption processes proceed with negligibly small energy losses. The emission and absorption lines have just the natural width (the Mössbauer line).

An Ir^{191} crystal emits γ-quanta with an energy of 129 keV. The width of the Mössbauer line of emission and absorption of γ-quanta is $\Gamma = 4{\cdot}6\times10^{-6}$ V. Suppose that the crystal moves with velocity v when emitting γ-quanta, and is at rest when absorbing quanta. Find the least source velocity v which can be recorded as a function of the absorption. Suppose that it is possible to record reliably a Doppler shift of the moving source γ-quanta frequency equal to 1/6 the line width.

662. In order for the Mössbauer line to have an intensity sufficient for practical applications, the energy loss R on free nuclear recoil (see Problems 658 and 659) must be less than or of the order of $2kT_D$, where T_D is the Debye temperature of the crystal. Determine the region of γ-quanta energies and mass numbers A in which the Mössbauer effect may be observed in practice, assuming that T_D varies between 160 and 480°K for different crystals.

663. By using the Mössbauer effect, it is possible to measure the gravitational frequency shift (see also Problem 501). Use has been made for this purpose of the γ-rays emitted by an excited Fe^{57} nucleus (energy of the γ-rays $E_{12} = 14{\cdot}4$ keV, line width $\Gamma = 3 \times \times 10^{-13} E_{12} \approx 4 \times 10^{-9}$ eV). For what height difference between the receiver (absorber) and source is the γ-line displaced 1 per cent of the line width (a change in the absorption of the γ-rays can already be noticed here).

664. In the conditions of the previous problem the γ-ray absorption varies not only as a function of the height difference between the receiver and source, but also with the temperature difference δT between the receiver and source. What is the cause of this effect and what change in the height difference corresponds in the experiments with Fe^{57} (from the point of view of the γ-ray absorption variation) to a temperature difference $\delta T = 1$ °C?

ANSWERS AND SOLUTIONS

CHAPTER I

MOLECULAR PHYSICS AND THERMODYNAMICS

§ 1. Thermometry. Calorimetry. Thermal Expansion

1. $t°C = 1{\cdot}475\, t°\mathrm{Fl} - 18{\cdot}75°$.

2. $t°\mathrm{C} = -\frac{2}{3}t°\mathrm{D} + 100°$.

3. $t = -38\frac{2}{3}\,°\mathrm{C}$.

4. $t° = T_H \dfrac{t_i - t_0}{t_H - t_0}$.

5. $t_m = \dfrac{t(t_H - t_0)}{100} + t_0 = 67{\cdot}7°$*.

6. $\dfrac{l}{l_1} = \dfrac{\alpha - 3\beta}{\alpha_1 - 3\beta}$.

7. The thermometer will give identical readings at two different temperatures t_1 and t_2 between 0° and 7·9°, where $t_1 + t_2 = 7{\cdot}9°$.

8. $t_1 = \dfrac{p_1 - p_0}{p_0\alpha_p - p_1\alpha}$.

9. $x^0 = t + \dfrac{k}{m}\,\Delta t = 33{\cdot}4°$.

10. $\tau = 100°[\ln(1 + \alpha t)/\ln(1 + 100\alpha)]$, where α is the volumetric expansion coefficient of the gas.

* Degrees centigrade are always to be understood unless there is a indication to the contrary.

11. $\beta = \dfrac{1}{p_0}\left(\dfrac{\partial p}{\partial T}\right)_v = -\dfrac{\left(\dfrac{\partial v}{\partial T}\right)_p}{p_0\left(\dfrac{\partial v}{\partial p}\right)_T} = \dfrac{\alpha v_0}{p_0 v_0 \gamma} = 46\ \text{deg}^{-1}.$

12. An increase of 640 atm.

13. $t = \dfrac{r_t - r_{18}}{r_{18}\varkappa} + 18° = 54{\cdot}1°.$

14. An accuracy $\Delta t = \Delta R/R\varkappa = 0{\cdot}0025°.$

15. $t = \dfrac{m' t_1 - m\lambda}{m + m'}.$

16. $m = \dfrac{M(r - qt_1)}{t + 80} = 80\ \text{g}.$

17. $q_2 = \dfrac{m + q_1 m_1}{m_2}\,\dfrac{t - t_0}{t_2 - t} = 0{\cdot}0092\ \text{cal g}^{-1}\ \text{deg}^{-1}$

18. $q' = \dfrac{1}{m'}\left[(qm + q_1 m_1)\dfrac{t_1 - t_0}{t_1' - t_2'} - m_1' q_1'\right].$

19. $m = 0{\cdot}125$ kg.

20. 1·1 g.

21. $\alpha = \dfrac{p_1(1 + \alpha_1 t) - p_0}{p_0 t}.$

23. $\alpha_1 = \dfrac{p - p_1}{p_1(t_1 - t)} + \alpha.$

24. $\alpha = 3\beta + \dfrac{p - p_1}{p(t_1 - t)}.$

25. $H_0 = H_1[1 - t_1(\alpha - \beta)] = 748{\cdot}0\ \text{mm}.$

26. $\beta = \dfrac{a \tan \varphi}{10 l_0 (t_1 - t_0)} = 0{\cdot}0000183\ \text{deg}^{-1}.$

27. $S = \pi r^2[1 + (\beta_{\parallel} + \beta_{\perp})(t_2 - t_1)]$.

28. $V_2 = \pi r^2 l(1 + [t_2 - t_1)(\beta_{\parallel} + 2\beta_{\perp})] = 16{\cdot}14\ \text{cm}^3$.

29. $\alpha = (h - h_0)/100\, h_0$, where h and h_0 are the liquid column heights at 100° and 0°.

30. $$x = \frac{1}{t}\left\{\frac{\varrho_0}{p}\left[\left(\frac{p}{\varrho_0} + \frac{P_0}{\delta_0}\right)(1 + \beta t) - \frac{P_t}{\delta_0}(1 + \alpha t)\right] - 1\right\}.$$

31. $n_2 - n_1 \approx 9{\cdot}5$ revolutions.

32. The water level is unchanged.

33. $P = E\beta S = 25{\cdot}2$ kg.

34. $P = E\beta(t_1 - t_0)\, S = 1{\cdot}41 \times 10^5$ kg.

§ 2. Thermal Conductivity

35. $m = \tau Sk(t_1 - t_2)/\lambda l = 54$ g, λ is the latent heat of melting of ice, equal to 80 cal g^{-1}.

36. $t_2 - t_1 = m\lambda l/\tau Sk = 0{\cdot}013°$, where λ is the latent heat of vaporisation of water, equal to 539 cal g^{-1} approximately.

37. $$t_2 - t_1 = \frac{m\lambda}{\tau S}\left(\frac{l}{k} + \frac{l_1}{k_1}\right) \approx 2°.$$

38. $$t_1 = \frac{k_1(t + t_3) + kt}{2k_1 + k} \approx 92{\cdot}8°, \quad t_2 = \frac{k_1(t + t_3) + kt_3}{2k_1 + k} \approx 7°.$$

39. $$Q = \frac{S\alpha k(t_1 - t_4)}{\alpha l + 2k}\tau = 1550\ \text{cal};$$

$$t_2 = \frac{k(t_1 + t_4) + \alpha l t_1}{\alpha l + 2k} = 11°; \quad t_3 = \frac{k(t_1 + t_4) + \alpha l t_4}{\alpha l + 2k} = -1°.$$

40. $$M = \frac{k\alpha S\tau(t_1 - t_2)}{(2k + \alpha L)r} = 1{\cdot}21\ \text{ton}.$$

41. $$\tau = \frac{m_1 m_2 c_1 c_2 L}{kS(m_1 c_1 + m_2 c_2)} \ln 2.$$

42. $t_2 = \dfrac{kt_1 + L\alpha t_3}{k + \alpha L}$.

43. (1) $t_2 \to t_1$ if $L \to 0$.

(2) $t_2 \to t_3$ if $k \to 0$.

44. $\tau = \dfrac{mc}{\alpha S} \ln \dfrac{t_1 - t_3}{t_2 - t_3}$.

45. $t_R = t_1 - \dfrac{t_1 - t_2}{\ln \dfrac{R_2}{R_1}} \ln \dfrac{R}{R_1}$.

46. $t_R = \dfrac{t_2 - t_1}{R_1 - R_2} \dfrac{R_1 R_2}{R} + \dfrac{t_1 R_1 - t_2 R_2}{R_1 - R_2}$.

47. $t = t_0 + 0{\cdot}24 \dfrac{I^2 \varrho (R^2 - r^2)}{4\pi^2 k R^4}$.

48. $x = \sqrt{\dfrac{2k(t_1 - t_2)}{\lambda \varrho} \tau} = 11{\cdot}2$ cm.

49. Consider the heat balance in the rod volume between the sections x and $x + dx$. The amount of heat flowing into this volume from the left during time $d\tau$ is $-k(\partial t/\partial x)Sd\tau$. The amount leaving from the right is $-k(\partial t/\partial x)_{x+dx}Sd\tau$. In addition, an amount of heat $\alpha p\, dx(t - t_3)d\tau$ leaves the volume via its lateral surface as a result of conduction. On the other hand, the amount of heat arriving in the volume is $Sdxc\varrho dt$. Thus, $-k(\partial t/\partial x)Sd\tau - [-k(\partial t/\partial x)_{x+dx}Sd\tau] - \alpha p dx(t - t_3)d\tau = Sdxc\varrho dt$, and consequently,

$$\frac{\partial t}{\partial \tau} = \frac{k}{c\varrho} \frac{\partial^2 t}{dx^2} - \frac{\alpha p}{c\varrho S}(t - t_3).$$

50. $t = t_3 + \dfrac{(t_2 - t_3) \sinh \beta x + (t_1 - t_3) \sinh \beta (l - x)}{\sinh \beta l}$,

where $\beta = \sqrt{\dfrac{\alpha}{k} \dfrac{P}{S}}$.

51. $t = (t_1 - t_2)\sinh\beta(l - x)/\sinh\beta l + t_2$. If $\beta l \gg 1$, $\beta(l - x) \gg 1$, then $t = t_2 + (t_1 - t_2)e^{-\beta x}$. If, moreover, $\beta x \gg 1$, then $t \approx t_2$.

52. $k_2 = k_1 \dfrac{x_2^2}{x_1^2}$.

53. $k_2 = \dfrac{d_2(t_1 - t_2)}{d_1(t_2 - t_3)} k_1 = 0{\cdot}00033$ cal deg^{-1}cm^{-1} sec^{-1}.

56. $t = t_1 e^{-\sqrt{\frac{\omega}{2}}\frac{x}{a}} \cos\left(\omega\tau - \sqrt{\dfrac{\omega}{2}}\dfrac{x}{a}\right) + t_0$.

57. $v = 1/\sqrt{365} = 0{\cdot}052$ m per day.

58. $\dfrac{\gamma_1}{\gamma_2} = \sqrt{\dfrac{T_2}{T_1}} = \sqrt{\dfrac{1}{365}} = \dfrac{1}{19}$.

59. It can easily be verified by substitution that expression (1) satisfies the heat conduction equation

$$\frac{\partial t}{\partial \tau} = a^2 \frac{\partial^2 t}{\partial x^2}, \tag{2}$$

the initial condition

$$t = t_0 \quad \text{for} \quad \tau = 0,\ x \geqslant 0, \tag{3}$$

and the boundary conditions

$$\begin{aligned} t &= 0 \quad \text{for} \quad x = 0,\ \tau > 0, \\ t &= t_0 \quad \text{for} \quad x = \infty,\ \tau > 0. \end{aligned} \tag{4}$$

It remains to show that the solution of the heat conduction equation satisfying these conditions is unique. Suppose there exists a second solution of equation (1): $t_1 = t_1(\tau, x)$, satisfying the same initial and boundary conditions. The difference $t_2 = t_1 - t$ will now satisfy the heat conduction equation:

$$\frac{\partial t_2}{\partial \tau} = a^2 \frac{\partial^2 t_2}{\partial x^2}, \tag{5}$$

the initial condition: $t_2 = 0$ for $\tau = 0$, $x > 0$ and the boundary conditions: $t_2 = 0$ for $x = 0$, $x = +\infty$, $\tau > 0$. We obtain from (5):

$$\frac{\partial}{\partial\tau}\left(\frac{1}{2}t_2^2\right) = a^2\frac{\partial}{\partial x}\left(t_2\frac{\partial t_2}{\partial x}\right) - a^2\left(\frac{\partial t_2}{\partial x}\right)^2,$$

whence integration gives us:

$$\frac{\partial}{\partial\tau}\int_0^\infty \frac{1}{2}t_2^2 dx = a^2 t_2 \frac{\partial t_2}{\partial x}\bigg|_0^\infty - a^2\int_0^\infty \left(\frac{\partial t_2}{\partial x}\right)^2 dx,$$

or, in view of the boundary conditions:

$$\frac{\partial}{\partial\tau}\int_0^\infty \frac{1}{2}t_2^2 dx = -a^2\int_0^\infty \left(\frac{\partial t_2}{\partial x}\right)^2 dx \leqslant 0. \tag{6}$$

We conclude from this that the integral $\int_0^\infty \frac{1}{2}t_2^2\, dx$ cannot increase with time. This is only possible when $t_2(\tau, x) = 0$, and the uniqueness of the solution is proved.

60. $\tau = \frac{1}{T}\left(\frac{2t_0}{v\frac{\partial t}{\partial x}}\right)^2 = 4\times 10^{10}$ days (T is the length of a day).

61. $p = \alpha\frac{ELQ}{2kS}$.

§ 3. Gas Laws. The Equation of State

62. $\varrho = \frac{(P-p)\,760}{V(H-h)}$.

63. ≈ 105 g.

64. $n = \dfrac{\ln\frac{p_2}{p_1}}{\ln\frac{V}{V+v}}$.

65. $H = \frac{(l'+l)h}{l-l'}$ mm Hg.

66. $\frac{1}{2}\left(H + l + l' - \sqrt{(H + l + l')^2 - 4l'H}\right)$ cm.

67. $\dfrac{H + l - \sqrt{H^2 + l^2}}{2}$.

68. $\approx 0{\cdot}004$ cm^2.

69. $\approx 4{\cdot}3$ mm.

70. Instead of 0·35 mm Hg, the manometer will read 0·33 mm Hg.

71. 10·9 litres.

72. 1·15 g.

73. $V = \dfrac{Q}{\delta_0\left(\dfrac{1}{1 + \alpha t_1} - \dfrac{1}{1 + \alpha t_2}\right)} = 1000 \text{ m}^3$

(α is the expansion coefficient of the gases).

74. $Q = 7{\cdot}2$ g.

75. $p = d_0 l\left(\dfrac{1}{1 + \alpha t_2} - \dfrac{1}{1 + \alpha t_1}\right) = 14$ mm water

(α is the expansion coefficient of the gases).

76. $p_1 = \dfrac{1 + \alpha t}{1 + \alpha t_1}\,\dfrac{L - h_1}{L - h}\,(H - h_1)$

(α is the expansion coefficient of the gases).

77. $$h_1 = -\tfrac{1}{2}(2l + H_1 - h) + \sqrt{\frac{1}{4}(2l + H_1 - h)^2 + \frac{2T_1}{T_0}(H_0 + h)\,l - H_1(2l - h)}.$$

78. $m = \dfrac{2P\sigma}{3RTd}\,M = 488$ g

(M is the molecular weight of nitrogen).

79. $\left(p + \frac{a\nu^2}{V^2}\right)(V - \nu b) = \nu RT.$

80. $p_{cr}V_{cr} = 3RT_{cr}/8.$

81. $p_{cr} = 50$ atm; $T_{cr} = 151\,°K.$

82. $V_{cr} = \frac{3RT_{cr}}{8p_{cr}} = 128\ \text{cm}^3.$

83. $b = 39{\cdot}4\ \text{cm}^3\,\text{mole}^{-1}$; $a = 1{\cdot}39 \times 10^6\ \text{atm cm}^6\,\text{mole}^{-2}.$

84. $p = \frac{a}{V^2} = \frac{5{\cdot}47 \times 10^6}{18^2} \approx 17000$ atm.

85. $V = \frac{8p_{cr}V_1\mu}{3RT_{cr}\varrho} = 2{\cdot}8\ \text{cm}^3.$

86. $T_{cr}^2 = \frac{8a}{27(b + c)R}$; $p_{cr}^2 = \frac{Ra}{216(b + c)^3}$; $v_{cr} = 3b + 2c.$

87. $T_{cr}^2 = \frac{8a}{27bR}$; $p_{cr}^2 = \frac{Ra}{216b^3}$; $v_{cr} = 3b.$

88. $p_{cr}v_{cr} = 3RT_{cr}/8.$

89. $\lambda = \int_{v_l}^{v_v} \frac{a}{v^2}\,dv = a\left(\frac{1}{v_l} - \frac{1}{v_v}\right) \approx \frac{a}{v_l} = v_l\pi;\quad \pi = \frac{\lambda}{v_l} = \lambda\varrho.$

90. Let p be the gas pressure in the evacuated vessel and p_1 the pressure at the end of the capillary adjacent to the pump (the pressure in the pump). Let m be the mass of gas in the evacuated vessel, and V its volume. Then

$$\frac{dm}{dt} = \frac{p_1 - p}{w}. \tag{1}$$

The volume dv occupied by the mass dm of gas at pressure p_1 is given by $p_1 dv = -dm(RT/\mu)$, whence

$$p_1 K = -\frac{RT}{\mu}\frac{dm}{dt}. \tag{2}$$

We have for the pressure p in the evacuated vessel: $pV = mRT/\mu$, so that

$$V\frac{dp}{dt} = \frac{RT}{\mu}\frac{dm}{dt}. \qquad (3)$$

On eliminating p_1 and dm/dt from (1), (2) and (3) and integrating, we obtain:

$$p = p_0 e^{-\frac{t}{V\left(\frac{\mu w}{RT}+\frac{1}{K}\right)}}. \qquad (4)$$

91. $\tau = \frac{V}{K}\ln\frac{p_0}{p} \approx 370$ sec.

92. $\tau = \left(2\cdot 18 \times 10^4 \frac{1}{RD^3}\sqrt{\frac{\mu}{T}} + \frac{1}{K}\right) V \ln\frac{p_0}{p} = 64\cdot 5$ sec

(μ is the molecular weight of the gas).

93. $M = \frac{\pi\mu}{RT}\,\frac{p_1^2 - p_2^2}{256\,\eta l}\,d^4$

(μ is the molecular weight of the gas).

94. $\tau = \frac{128\eta l V}{\pi p_2 d^4}\ln\frac{p_1 + 3p_2}{p_1 + p_2}$

(η is the coefficient of internal friction of the gas).

95. $p = \frac{p_1V_1T_2 + p_2V_2T_1}{V_1T_2 + V_2T_1} = 224$ mm Hg

(T_1 and T_2 are the absolute temperatures of the vessels).

96. It can be assumed without loss of generality that the cross-sectional area of the cylinder is unity. The co-ordinate origin is located on the cylinder base, with the x axis vertically upwards. First of all, if the gas is in equilibrium, the pressure p must be a function of x only. Otherwise, the pressure gradient would have a horizontal component, which would not be balanced by the external forces, with the result that motion would be produced in the gas. If the pressure at the base is p_0, and at the cover p, we must have by hypothesis:

$$p_0 - p = \int_0^x g\varrho\, dx,$$

and this equation must hold whatever x. We obtain by differentiation:

$$\frac{\partial p}{\partial x} = -g\varrho.$$

On substituting $p = RT\varrho/\mu$ in this and integrating, we obtain the barometric formula.

§ 4. The First and Second Laws of Thermodynamics and their Applications

97. $v = 340\,\mathrm{m\,sec^{-1}}$.

98. $Q = 1{\cdot}28 \times 10^9$ erg.

99. $Q = 2RT \ln \dfrac{p_1}{p}$.

100. $Q = 580$ cal.

101. $E = \dfrac{2\pi RPN}{(M + w)\, c\Delta t}$

($c = 1\,\mathrm{cal\,g^{-1}\,deg^{-1}}$ is the specific heat of water).

102. $E = \dfrac{1000R\gamma}{\mu c_p(\gamma - 1)} = 427\,\mathrm{kg\,m\,cal^{-1}}$.

103. $pV^k = \text{const.}$, where $k = (c_p - c)/(c_v - c)$. (1) $V = \text{const.}$, (2) $p = \text{const.}$, (3) $pV^\gamma = \text{const.}$ and (4) $pV = \text{const.}$

104. (1) The gas cools on expansion, its temperature being proportional to $\sqrt{p}$

(2) $c = c_v - R$. Heat must be taken from the gas when it expands.

105. The gas heats on expansion, its temperature being proportional to $\sqrt{V}$; $c = c_p + R$. Heat must be supplied to the gas when it expands.

106. $C = \nu(3c_v - 2c_p) = -0{\cdot}163\,\mathrm{cal\,deg^{-1}}$, where $\nu = 0{\cdot}163$ is the number of moles.

107. $c = \frac{1}{2}(c_v + c_p)$.

109. 29,000 cal.

110. 67,700 cal.

111. $$T = \frac{5p_1V_1 + 3p_2V_2}{\dfrac{5p_1V_1}{T_1} + \dfrac{3p_2V_2}{T_2}} = 352\,^\circ\text{K} = 79\,^\circ\text{C};$$

$$p = \frac{T}{V_1 + V_2}\left(\frac{p_1V_1}{T_1} + \frac{p_2V_2}{T_2}\right) = 1{\cdot}23 \text{ atm.}$$

112. Zero.

113. $VT^{\frac{1}{\gamma-1}} e^{-\frac{\alpha T}{R}} = \text{const.}$

114. $Q = 217$ cal.

115. $Q = 163$ cal.

116. The proof follows from the fact that the internal energy of a given mass of gas is $U = pV/(\gamma - 1)$, where V is the volume of the gas.

117. $Q = 3{\cdot}72$ cal.

118. $Q = 90$ cal.

119. $$\Delta U = \frac{p\Delta V}{\gamma - 1} = 150 \text{ kgm.}$$

120. $$Q = \frac{t}{\gamma}(mc_p + m_1c_{1p}) = 300 \text{ cal.}$$

121. $p_t = (2p_0/3)(1 + \alpha C/c)$, where p_0 is the initial pressure of the mixture, α is the thermal expansion coefficient.

122. Since heating leaves the volume of the system unchanged, no work is done. The required amount of heat is therefore equal to the increment in the internal energy of the system and is thus independent of the method by which the system passes from its initial to its final state. This passage may be realised in two stages.

1. We heat the water from 0° to 100° in such a way that no vaporisation occurs. The amount of heat required for this is $Q_1 = 18 \times 100 = 1800$ cal.

2. We vaporise the water at constant temperature $t = 100°$. The amount of heat required is $Q_2 = U_v - U_l$, where U_v and U_l are the internal energies of a mole of water vapour and liquid water at 100° and atmospheric pressure. To find $U_v - U_l$ we use the first law of thermodynamics $q = U_v - U_l + A$, where q is the heat of vaporisation per mole ($q = 539 \times 18 = 9710$ cal), and A is the work against the constant external pressure ($A = pV_v = RT = 1{\cdot}98 \times 373 = 739$ cal). Hence $Q_2 = U_v - U_l = q - A = 8970$ cal.

$$Q = Q_1 + Q_2 = 1800 + 8970 = 10{,}770 \text{ cal}.$$

123. $dQ = dU + p\,dV = \left(\frac{\partial U}{\partial T}\right)_V dT + \left[\left(\frac{\partial U}{\partial V}\right)_T + p\right] dV.$

On first putting $V = \text{const}$, then $p = \text{const}$, we obtain:

$$c_v = \left(\frac{\partial U}{\partial T}\right)_V; \quad c_p = \left(\frac{\partial U}{\partial T}\right)_V + \left[\left(\frac{\partial U}{\partial V}\right)_T + p\right]\left(\frac{\partial V}{\partial T}\right)_P,$$

whence

$$c_p - c_v = \left[\left(\frac{\partial U}{\partial V}\right)_T + p\right]\left(\frac{\partial V}{\partial T}\right)_P.$$

124. It follows from the solution of the previous problem that

$$dQ = c_v dT + \frac{c_p - c_v}{\left(\frac{\partial V}{\partial T}\right)_P} dV.$$

For an adiabatic process $dQ = 0$. Hence

$$dT_{\text{ad}} + \frac{\gamma - 1}{\left(\frac{\partial V}{\partial T}\right)_P} dV_{\text{ad}} = 0.$$

On substituting in this

$$dT_{\text{ad}} = \left(\frac{\partial T}{\partial V}\right)_P dV_{\text{ad}} + \left(\frac{\partial T}{\partial p}\right)_V dp_{\text{ad}},$$

we obtain:

$$\left(\frac{\partial V}{\partial p}\right)_{\text{ad}} = -\frac{1}{\gamma}\left(\frac{\partial T}{\partial p}\right)_V \left(\frac{\partial V}{\partial T}\right)_P.$$

On comparing this with

$$\left(\frac{\partial V}{\partial p}\right)_T = -\left(\frac{\partial T}{\partial p}\right)_V \left(\frac{\partial V}{\partial T}\right)_p,$$

we obtain the required result.

125. Obviously, *ceteris paribus*, the speed of sound is the greater, the greater the force tending to return a deviated air particle to the equilibrium position, i.e. the greater the pressure difference between points of compression and rarefaction. The temperature rise at a point of compression increases the air pressure, whilst the temperature drop at a point of rarefaction reduces the pressure. Both lead to an increase in the pressure difference between points of compression and rarefaction, and hence to an increase in the speed of sound in the gas.

127. 1260 m sec^{-1}.

128. 970 m sec^{-1}.

129. $\gamma = 1{\cdot}41$.

130. $\dfrac{v}{v_1} = 4{\cdot}86$.

131. $\gamma = \dfrac{c_p}{c_v} = 1{\cdot}7$.

132. $\dfrac{p_2}{p_1} = \left(\dfrac{V_1}{V_2}\right)^\gamma; \quad p_2 = \left(\dfrac{1}{2}\right)^{1\cdot 7} = 0{\cdot}308$ atm.

134. $\gamma = \dfrac{\ln \dfrac{p_0}{p_1}}{\ln \dfrac{p_2}{p_1}}$.

135. $\gamma = \dfrac{V}{lS}\dfrac{T_1^2 - T_2^2}{T_2^2}$.

136. $T - T_0 = mv^2/2\nu c_v \approx 28{,}000\,^\circ$K, ν is the number of moles:

$$\frac{\varrho}{\varrho_0} = \left(\frac{T}{T_0}\right)^{\frac{1}{\gamma-1}} \approx 1000; \quad \frac{p}{p_0} = \left(\frac{\varrho}{\varrho_0}\right)^\gamma \approx 10^5.$$

137. At mechanical equilibrium the temperature T, density ϱ and pressure p of the air depend only on the height z above the Earth's surface, whilst $p = C\varrho T$, where C is independent of z. Thus, when z varies,

$$\frac{\partial}{\partial p} = \frac{d}{dp} + \frac{dT}{T},$$

whence we find for the equilibrium density at the height $z + dz$:

$$\varrho(z + dz) = \varrho(z) + d\varrho = \varrho + \frac{\varrho}{p} dp - \varrho \frac{dT}{T}. \tag{1}$$

Suppose now that, as a result of random disturbances, a small mass of air has been shifted from the height z to $z + dz$. The pressure inside the mass will be equal to the pressure of the surrounding air, so that its density must have changed. Since the thermal conduction of air is small, the process can be regarded as adiabatic, and hence $p = \text{const}\, \varrho^\gamma$. We thus have, for the density change $d\varrho^*$ in the mass that has shifted:

$$\frac{dp}{p} = \gamma \frac{d\varrho^*}{\varrho},$$

and for the density itself:

$$\varrho^*(z + dz) = \varrho(z) + d\varrho^* = \varrho + \frac{1}{\gamma} \frac{\varrho}{p} dp. \tag{2}$$

Suppose that $dz > 0$ and $\varrho^*(z + dz) > \varrho(z + dz)$. The displaced mass of air, being heavier than the surrounding air, must now return to its equilibrium position, i.e. the equilibrium is stable. When $dz > 0$ and $\varrho^*(z + dz) < \varrho(z + dz)$, it will be unstable. We thus obtain the following stability conditions from (1) and (2)

$$\frac{1}{\gamma} \frac{\varrho}{p} dp \geqslant \frac{\varrho}{p} dp - \varrho \frac{dT}{T} \quad \text{for} \quad dz > 0. \tag{3}$$

At mechanical equilibrium,

$$\frac{dp}{dz} = -\varrho g. \tag{4}$$

On eliminating dp, we obtain:

$$\frac{dT}{dz} \geqslant -\frac{T}{p} \frac{\gamma - 1}{\gamma} \varrho g = -\frac{g}{c_p} \approx -0{\cdot}1 \text{ deg m}^{-1}, \tag{5}$$

where c_p is the specific heat at constant pressure. The equality sign corresponds to neutral equilibrium. The corresponding stratification of the atmosphere is described as adiabatic.

138. $p = p_0(1 - az/T_0)^n$; $p/T^n = \text{const}$, where T_0 is the absolute temperature at the Earth's surface; $n = Mg/Ra$; R is the gas constant, M is the molecular weight of air. In the limiting case, when $a \to 0$, the barometric formula is obtained:

$$p = p_0 e^{-\frac{Mgz}{RT_0}}.$$

Hint. We have assumed that

$$\frac{dT}{dz} = -a.$$

The equilibrium condition is

$$\frac{dp}{dz} = -\varrho g.$$

Finally, on the basis of the perfect gas law

$$p = \frac{R}{M}\varrho T.$$

The formulae given in the answer can be obtained from these three equations.

139. $z = T_0/a$. For adiabatic stratification (see the solution to Problem 137),

$$z = \frac{gT_0}{c_p} \approx 28 \text{ km}.$$

It follows from the answer that the temperature gradient cannot be the same throughout the atmosphere.

140. Cobalt = 6·14; Gold = 6·15.

141. $\eta = (T_1 - T_2)/(T_1 + c_p(T_1 - T_2)/R \ln (P/p))$, where $T_1 > T_2$, $P > p$.

142. $$\eta = \frac{(\gamma - 1)(T_1 - T_2)\ln\dfrac{V_1}{V_2}}{(\gamma - 1)T_1 \ln\dfrac{V_1}{V_2} + (T_1 - T_2)}, \quad \text{where} \quad \gamma = \frac{c_p}{c_v}.$$

144. If the process is cyclical, the heat borrowed from the heat reservoir cannot be entirely converted into work, since this would contradict the second law of thermodynamics. If the process is not cyclical, total conversion of the heat into work is possible. For instance, if an ideal gas is in thermal contact with a heat reservoir and undergoes isothermal expansion, performing work against the external forces, its internal energy will meantime remain unchanged, since it is independent of the volume and depends only on the temperature. Hence all the heat taken by the gas from the reservoir must be converted into work.

145. The heat restored by the engine in its operation to the water of the heating system (cooler) is

$$Q' = q\frac{T_2}{T_1}.$$

The work of the engine,

$$A = q\frac{T_1 - T_2}{T_1}$$

is expended on operating the cooling machine. The latter takes from the cooler (sub-soil water) heat Q_3 and transmits to the heater (water of the heating system) heat Q''. Here,

$$Q'' = \frac{T_2}{T_3}Q_3;$$

$$Q'' - Q_3 = Q''\frac{T_2 - T_3}{T_2} = A;$$

$$Q'' = A\frac{T_2}{T_2 - T_3} = q\frac{T_1 - T_3}{T_1}\,\frac{T_2}{T_2 - T_3}.$$

The total amount of heat received by the heated location is

$$Q = Q' + Q'' = q\frac{T_2(T_1 - T_3)}{T_1(T_2 - T_3)} \approx 20000 \text{ cal kg}^{-1}.$$

146. On the p, V diagram (Fig. 20) we take two indefinitely close isotherms 12 and 34 and two indefinitely close adiabats 23 and 41 and apply Carnot's theorem to the cycle 1234. The heat Q_1 received by the system on the isotherm 12 is equal to $Q_1 = A_1 + \Delta U$, where $A_1 = p\Delta V$ is the work done by the system on the isotherm 12, and $\Delta U = (\partial U/\partial V)_T \Delta V$ is the change in the internal energy on this isotherm. The work of the cycle is represented by the area 1234. This area can be calculated, discounting higher order magnitudes, by replacing 1234 by a parallelogram, the area of which is obviously equal to the area of the parallelogram 1256, i.e. $A = \Delta p \cdot \Delta V = (\partial p/\partial T)_V \Delta T \Delta V$, where $\Delta T = T_1 - T_2$. By Carnot's theorem,

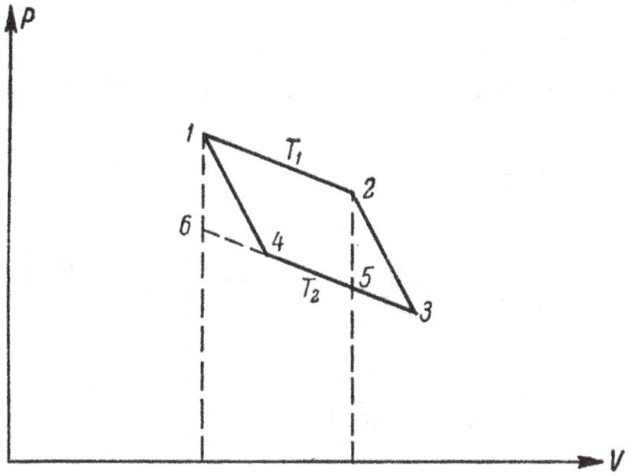

FIG. 20

$A/Q_1 = \Delta T/T_1$. On substituting in this the expressions for A and Q_1, we obtain the first of the formulae which are to be proved. The second formula is obtained from the first by differentiation with respect to T at constant V.

147. $U = \nu(c_v T - a\nu/V)$, where ν is the number of moles and the constants c_v, a refer to 1 mole.

148. $U = \nu(c_{v\infty} T - a\nu/V)$, where $c_{v\infty}$ is the molar specific heat of the gas at constant volume in a state of infinite rarefaction, when the gas behaves as though ideal. The defect of the solution is that it does not provide a proof of the independence of c_v on the volume of the gas.

149. $\Delta T = \dfrac{a}{c_v}\left(\dfrac{1}{V_1} - \dfrac{1}{V_2}\right) = 0{\cdot}24°$.

150. The gas cools. Its temperature and pressure are

$$T' = T - \frac{a}{2c_v}\frac{(V_2 - V_1)^2}{V_1V_2(V_1 + V_2)};$$

$$p' = \frac{2RT'}{V_1 + V_2 - 2b} - \frac{4a}{(V_1 + V_2)^2}.$$

151. $T' - T = -a\nu/2Vc_v = -0{\cdot}0055°$, where $\nu = 0{\cdot}041$ is the number of moles.

152. $T' - T = (a/c_v)(1/V_2 - 1/V_1) = -0{\cdot}013°$, where $V_1 = 20$ litres and $V_2 = 200$ litres are the corresponding molar volumes.

153. $Q = a\left(\frac{1}{V_1} - \frac{1}{V_2}\right).$

154. $$Q = \frac{c_v}{R}\left\{\left(p + \frac{a}{V_2^2}\right)(V_2 - b) - \left(p + \frac{a}{V_1^2}\right)(V_1 - b)\right\} + a\left(\frac{1}{V_1} - \frac{1}{V_2}\right).$$

155. According to the first law of thermodynamics the heat of vaporisation of 1 mole of liquid is equal to $q = U_v - U_l + A$, where U_v and U_l are the internal energies of the vapour and liquid, and $A = p(V_v - V_l)$ is the work done against the constant external pressure. $U_v - U_l$ is found from the equation

$$\left(\frac{\partial U}{\partial V}\right)_T = T\left(\frac{\partial p}{\partial T}\right)_V - p = \frac{a}{V^2},$$

which gives $U_v - U_l = a(1/V_l - 1/V_v)$. Hence,

$$q = V_v\left(p - \frac{a}{V_v^2}\right) - V_l\left(p - \frac{a}{V_l^2}\right)$$

$$= V_v\left(\frac{RT}{V_v - b} - \frac{2a}{V_v^2}\right) - V_l\left(\frac{RT}{V_l - b} - \frac{2a}{V_l^2}\right).$$

156. $$c_p - c_v = T\left(\frac{\partial p}{\partial T}\right)_V\left(\frac{\partial V}{\partial T}\right)_p = -T\left(\frac{\partial V}{\partial T}\right)_p^2\left(\frac{\partial p}{\partial V}\right)_T.$$

157. $$c_p - c_v = \frac{R}{1 - \dfrac{2a(V-b)^2}{RTV^3}}.$$

158. $c_p - c_v = Tv\alpha^2/\beta = 0{\cdot}0041$ cal g^{-1} deg^{-1}; $\gamma = 1{\cdot}14$; $A/(c_p - c_v) = P_0\beta/T\alpha = 7{\cdot}9 \times 10^{-5}$. Thus practically the entire difference $c_p - c_v$ goes into increasing the internal energy of the mercury.

159. See the answer to Problem 156.

160. (1) It gets cooler. (2) It gets hotter. The answer follows from the identity $(\partial T/\partial p)_v = -(\partial T/\partial V)_p \cdot (\partial V/\partial p)_T$, provided we take into account the condition for the stability of a physically uniform and isotropic substance (see the previous problem).

161. Let l, τ, T and S be the length, tension and entropy of the strap. Only two of these four quantities are independent, the other two being functions of them. Thus the indentity follows:

$$\left(\frac{\partial T}{\partial l}\right)_S \left(\frac{\partial l}{\partial S}\right)_T \left(\frac{\partial S}{\partial T}\right)_l = -1. \tag{1}$$

It follows from the first law, written in the form $d(U-TS) = -SdT + \tau dl$, that

$$\left(\frac{\partial S}{\partial l}\right)_T = -\left(\frac{\partial \tau}{\partial T}\right)_l$$

or

$$\left(\frac{\partial l}{\partial S}\right)_T = -\left(\frac{\partial T}{\partial \tau}\right)_l.$$

Further, since T, τ, l are connected by a functional relationship, we have identically,

$$\left(\frac{\partial l}{\partial S}\right)_T = \left(\frac{\partial l}{\partial \tau}\right)_T \left(\frac{\partial T}{\partial l}\right)_\tau.$$

On substituting this in (1), we get

$$\frac{c_l}{T}\left(\frac{\partial T}{\partial l}\right)_S \left(\frac{\partial l}{\partial \tau}\right)_T \left(\frac{\partial T}{\partial l}\right)_\tau = -1,$$

where $c_l = T(\partial S/\partial T)_l$ is the specific heat at constant length. It is positive for all bodies: $c_l > 0$. The quantity $(\partial l/\partial \tau)_T$ is also positive for all bodies. Consequently,

$$\left(\frac{\partial T}{\partial l}\right)_S \left(\frac{\partial T}{\partial l}\right)_\tau < 0.$$

By hypothesis, $(\partial l/\partial T)_\tau < 0$ for the rubber strap, and hence $(\partial T/\partial l)_S > 0$. It follows from this that the strap heats up if it is elongated adiabatically.

162. We first write the first law of thermodynamics $\delta Q = dU + pdV$ in the form $\delta Q = dH - Vdp$. We then take on the p, V diagram (Fig. 20, page 131) two indefinitely close isotherms 12 and 34 and two indefinitely close adiabats 23 and 41 and apply Carnot's theorem to the cycle 1234. The heat Q_1 received by the system on isotherm 12 is $Q_1 = H_2 - H_1 - V(p_2 - p_1)$. Since the change in enthalpy $H_2 - H_1$ takes place along the isotherm, $Q_1 = [(\partial H/\partial p)_T - V] \times (p_2 - p_1)$. The work A of the cycle is represented by the area 1234. Discounting higher order quantities, the area of 1234 can be regarded as a parallelogram. The area of this parallelogram is equal to the area of the parallelogram 1256. This latter is in turn equal to the base 61 multiplied by the height $(V_2 - V_1)$. Since the points 1 and 6 correspond to the same volumes, but different temperatures, the length of the base 61 is $(\partial p/\partial T)_V (T_1 - T_2)$. We thus have for the work of the cycle: $A = (\partial p/\partial T)_V (T_1 - T_2)(V_2 - V_1)$ or, using the identity $(\partial p/\partial V)_V = -(\partial V/\partial T)_p (\partial p/\partial V)T$, $A = -(\partial V/\partial T)_p \times (T_1 - T_2)(p_2 - p_1)$. By Carnot's theorem, $A/Q_1 = (T_1 - T_2)/T_1$. On substituting the values for A and Q_1 in this, we obtain the first of the required formulae. The second is obtained by differentiation of the first with respect to p, since $c_p = (\partial H/\partial T)_p$.

163. The Joule–Thomson effect is characterised by constant enthalpy. Thus

$$dH \equiv c_p dT + \left[V - T\left(\frac{\partial V}{\partial T}\right)_p\right] dp = 0,$$

whence

$$\left(\frac{\partial T}{\partial p}\right)_H = \frac{T\left(\frac{\partial V}{\partial T}\right)_p - V}{c_p}.$$

164. $$\left(\frac{\partial T}{\partial p}\right)_H = \frac{\dfrac{2a}{RT} - b}{c_p}.$$

165. $\Delta T = -b\Delta p/c_p > 0$ ($\Delta p < 0$; Δp and ΔT are assumed small).

166. $\Delta T = +\dfrac{2a\Delta p}{RTc_p}$ (Δp small).

167. $T_i = \dfrac{27}{4}T_k = \dfrac{2a}{Rb}$.

168. $T < T_i = 35{\cdot}8°$ K.

169.

	$T_i°K$	$\Delta T°$
Nitrogen	800	$-0{\cdot}0014$
Hydrogen	206	$+0{\cdot}0001$
Helium	33·4	$+0{\cdot}0003$

170. $$\Delta T = \frac{1}{c_p}\left(\frac{RT}{V-b}b - \frac{2a}{V}\right);$$

$$\Delta T_{\text{nitrogen}} = -35°;$$

$$\Delta T_{\text{hydrogen}} = +11°;$$

$$\Delta T_{\text{helium}} = +34°.$$

171. A hyperbola: $T = 2a(V-b)/RbV$ (see Figs. 21 and 22). (The temperature is in degrees centigrade, the volume in cubic centimetres.) The asymptotes, represented by dotted lines, intersect the axis of ordinates at the points of inversion of the Joule–Thomson effect.

172. Let the point A on the p, V diagram (Fig. 23) represent the state of a gram of the liquid at the temperature T and pressure p, equal to the pressure of its saturated vapour at this temperature. We shall communicate heat to the system in such a way that the pressure and temperature remain constant. The liquid will now vaporise, and saturated vapour will be present above it at any instant. Let B represent the state in which the entire liquid has become vapour. The heat received by the system on the isotherm AB will now be equal to the heat of vaporisation q. We lower the vapour temperature adiabatically by the infinitesimal amount dT (the point C), then return the system to its initial state along the isotherm CD and the adiabat DA. The work done by the system is equal to the

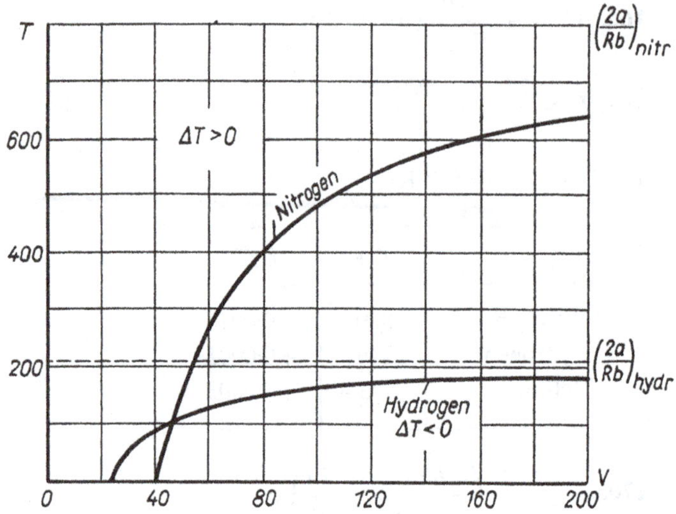

FIG. 21

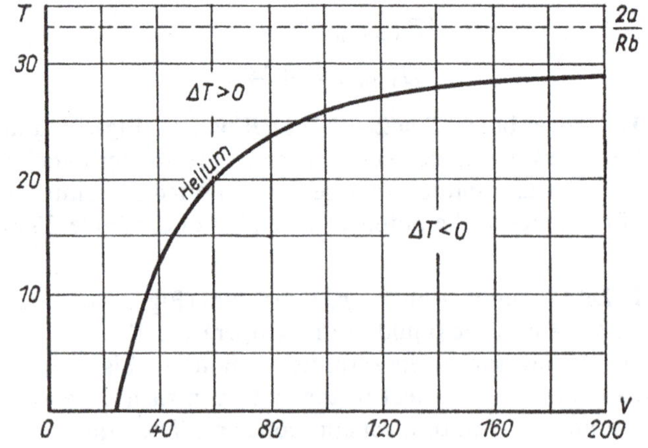

FIG. 22

area of the parallelogram $ABCD$. On expressing it in terms of v_v, v_l and dT, and applying Carnot's theorem, we easily obtain:

$$dp/dT = q/T(v_v - v_l)$$

(the Clausius–Clapeyron formula).

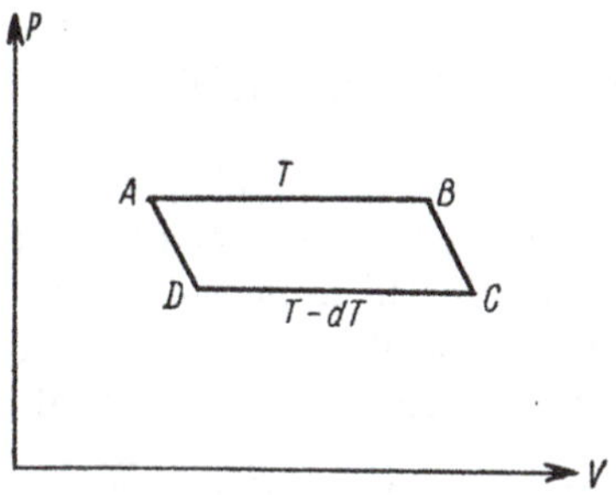

FIG. 23

173. $p \approx (1 + q\Delta T/\nu RT^2)p_0 = 1{\cdot}035$ atm, where q is the heat of vaporisation, $\nu = 1/18$ is the number of moles in 1 g water, p_0 is the atmospheric pressure.

174. $\Delta m \approx (\mu Vp/RT^2)[(q\mu/RT) - 1)]\Delta T \approx 0{\cdot}075$g, where $V \approx 4$ l is the volume of vapour, p is its pressure, R is the universal gas constant.

175. The heat of sublimation is $q = q_1 + q_2 = 676\ \mathrm{cal\,g^{-1}}$. On substituting this in the Clausius–Clapeyron equation $dp/dT = q/T(v_v - v_s) \approx q/Tv_v$ and determining the specific volume of the water vapour from the equation $pv_v = RT/\mu$, we easily find that, for $\Delta T = -1°$, $\Delta p = -0{\cdot}38$ mm Hg, and the pressure of the saturated vapour over the ice at $t = -1°$ is $p_{-1} = 4{\cdot}20$ mm Hg.

176. By the first law, $\delta Q = dH - Vdp$. Since $(\partial H/\partial p)_T = 0$ for an ideal gas (see Problem 163), we obtain from this, for the required specific heat: $c = (\partial H/\partial T)_p - Vdp/dT$. In the process in question dp and dT are connected by the equation $dp/dT = q/T(v_v - v_l) \approx q\mu/TV$ (μ is the molecular weight). Hence $c = c_p - \mu q/T$.

177. By the first law, the heat received by 1 mole of vapour is $\delta Q = dH_v - V_v dp$, and the molar heat of vaporisation q satisfies $\mu q = H_v - H_l$, where H_v and H_l are the molar enthalpies of the saturated vapour and the liquid, H_v being dependent on T only. On differentiating the last relationship with respect to T, we find $\mu dq/dT = dH_v/dT - dH_l/dT$. For the liquid $dH_l = c_p dT + V_l dp$, where the last term can be neglected. Hence $dH_v = \mu(dq/dT)dT + c_p dT$. In the process in question dp and dT are connected by $dp/dT = q/T(v_v - v_l) \approx \mu q/TV_v$. As a result, we obtain for the specific heat of the saturated vapour:

$$c = \delta Q/dT = c_p - \mu q/T + \mu dq/dT.$$

Here, c_p is the specific heat of the liquid, whereas in the approximate formula of the previous problem c_p was to be understood as the specific heat of the vapour. This approximate formula yields a lower value for the absolute value of c than the more accurate formula of the present problem. The error does not exceed 10 per cent.

178. On adiabatic compression the water vapour becomes unsaturated, on adiabatic expansion it becomes supersaturated. (The production of supersaturated water vapour by adiabatic expansion is used in a cloud chamber.)

180. $$t = \frac{p_0 - p_1}{\dfrac{p_2 - p_1}{t_2 - t_1} + \dfrac{q}{T(v_1 - v_2)}} = 0{\cdot}0075°;$$

$$p = \frac{p_2 - p_1}{t_2 - t_1} t + p_1 = 4{\cdot}582 \text{ mm Hg}.$$

181. In phase transitions of the first kind the ratio c/a changes with a jump at the point Θ. In phase transitions of the second kind the ratio changes continuously, and becomes unity at the temperature Θ.

182. We shall prove, for instance, the second relationship. We can write for the differential of the entropy of each phase:

$$dS = \left(\frac{\partial S}{\partial T}\right)_p dT + \left(\frac{\partial S}{\partial p}\right)_T dp = \left(\frac{c_p}{T}\right) dT - \left(\frac{\partial V}{\partial T}\right)_p dp.$$

If the points (T, p) and $(T + dT, p + dp)$ both lie on the equilibrium curve, we have

$$d(S_2 - S_1) = d\Delta S = 0$$

(S_1 is the entropy of one, S_2 of the other phase). This means that

$$\frac{\Delta c_p}{T}\,dT - \Delta\left(\frac{\partial V}{\partial T}\right)_p dp = 0$$

whence the required relationship follows. The other three relationships are proved in the same way.

183. $\Delta T = \dfrac{T(v_w - v_i)\,p}{q} = -0{\cdot}88°;\quad \dfrac{\Delta m}{m} = -\dfrac{c_i \Delta T}{q} = 0{\cdot}0066.$

The last result is most easily obtained from the condition that the entropy be constant during the process.

185. $v_v = v_l + \left(\dfrac{q}{T}\right)\left(\dfrac{dT}{dp}\right) \approx 1700\ \text{cm}^3\,\text{g}^{-1}.$

186. The bodies A and B can exchange internal energy by means of heat exchange and can perform work on one another. Since they are situated in a rigid adiabatic envelope, the changes in their internal energies in an elementary process are connected by $dU_A = -dU_B$. Since action and reaction are equal, $\delta A_A = -\delta A_B$, where δA_A is the work done by A on B, and δA_B is the work done by B on A. Thus $(dU + \delta A)_A = -(dU + \delta A)_B$, or $\delta Q_A = -\delta Q_B$. The amount of heat received by A is equal to the amount of heat released by B. According to the Clausius postulate, the only processes that can occur in the system are those in which heat passes from the hotter to the cooler body. It follows from this that $\delta Q_A < 0$, $\delta_B Q > 0$, since $T_A > T_B$. On applying the Clausius inequality to each body, we obtain

$$\Delta S_A \geqslant \int \frac{\delta Q_A}{T_A}, \quad \Delta S_B \geqslant \int \frac{\delta Q_B}{T_B}.$$

On adding these inequalities and noting that $S_A + S_B = S$, we find that

$$\Delta S \geqslant \int \left(\frac{\delta Q_A}{T_A} + \frac{\delta Q_B}{T_B}\right) > \int \delta Q_B\left(\frac{1}{T_B} - \frac{1}{T_A}\right) > 0.$$

188. $\Delta S = mc \ln T_2/T_1$, where m is the mass of the substance.

189. $\Delta S = 63\ \text{cal}\,\text{deg}^{-1}$.

190. $\Delta S = 3{\cdot}2\ \text{cal}\,\text{deg}^{-1}$.

191. $\Delta S = (RM/\mu)\ln(V_2/V_1)$, where μ is the molecular weight of the gas.

192. $$\Delta U = U_2 - U_1 = \frac{pV^k}{\gamma - 1}\left(\frac{1}{V_2^{k-1}} - \frac{1}{V_1^{k-1}}\right),$$

where $$\gamma = \frac{c_p}{c_v}; \quad \Delta S = S_2 - S_1 = (kc_v - c_p)\ln\frac{V_1}{V_2}.$$

For an isothermal process: $\Delta U = 0$; $\Delta S = R\ln V_2/V_1$.

For an adiabatic process: $\Delta U = [pV^\gamma/(\gamma - 1)](1/V_2^{\gamma-1} - 1/V_1^{\gamma-1})$; $\Delta S = 0$.

193. $$\Delta U = -\frac{3}{2}p_1V_1\left(1 - \frac{V_1^2}{V_2^2}\right) = -625\ \text{cal mol}^{-1}.$$

$$\Delta S = -2R\ln\frac{V_2}{V_1} \approx -4\ \text{cal deg}^{-1}\text{mol}^{-1}.$$

$$Q = -P_1V_1\left(1 - \frac{V_1^2}{V_2^2}\right) \approx -417\ \text{cal mole}^{-1}.$$

The system releases, and does not absorb, heat.

194. $$\Delta U = \frac{5}{2}p_1V_1\left(\frac{V_1}{V_2} - 1\right) = -117\ \text{cal}.$$

$$Q = \frac{3}{2}p_1V_1\left(\frac{V_1}{V_2} - 1\right) = -70\ \text{cal}.$$

$$\Delta S = -\frac{3}{2}\frac{p_1V_1}{T_1}\ln\frac{V_2}{V_1} = -0{\cdot}20\ \text{cal deg}^{-1}.$$

195. $\Delta S = 4{\cdot}56\ \text{cal deg}^{-1}$.

196. $\Delta S = R(M_1/\mu_1 + M_2/\mu_2)\ln 2$.

197. $$S_2 - S_1 = \frac{R}{2}(5\nu_1 + 3\nu_2)\ln\frac{5\nu_1T_1 + 3\nu_2T_2}{5\nu_1 + 3\nu_2}$$
$$- \frac{R}{2}(5\nu_1\ln T_1 + 3\nu_2\ln T_2) + R(\nu_1 + \nu_2)\ln 2 = 0{\cdot}16\ \text{cal deg}^{-1},$$

where $\nu_1 = 0{\cdot}0402$ is the number of moles of hydrogen, $\nu_2 = 0{\cdot}0948$ is the number of moles of helium.

198. $\Delta U = U - U_0 = \frac{M}{\mu} c_v T_0 (2^{\gamma-1} - 1);$

$$\Delta S = S - S_0 = \frac{M}{\mu} c_v (\gamma - 1) \ln 2, \quad \text{where} \quad \gamma = \frac{c_p}{c_v}.$$

199. $S = c_v \ln T + R \ln (V - b) + \text{const}$. The equation of the adiabat is obtained by equating this expression to a constant.

200. $\left(p + \frac{a}{V^2}\right)(V - b)^{\frac{R + c_v - c}{c_v - c}} = \text{const}.$

201. $s = c_p \ln T + \frac{q(T)}{T} \xi + \text{const},$

where c_p is the specific heat of the liquid, $q(T)$ is the heat of vaporisation at the temperature T, ξ is the ratio of the mass of vapour to the total mass of the system.

202. $v^2 = 2c_p T_1 \left(1 - \frac{T_2}{T_1}\right) = 2c_p T_1 \left[1 - \left(\frac{p_2}{p_1}\right)^{\frac{\gamma-1}{\gamma}}\right].$

For carbon dioxide $v \approx 460 \text{ m sec}^{-1}$.

203. $T = T_0 - \frac{\mu v^2}{2c_p} = 194°\text{K}; \quad p_0 = p\left(\frac{T_0}{T}\right)^{\frac{\gamma}{\gamma-1}} = 3{\cdot}1 \text{ atm}$

(μ is the molecular weight, c_p is the molar specific heat, p is the atmospheric pressure).

204. $v = \sqrt{2 \frac{c_p}{\mu} T}.$

This maximum velocity is reached when the gas flows adiabatically into a vacuum (or in practice, when $P/p \gg 1$, where P is the gas pressure in the flask, p is the external pressure).

205. $\frac{M_0}{M} = e^{\frac{v}{v_0}} \approx 22, \quad \text{where} \quad v_0 = \sqrt{2 \frac{c_p}{\mu} T} \approx 2{\cdot}58 \text{ km sec}^{-1}.$

206. We can write for the required ratio (see the discussion in § 94 of L.D. Landau and E.M. Lifshitz, *Electrodynamics of Continuous Media*, Pergamon Press, Oxford, 1960)

$$\frac{I_\omega}{I_{\omega-\delta\omega}+I_{\omega+\delta\omega}} = \frac{\left(\frac{\partial V}{\partial s}\right)_p^2 \overline{\Delta s^2}}{\left(\frac{\partial V}{\partial p}\right)_s^2 \overline{\Delta p^2}} = -\left(\frac{\partial V}{\partial s}\right)_p^2 \left(\frac{\partial s}{\partial T}\right)_p \left(\frac{\partial p}{\partial V}\right)_s,$$

where we have made use of the expressions for $\overline{\Delta p^2}$ and $\overline{\Delta s^2}$, and of the formula $c_p = T(\partial s/\partial T)_p$. Since the differential of the specific enthalpy $dh = T\,ds + V\,dp$ is a total differential, we have $(\partial T/\partial p)_s = (\partial V/\partial s)_p$. Hence

$$\frac{I_\omega}{I_{\omega-\delta\omega}+I_{\omega+\delta\omega}} = -\left(\frac{\partial T}{\partial p}\right)_s \left(\frac{\partial p}{\partial V}\right)_s \left(\frac{\partial V}{\partial s}\right)_p \left(\frac{\partial s}{\partial T}\right)_p$$

$$= -\left(\frac{\partial T}{\partial V}\right)_s \left(\frac{\partial V}{\partial T}\right)_p,$$

or, using the identity $(\partial T/\partial V)_s (\partial V/\partial s)_T (\partial s/\partial T)_V = -1$,

$$\frac{I_\omega}{I_{\omega-\delta\omega}+I_{\omega+\delta\omega}} = \left(\frac{\partial V}{\partial T}\right)_p \left(\frac{\partial s}{\partial V}\right)_T \left(\frac{\partial T}{\partial s}\right)_V = \frac{\left(\frac{\partial V}{\partial T}\right)_p \left(\frac{\partial s}{\partial V}\right)_T}{\left(\frac{\partial s}{\partial T}\right)_V}.$$

Regarding the entropy s as a function of T and V, we obtain:

$$\left(\frac{\partial s}{\partial T}\right)_p = \left(\frac{\partial s}{\partial T}\right)_V + \left(\frac{\partial s}{\partial V}\right)_T \left(\frac{\partial V}{\partial T}\right)_p.$$

Finally:

$$\frac{I_\omega}{I_{\omega-\delta\omega}+I_{\omega+\delta\omega}} = \frac{\left(\frac{\partial s}{\partial T}\right)_p - \left(\frac{\partial s}{\partial T}\right)_V}{\left(\frac{\partial s}{\partial T}\right)_V} = \frac{c_p - c_v}{c_v}$$

(the Landau–Placzek formula).

§ 5. Properties of Liquids. Surface Tension. Solutions

207. $\delta = \delta_0(1 + \beta p) = 1{\cdot}054\ \text{gcm}^{-3}$.

208. $\eta = \dfrac{\pi d^4 p\tau}{128\, lV} \approx 0{\cdot}01\ \text{gcm}^{-1}\,\text{sec}^{-1}$ (p is the pressure difference).

209. $\sigma = \dfrac{gDh\delta}{4} \approx 80\ \text{dyne cm}^{-1}$.

210. $\sigma = mg/\pi d \approx 70\ \text{dyne cm}^{-1}$ (m is the mass of the drop).

211. The arm of the balance from which the capillary is suspended falls.

212. $h_1 - h_2 = \dfrac{4\sigma(d_2 - d_1)}{\varrho g\, d_1 d_2}$.

213. $d\sigma/dT = -q/T$, where q is the amount of heat consumed in increasing isothermally the surface of the liquid by unity (the latent heat of formation of the surface). The problem is solved in the same way as Problem 172.

214. $\Delta(h_1 - h_2) = \dfrac{4\Delta\sigma(d_2 - d_1)}{\varrho g\, d_1 d_2} \approx 24{\cdot}2\ \text{mm}$.

215. $p = \dfrac{4\sigma}{d} \approx 19{\cdot}8\ \text{kgcm}^{-2}$.

216. $p = \dfrac{8\sigma}{d} \approx 0{\cdot}29\ \text{mm Hg}$.

217. $h \approx \dfrac{2\sigma}{\varrho g a} = 35\ \text{cm}$.

218. d_2 is found from the equation

$$\left(p_0 + \varrho g h + \frac{4\sigma}{d_1}\right) d_1^3 = \left(p_0 + \frac{4\sigma}{d_2}\right) d_2^3,$$

where p_0 is the atmospheric pressure. Since $4\sigma/d_1 \ll p$ and $4\sigma/d_2 \ll p_0$, these terms can be discarded (i.e. surface tension is neglected). This gives: $d_2 = 5{\cdot}3 \times 10^{-3}$ cm.

219. $$h = \frac{p + \varrho gl + \frac{2\sigma}{r} - \sqrt{\left(p + \varrho gl + \frac{2\sigma}{r}\right)^2 - \frac{8\sigma\varrho gl}{r}}}{2\varrho g}$$

$$\approx \frac{2\sigma l}{r\left(p + \varrho gl + \frac{2\sigma}{r}\right)}$$

(p is the atmospheric pressure).

220. $\Delta T > \frac{4\sigma}{pr} T.$

221. $p = 8p_0 + \frac{24\sigma}{r}.$

222. $h = \frac{2\sigma \cos \vartheta}{d\varrho g} = 3$ cm.

223. $h = \frac{\sigma \cos \vartheta}{\varrho g \sin \frac{\alpha}{2}} \frac{1}{x} \approx \frac{2\sigma \cos \vartheta}{\varrho g \alpha} \frac{1}{x}.$

224. $F = \frac{2\sigma m}{\varrho d^2} \cos \vartheta = 1{\cdot}46 \times 10^9$ dyne $= 1490$ kg.

225. $F = \frac{2\sigma\varrho \cos \vartheta}{m} \pi^2 R^4 = 64$ kg

(m is the mass of the mercury).

226. $F = \frac{2\sigma^2 l \cos^2 \vartheta}{\varrho g d^2} = 1{\cdot}56$ kg.

227. The pressure inside the liquid at the level of the point A (Fig. 5, page 39) is $p = p_0 - \varrho g y$, where p_0 is the atmospheric pressure. The same pressure can be expressed by Laplace's formula

$p = p_0 - \sigma K$, where K is the absolute value of the liquid surface curvature at the point A. Hence

$$\varrho g y = \sigma K. \tag{1}$$

By definition of the curvature, $K = -d\varphi/ds$, where ds is the element of arc, regarded as positive when in an upwards direction. It is connected with dx and dy by: $dx = ds \cos\varphi$; $dy = ds \sin\varphi$. Hence

$$K = -\frac{d\varphi}{dx}\cos\varphi = -\frac{d\varphi}{dy}\sin\varphi.$$

On substituting these expressions in (1), we get the two equations:

$$\varrho g y\, dy + \sigma \sin\varphi\, d\varphi = 0, \tag{2}$$

$$\varrho g y\, dx + \sigma \cos\varphi\, d\varphi = 0. \tag{3}$$

On integrating (2) with the initial condition $\varphi = \pi$ at $y = 0$, we get

$$y = 2\sqrt{\frac{\sigma}{\varrho g}}\cos\frac{\varphi}{2}. \tag{4}$$

Substitution of this expression in (3) leads to the equation

$$dx = -\sqrt{\frac{\sigma}{\varrho g}}\cos\frac{\varphi}{2}\, d\varphi + \frac{1}{2}\sqrt{\frac{\sigma}{\varrho g}}\,\frac{d\varphi}{\cos\frac{\varphi}{2}},$$

integration of which, with the initial condition $x = 0$ at $\varphi = \frac{1}{2}\pi$, gives:

$$x = 2\sqrt{\frac{\sigma}{\varrho g}}\left[\frac{1}{\sqrt{2}} - \sin\frac{\varphi}{2}\right] + \sqrt{\frac{\sigma}{\varrho g}}\ln\frac{\tan\frac{\varphi+\pi}{4}}{\tan\frac{3\pi}{8}}. \tag{5}$$

228. The minimum thickness $D = MN$ of the liquid column when the plate is raised to its maximum height h (Fig. 5, page 39) is determined from the requirement that $\varphi = 0$ when $y = h$. On substituting $x = \frac{1}{2}(a - D)$, $\varphi = 0$ in formula (5) of the previous problem, we obtain:

$$D = a - 2\sqrt{\frac{\sigma}{\varrho g}}\left[\sqrt{2} - \ln\tan\frac{3\pi}{8}\right] = a - 1{\cdot}066\sqrt{\frac{\sigma}{\varrho g}}. \qquad (1)$$

If $a < 1{\cdot}066\sqrt{\sigma/\varrho g}$, the minimum value of D is zero. In this case the limiting value $\varphi = 0$ of the angle is not reached.

Let $a > 1{\cdot}066\sqrt{\sigma/\varrho g}$. The maximum height h is now determined from (4) of the previous problem, if we put $\varphi = 0$;

$$h = 2\sqrt{\frac{\sigma}{\varrho g}}. \qquad (2)$$

The difference between the atmospheric and hydrostatic pressures on the plate is directed downwards and is equal to ϱgh. Hence

$$F = q + \varrho gha = q + 2a\sqrt{\varrho g\sigma}. \qquad (3)$$

We now take the second case: $a < 1{\cdot}066\sqrt{\sigma/\varrho g}$. In this case

$$h = 2\sqrt{\frac{\sigma}{\varrho g}}\cos\frac{\varphi}{2}, \qquad (4)$$

where φ is determined from the transcendental equation

$$\frac{a}{2} = 2\sqrt{\frac{\sigma}{\varrho g}}\left[\frac{1}{\sqrt{2}} - \sin\frac{\varphi}{2}\right] + \sqrt{\frac{\sigma}{\varrho g}}\ln\frac{\tan\dfrac{\varphi+\pi}{4}}{\tan\dfrac{3\pi}{8}}. \qquad (5)$$

When finding F, we have to remember that the plate is pulled downwards in the present case by an extra force of surface tension $2\sigma\sin\varphi$. On taking account of this force,

$$F = q + 2a\sqrt{\varrho g\sigma}\cos\frac{\varphi}{2} + 2\sigma\sin\varphi. \qquad (6)$$

If $a \ll \sqrt{\sigma/\varrho g}$, the second term in this formula can be neglected. On also neglecting the term $\frac{1}{2}a$ in (5), we find $\varphi = \frac{1}{2}\pi$. Thus, when $a \ll \sqrt{\sigma/\varrho g}$: $F = q + 2\sigma$, $h = \sqrt{2\sigma/\varrho g}$.

229. We take as the y axis the vertical tangent to the lateral liquid surface, and as the x axis a horizontal line perpendicular to the length of the plate and touching the liquid surface at infinity (Fig. 24). The equation of the lateral liquid surface is now:

$$x = 2\sqrt{\frac{\sigma}{\varrho g}}\left[\frac{1}{\sqrt{2}} - \cos\frac{\varphi}{2}\right] + \sqrt{\frac{\sigma}{\varrho g}}\ln\frac{\tan\frac{\pi}{8}}{\tan\frac{\varphi}{4}}, \tag{1}$$

$$y = -2\sqrt{\frac{\sigma}{\varrho g}}\sin\frac{\varphi}{2}. \tag{2}$$

The minimum distance $D = MN$ when the plate submersion is a maximum $|y|_{max}$ is determined from the requirement that $\varphi = \pi$, which gives

$$D = a - 2\sqrt{\frac{\sigma}{\varrho g}}\left(\sqrt{2} + \ln\tan\frac{\pi}{8}\right) = a - 1{\cdot}066\sqrt{\frac{\sigma}{\varrho g}}. \tag{3}$$

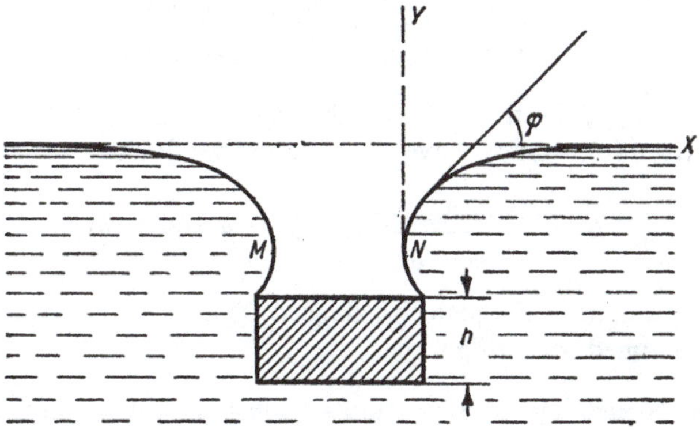

FIG. 24

If $a < 1{\cdot}066\sqrt{\sigma/\varrho g}$, then $D = 0$, and the limiting value $\varphi = \pi$ is not reached.

We first take the case $a > 1{\cdot}066\sqrt{\sigma/\varrho g}$. In this case the maximum depth of submersion of the upper face of the plate is determined from (2) in which we put $\varphi = \pi$. It is equal to $|y|_{max} = 2\sqrt{\sigma/\varrho g}$. The pressure difference $\varrho g(h + |y|_{max})$ will now act in an upwards direction on the face of the plate, and must balance the weight of the plate. The maximum plate thickness before it sinks is given by the condition $\varrho g(h + |y|_{max}) = \varrho_0 g$, i.e.

$$h = \frac{2}{\varrho_0 - \varrho}\sqrt{\frac{\sigma\varrho}{g}}. \tag{4}$$

We now take the case $a < 1{\cdot}066\sqrt{\sigma/\varrho g}$. In this case

$$|y|_{max} = 2\sqrt{\frac{\sigma}{\varrho g}}\sin\frac{\varphi}{2}, \tag{5}$$

where φ is given by the equation

$$\frac{a}{2} = 2\sqrt{\frac{\sigma}{\varrho g}}\left[\frac{1}{\sqrt{2}} - \cos\frac{\varphi}{2}\right] + \sqrt{\frac{\sigma}{\varrho g}}\ln\frac{\tan\frac{\pi}{8}}{\tan\frac{\varphi}{4}}. \tag{6}$$

We obtain for the maximum plate thickness:

$$h = \frac{2}{\varrho_0 - \varrho}\sqrt{\frac{\sigma\varrho}{g}}\sin\frac{\varphi}{2} + \frac{2\sigma\sin\varphi}{ga(\varrho_0 - \varrho)}. \tag{7}$$

If $a \ll \sqrt{\sigma/\varrho g}$, the first term on the right can be neglected. As is clear from (6), we now have $\varphi = \frac{1}{2}\pi$, and we find:

$$h = \frac{2\sigma}{ga(\varrho_0 - \varrho)} \quad \text{or} \quad 2\sigma = gah(\varrho_0 - \varrho), \tag{8}$$

i.e. the weight of the plate is balanced by the surface tension and the Archimedean lifting force.

230. Neglecting the curvature of the plate circumference, we obtain:

$$F \approx 2\pi r^2\sqrt{\varrho g\sigma} \approx 110 \text{ g}.$$

231. $h = \sqrt{\dfrac{2\sigma}{\varrho g}(1 - \sin\vartheta)}$.

232. The surfaces of the liquid and needle diverge tangentially at the point A (Fig. 25). The surface tension force $F_1 = 2\sigma\sin\vartheta$ acts upwards per unit length of the needle. A hydrostatic pressure force, also directed upwards, likewise acts on the needle. If the part ACB of the needle were to be replaced by liquid, the hydrostatic pressure force would be $F_2 = \varrho gh \cdot AB = 2\varrho ghr \sin\vartheta$, where r is the needle radius and ϱ the density of the liquid. Due to the fact that the part ACB is submerged in the liquid, an additional hydrostatic force F_3 acts on the needle, equal to the weight of water displaced by ACB, i.e. $F_3 = gr^2(\vartheta - \sin\vartheta\cos\vartheta)$. The sum of the three forces F_1, F_2, F_3 must balance the weight of unit length of the needle. This gives:

$$2\sigma\sin\vartheta + 2\varrho ghr\sin\vartheta + \varrho gr^2(\vartheta - \sin\vartheta\cos\vartheta) = \varrho_0 g\pi r^2.$$

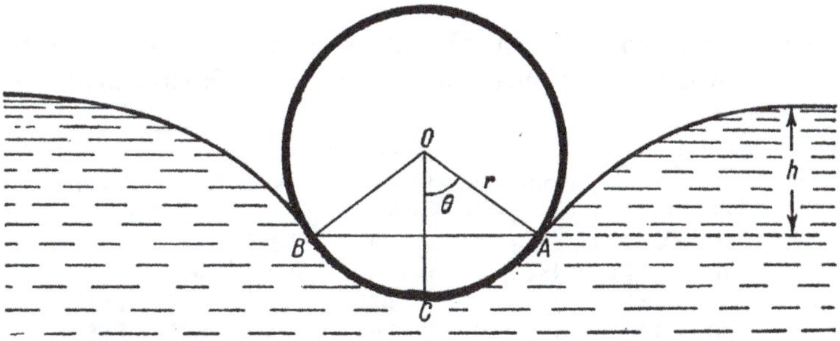

FIG. 25

The angle ϑ and the height h are connected by $h = 2\sqrt{\sigma/\varrho g}\cdot\sin\frac{1}{2}\vartheta$ (see the solution to Problem 229), and the previous equation takes the form

$$\left[\pi\varrho_0 - \varrho\left(\vartheta - \frac{1}{2}\sin 2\vartheta\right)\right]r^2 - 4r\sqrt{\frac{\varrho\sigma}{g}}\sin\vartheta\sin\frac{\vartheta}{2} - \frac{2\sigma\sin\vartheta}{g} = 0. \quad (1)$$

We obtain for D and H:

$$D = 2r\sin\vartheta + 2\sqrt{\frac{\sigma}{\varrho g}}\left\{2\cos\frac{\vartheta}{2} + \ln\tan\frac{\vartheta}{4}\right\} - 2\sqrt{\frac{\sigma}{\varrho g}}\left\{\sqrt{2} + \ln\tan\frac{\pi}{8}\right\}, \quad (2)$$

$$H = 2r\sin^2\frac{\vartheta}{2} + 2\sqrt{\frac{\sigma}{\varrho g}}\sin\frac{\vartheta}{2}. \quad (3)$$

After substituting the numerical values:

$$\left[24{\cdot}5 - \left(\vartheta - \frac{1}{2}\sin 2\vartheta\right)\right] r^2$$

$$- 1{\cdot}091 \sin\vartheta \sin\frac{\vartheta}{2}\cdot r - 0{\cdot}1488 \sin\vartheta = 0, \qquad (4)$$

$$D = 2r\sin\vartheta + 1{\cdot}091\cos\frac{\vartheta}{2} + 1{\cdot}256\log_{10}\tan\frac{\vartheta}{4} - 0{\cdot}291. \quad (5)$$

(It is assumed here that all the lengths are expressed in centimetres.) The following table is obtained on assigning different values to ϑ:

$\vartheta°$	r mm	H mm	D mm	$\vartheta°$	r mm	H mm	D mm
0	0	0	—	80	0·955	4·29	—
10	0·328	0·481	—	90	0·990	4·85	1·98
20	0·471	0·975	—	100	1·005	5·35	1·91
30	0·583	1·49	—	110	1·001	5·82	1·68
40	0·680	2·03	—	120	0·977	6·20	1·24
50	0·763	2·58	—	130	0·922	6·45	0·65
60	0·840	3·15	—	139	0·846	6·59	0·04
70	0·903	3·72	—	139°30′	0·842	6·60	0·00

The greatest radius r is obtained with $\vartheta \approx 100°$ and is approximately 1 mm. If $r > 0{\cdot}842$ mm, the needle has two equilibrium positions: one with $\vartheta \lesssim 100°$, the other with $\vartheta \gtrsim 100°$. If $r < 0{\cdot}842$ mm, there is only one equilibrium position with $\vartheta \lesssim 60°$, since in this case, when $\vartheta \gtrsim 60°$, formula (5) gives a negative value for D. The maximum depth of submersion H is obtained with $r \approx 0{\cdot}842$ mm and is approximately 6·60 mm.

233. The plates are attracted in cases (1) and (2). In case (3) they are repelled.

234. $\sigma = \dfrac{(2\pi R - l)ES}{2\pi R^2}$.

235. The amount of heat received by the film on stretching is $\delta Q = q\,dS + C\,dT$, where q is the heat of formation of unit area of film, C is its specific heat. Since (see Problem 213) $q = -T d\sigma/dT$, then $\delta Q = -T(d\sigma/dT)\,dS + C\,dT$. Using this relationship, we easily obtain $\Delta T = (2T/\varrho lc)(d\sigma/dT) = -0{\cdot}0195°$.

236. The time t is connected with the bubble radius by

$$t = (2\eta l/\sigma r^4)(R_0^4 - R^4).$$

The bubble disappears after

$$t = (2\eta l/\sigma r^4)R_0^4 = 7{\cdot}2 \times 10^3 \text{ sec} = 2 \text{ hr}.$$

237. $t = (2/7a^2)\sqrt{2p\mu/\sigma RT}\,r_0^{7/2} \approx 630$ sec $= 10{\cdot}5$ min, where R is the universal gas constant. (See the answer to the previous problem.)

238. $T \sim \sqrt{\dfrac{\varrho r^3}{\sigma}}$.

239. $l \sim \sqrt{\dfrac{\varrho g h}{\sigma}}$.

240. 100·59°

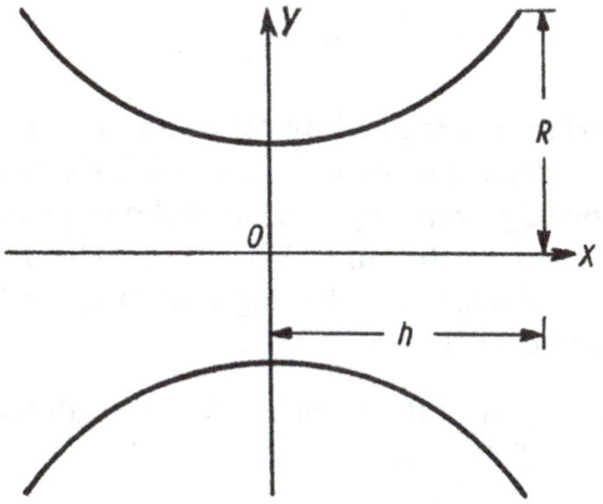

FIG. 26

241. From symmetry, the film is a surface of revolution about the line through the centres of the rings. We intersect the film surface by an arbitrary plane through the axis of revolution, which we take as the xy plane (Fig. 26). Since the pressures on both sides of the film are the same, its total curvature $1/R_1 + 1/R_2$ must be zero.

The radius of curvature R_1 of the normal section of the film lying in the xy plane is given by $1/R_1 = -y''/(1+y'^2)^{3/2}$ (it is negative). The radius of curvature of the section perpendicular to it is easily found by using the familiar theorem of differential geometry, which gives $y = R_2 \cos\alpha$, whence $R_2 = y\sqrt{1+y'^2}$ (it is positive). The differential equation for the axial section of the film is therefore

$$\frac{y''}{1+y'^2} - \frac{1}{y} = 0. \tag{1}$$

We use the substitution $y' = \sinh\vartheta$. Then $1 + y'^2 = \cosh^2\vartheta$, $y = \cosh\vartheta/(d\vartheta/dx)$. On differentiating the last relationship and noting that $y' = \sinh\vartheta$, we find that $d\vartheta/dx = 0$, whence $\vartheta = ax + b$, where a and b are constants. The constants a and b are found from the boundary conditions: $y = R$ when $x = \pm h$. Obviously, $b = 0$, since, from symmetry, y must be an even function of x. Finally,

$$y = \frac{1}{a}\cosh ax = \frac{1}{2a}(e^{ax} + e^{-ax}), \tag{2}$$

where the constant a is given by

$$aR = \cosh ah. \tag{3}$$

The film surface is obtained by revolution of curve (2) about the x axis. It is termed a catenoid. Equation (3) is most easily investigated and solved graphically. It is easily shown by using this method that (3) only has a solution if $R/h > 1{\cdot}51$. This means that, to be able to form a film between the rings, the distance $2h$ between them must not exceed $2R/1{\cdot}51 = 1{\cdot}33R$.

242. The radius r of the cylindrical film is half the radius R of the spherical part of the film.

243. The shape of the lateral surface of the film is determined by the requirement that the total curvature $1/R_1 + 1/R_2$ remain constant. (As distinct from Problem 241, this constant is in general non-zero.) This leads to the differential equation

$$\frac{1}{y\sqrt{1+y'^2}} - \frac{y''}{(1+y'^2)^{3/2}} = \text{const} \equiv 2K. \tag{1}$$

(The notation is the same as in Problem 241.) On again using the substitution $y = \sinh\vartheta$, we obtain:

$$\frac{d}{dy}\left(\frac{1}{\cosh\vartheta}y\right) = 2Ky, \tag{2}$$

whence

$$\frac{1}{\cosh\vartheta} = Ky + \frac{A}{y}, \tag{3}$$

where A is a constant of integration. Having found $\sinh\vartheta$ from this with the aid of the formula $\sinh^2\vartheta = \cosh^2\vartheta - 1$ and recalling the notation $y = \sinh\vartheta$, we find:

$$x = \int \frac{Ky^2 + A}{\sqrt{y^2 - (Ky^2 + A)^2}}\,dy + B, \tag{4}$$

where B is a second constant of integration. The constants of integration A and B are found from the boundary conditions $y = R$ when $x = \pm h$. Formula (4) in conjunction with these boundary conditions provides the solution.

If $A = 0$, the integration in (4) is elementary and we have:

$$(x - a)^2 + y^2 = \frac{1}{K^2},$$

where a is a constant of integration. When $a = 0$ a circle of radius $R = 1/K$ is obtained, with centre at the origin. This solution corresponds to the case when the radius of the rings becomes zero. When $a = +1/K$ a circle is obtained with centre $x = +1/K$, whilst with $a = -1/K$, the centre is at $x = -1/K$. Both these circles have the same radius $R = 1/K$ and touch one another at the origin. These solutions correspond to the case when the distance between the rings is equal to half the radius of the rings.

245. When determining the surface tension we must bear in mind that the liquid is in equilibrium with its saturated vapour. Strictly speaking, we should not have spoken of the "surface tension of the liquid", but of the surface tension at the boundary between the two phases, liquid and gaseous, in equilibrium. At the critical temperature, however, the substance can only be in one phase, not in two. We might say formally that the two phases become identical.

Thus there cannot be a boundary between them, and the surface tension must be zero.

247. $p = p_0 \pm (2\sigma/r)\cdot(d_v/d_l)$. Here σ is the surface tension of the liquid, d_v is the vapour density, d_l the liquid density. The plus sign refers to liquids that do not wet the capillary, the minus sign to wetting liquids.

248. The stationary flux of vapour through any spherical surface of radius r concentric with the surface of the drop is

$$q = -D\cdot 4\pi r^2\left(\frac{d\varrho_v}{dr}\right) = \text{const},$$

whence

$$\varrho_v = \frac{q}{4\pi Dr} + \varrho_{v\infty}.$$

We find q from the condition that the vapour is saturated on the drop surfaces ($r = a$). This gives

$$q = 4\pi Da(\varrho_{v_\infty} - \varrho_{v_\infty}) = 4\pi Da\frac{\mu}{RT}(p_s - p_\infty),$$

where μ is the molecular weight of the vapour, p_s is the pressure of the saturated vapour at the temperature of the drop, p_∞ is the partial vapour pressure remote from the drop. On substituting this value of q in the earlier formula, we get

$$\varrho_v = \left(\frac{a}{r}\right)(\varrho_{v_s} - \varrho_{v\infty}) + \varrho_{v\infty}.$$

249. The stationary vapour diffusion equation and the relevant boundary conditions are

$$\nabla^2\varrho_v = 0,$$

$$\varrho_v = \begin{cases}\varrho_{v\infty} & \text{at } r = \infty\\ \varrho_{v_s} & \text{at the drop surface.}\end{cases}$$

The flux of vapour through any closed surface surrounding the drop is independent of the position and form of the surface. On taking as this surface the surface S of the drop itself, we can write for the flux

$$q = -D\oint_S \frac{\partial \varrho_v}{\partial n}\,dS,$$

where $\partial\varrho_v/\partial n$ is the derivative of ϱ_v in the direction of the outward normal $\boldsymbol{n}$ to the surface S.

Let us compare this problem with the electrostatic problem of the field of a charged conductor with the surface S. It is defined by the potential φ, which satisfies the conditions:

$$\nabla^2\varphi = 0,$$

$$\varphi = \begin{cases} \varphi_\infty \text{ at } r = \infty \\ \varphi_S \text{ on the surface } S. \end{cases}$$

The charge Q on the conductor is

$$Q = -\frac{1}{4\pi}\oint_S \frac{\partial\varphi}{\partial n}\,dS = C(\varphi_S - \varphi_\infty)$$

(C is the capacity of the drop).

Mathematically, the two problems are identical and have unique solutions. Hence

$$q = 4\pi CD(\varrho_{v_s} - \varrho_{v\infty}).$$

In the particular case of a sphere $C = a$, and we obtain the solution of the previous problem.

250. $\tau_{\text{vap}} = \dfrac{a^2}{2D}\dfrac{\varrho_l}{(1-f)\varrho_{v_s}} = \dfrac{a^2}{2D}\dfrac{RT\varrho_l}{(1-f)\mu p_v}$;

(1) $\tau_{\text{vap}} \simeq 37$ min; (2) $\tau_{\text{vap}} \simeq 0{\cdot}13$ sec.

251. The saturated vapour pressure p_{sa} at the drop surface is given by

$$p_{sa} - p_{s\infty} = \frac{RT}{\mu}(\varrho_{sa} - \varrho_{s\infty}) = \frac{2\sigma}{a}\frac{\varrho_{v\infty}}{\varrho_l}$$

(see Problem 247). But, according to the solution of Problem 248:

$$\varrho_v = \varrho_{v\infty} + \frac{a}{r}(\varrho_{sa} - \varrho_{s\infty}) = \varrho_{v\infty}\left[1 + \frac{2\sigma\mu}{r\varrho_l RT}\right].$$

The vapour density ϱ_v is therefore independent in this case of the drop radius a. The vapour flux

$$q = -4\pi a^2 D\left(\frac{d\varrho_v}{dr}\right)_{r=a} = 8\pi\sigma\mu D\,\frac{\varrho_{v\infty}}{\varrho_l RT}$$

is constant and also independent of the radius a. Hence

$$\tau_{vap} = \frac{4\pi}{3q}\varrho_l a^3 = \frac{\varrho_l^2 RT}{6\sigma\mu D\varrho_{v\infty}}a^3 = \left(\frac{\varrho_l RT}{\mu}\right)^2\cdot\frac{a^3}{6\sigma D p_{v\infty}}.$$

(1) $\tau_{vap} \simeq 225$ hr; (2) $\tau_{vap} \simeq 0{\cdot}8$ sec.

252. $p_{osm} = CRT/\mu = 3{\cdot}3$ atm, where C is the concentration, μ the molecular weight.

253. $t \approx 35°$.

254. $\mu \approx 360$.

255. $p_{osm} = [1 + \alpha(n-1)]\,(mRT/\mu v)$, where m is the mass of dissolved substance in the volume v.

256. $p_{osm} \approx 7{\cdot}5$ atm.

257. $p_0 - p_l = (\varrho_v/\varrho_s)p_{osm}$, where ϱ_v is the vapour density, ϱ_s the solution density.

258. $\dfrac{p_0 - p_l}{p_0} = k.$

259. $p_l = p_0(1-k) = 16{\cdot}7$ mm Hg.

260. By Raoult's law, the vapour density ϱ_{av} close to the drop surface is connected with the corresponding density $\varrho_{v\infty}$ remote from the drop by

$$\frac{\varrho_{va} - \varrho_{v\infty}}{\varrho_{v\infty}} = k,$$

where the ratio k of the number of moles of salt to the number of moles of solvent can be written in the form $k = Am/\varrho_{v\infty}r^3$, where A is a constant. Thus

$$\varrho_{va} = \varrho_{v\infty} + \frac{Am}{r^3}.$$

On now using the solution of Problem 248, we easily obtain

$$a^5 = a_0^5 + 5\,DAmt,$$

where a_0 is the drop radius at $t = 0$.

261. $T_b = T_0 + nRT_0^2/mq = 101{\cdot}75°$, where T_0 is the boiling-point of the pure solvent, n is the total number of moles of the dissolved substances and m is the mass of solvent.

262. $t = 100{\cdot}016°$.

263. $t = -nRT^2/mq = -0{\cdot}054°$, where T is the absolute freezing-point of the pure solvent, n is the number of moles of solute, and m is the mass of solvent.

264. $t = -\dfrac{q_2}{q_1}\left(\dfrac{T_1}{T_2}\right)^2 \Delta t = -0{\cdot}180°$.

265. $n = \dfrac{RT^2m}{qMA \cdot \Delta T} = 2$ (R is the universal gas constant).

§ 6. Kinetic Theory of Matter

266. $n = 3{\cdot}24 \times 10^{13}$.

267. $p = 1{\cdot}74 \times 10^{-4}$ mm Hg.

268. Let the piston move in the cylinder with a velocity u which is small compared with the mean velocity of the gas molecules. We take the cylinder axis as the x axis in a rectangular system of co-ordinates. We consider the reflexion from the piston of a molecule, the x component of the velocity of which relative to the cylinder wall is v_x.

We introduce a moving co-ordinate system connected with the piston. In this system the x component of the velocity of the molecule is $v_x - u$. After reflexion from the piston the x component of the velocity has the same magnitude in the moving co-ordinate system but reversed sign. Thus the molecule velocity after reflexion is $-(v_x - u)$ relative to the moving system, and $-(v_x - u) + u = -v_x + 2u$ relative to the cylinder wall.

The two remaining velocity components are unchanged by reflexion. The change in the kinetic energy of the molecule is therefore

$$\frac{m}{2}(v_x - 2u)^2 - \frac{m}{2}v_x^2 = -mv_x u,$$

if we neglect the term in u^2.

Let N_i be the number of molecules, the x component of the velocity of which is v_{ix}. The number of molecules of this type striking the piston per second is $N_i v_{ix} S/V$, where S is the piston area. The change in the kinetic energy of these molecules per second is $-SumN_i v_{ix}^2/V$, whilst the change in kinetic energy of the gas as a whole is

$$\frac{dE}{dt} = -\frac{Sum}{V}\sum N_i v_{ix}^2 = -\frac{SuNm}{V}\overline{v_x^2} = -\frac{1}{3}\frac{SuNm}{V}\overline{v^2}$$
$$= -\frac{2}{3}\frac{Su}{V}E.$$

On substituting $Su = dV/dt$ in this and integrating, we obtain $EV^{2/3} = \text{const}$. Finally, taking into account that $pV = 2E/3$, we get

$$pV^{5/3} = \text{const}.$$

269. The arguments used in solving the previous problem retain their force for a diatomic gas. The only difference is that, for a monatomic gas, the total energy E is the kinetic energy of the translational motion of the molecules, whereas in the case of a diatomic gas we have to add the kinetic energy of the rotations of the molecules. The rotational motion of the molecules is unchanged, however, by reflexion from the piston. As before, only the x-component of the translational motion of a molecule is affected. We can therefore write, as in the solution of the previous problem:

$$\frac{dE}{dt} = -\frac{1}{3}\frac{uSNm}{V}\overline{v^2}.$$

According to classical theory, the kinetic energy at thermal equilibrium is uniformly distributed over the degrees of freedom. Observing that a molecule of diatomic gas has five degrees of freedom, three translational and two rotational ones, we find for the total energy:

$$E = \frac{1}{2} N m\overline{v^2} + \frac{1}{3} N m\overline{v^2} = \frac{5}{6} N m\overline{v^2}.$$

Hence $dE/dt = -2SuE/5V$, whence $EV^{2/3} =$ const. Finally, noting that $pV = Nm\overline{v^2}/3 = 2E/5$, we find that

$$pV^{7/5} = \text{const.}$$

270. $\overline{v_x^2} = \dfrac{kT}{m}$; $\dfrac{\overline{mv_x^2}}{2} = \dfrac{kT}{2}$.

271. $\bar{v} \sim p^{1/5}$.

272. $\dfrac{n_1}{n_2} = \dfrac{v_1^2}{v_2^2} \cdot e^{\frac{M(v_2^2 - v_1^2)}{2RT}} = 0{\cdot}98$ (M is the molecular weight).

273. $v_m = \sqrt{\dfrac{2RT}{M}} = 342 \text{ m sec}^{-1}$

$$\bar{v} = \sqrt{\frac{8RT}{\pi M}} = 1{\cdot}13\, v_m = 386 \text{ m sec}^{-1};$$

$$\sqrt{\overline{v^2}} = \sqrt{\frac{3RT}{M}} = 1{\cdot}23\, v_m = 420 \text{ m sec}^{-1}.$$

274. $t = 153°$.

276. We first take the particular case when all the molecules have the same absolute values of the velocities, but their distribution over the velocities is isotropic. In this case the number of molecules per cm^3, the directions of the velocities of which lie inside the solid angle $d\Omega$, is $dn = n d\Omega/4\pi$, where n is the number of molecules per cubic centimetre. Let us consider the molecules that strike 1 cm^2 of wall at angles of incidence between ϑ and $\vartheta + d\vartheta$. In this case $d\Omega = 2\pi \times \sin\vartheta\, d\vartheta$, $dn = \frac{1}{2} n \sin\vartheta\, d\vartheta$. The number of collisions of molecules of this type per square centimetre of wall per second will be $dz = \frac{1}{2} nv \sin\vartheta \times \cos\vartheta\, d\vartheta$. On integrating this expression between 0 and $\frac{1}{2}\pi$, we find that $z = nv/4$.

If the absolute velocities of the molecules are different, we have to group the molecules so that they have about the same velocity in a given group. We easily find in this way that

$$z = \frac{1}{4} n\bar{v},$$

where $\bar{v}$ is the mean velocity of the molecules. For a Maxwell distribution:

$$z = \frac{n}{4}\sqrt{\frac{8RT}{\pi M}} = n\sqrt{\frac{RT}{2\pi M}}.$$

277. For an isotropic distribution $E = mn\overline{v^3}/8$, for a Maxwell distribution $E = n\sqrt{2k^3T^3/m\pi}$, where m is the mass of a molecule, n is the number of molecules per cubic centimetre.

278. $\tau = \dfrac{4V}{S\bar{v}} \ln 2.$

279. (1) $t = \dfrac{4V}{S\bar{v}} \ln \dfrac{p_0 - p_1}{p_0 - p_2} \approx \dfrac{4V}{S\bar{v}} \dfrac{p_2 - p_1}{p_0} \approx 1{\cdot}17$ sec.

(2) $t = \dfrac{4V}{S\bar{v}} \ln 2 \approx 6{\cdot}2 \times 10^4$ sec $= 17$ hr.

280. The equations for the balance of the nitrogen molecules are

$$\left.\begin{aligned} \frac{dN_N^{(1)}}{dt} &= -\frac{1}{4}\frac{S\bar{v}_N}{V}(N_N^{(1)} - N_N^{(2)}) \\ \frac{dN_N^{(2)}}{dt} &= -\frac{1}{4}\frac{S\bar{v}_N}{V}(N_N^{(2)} - N_N^{(1)}), \end{aligned}\right\} \qquad (1)$$

where $N_N^{(1)}$ and $N_N^{(2)}$ are the numbers of nitrogen molecules in the first and second halves of the vessel. Since $N_N^{(1)} + N_N^{(2)} = N_N = \text{const}$, the first equation reduces to the form

$$\frac{dN_N^{(1)}}{dt} = -\frac{S\bar{v}_N}{2V}\left(N_N^{(1)} - \frac{N_N}{2}\right).$$

On integrating this with the initial condition $N_N^{(1)} = N_N$ at $t = 0$, we get

$$\left.\begin{aligned} N_N^{(1)} &= \frac{N_N}{2}\left(1 + e^{-\frac{S\bar{v}_N}{2V}t}\right) \\ N_N^{(2)} &= \frac{N_N}{2}\left(1 - e^{-\frac{S\bar{v}_N}{2V}t}\right) \end{aligned}\right\} \tag{2}$$

Similarly, for the oxygen molecules:

$$\left.\begin{aligned} N_O^{(1)} &= \frac{N_O}{2}\left(1 - e^{-\frac{S\bar{v}_O}{2V}t}\right) \\ N_O^{(2)} &= \frac{N_O}{2}\left(1 + e^{-\frac{S\bar{v}_O}{2V}t}\right) \end{aligned}\right\}. \tag{3}$$

Since the initial pressures in the two halves are the same, $N_N = N_0 = N$. The pressure in the first half is

$$p_1 = \frac{1}{V}\{N_N^{(1)} + N_O^{(1)}\}\, kT = p\left\{1 + \frac{e^{-\frac{S\bar{v}_N}{2V}t} - e^{-\frac{S\bar{v}_O}{2V}t}}{2}\right\}. \tag{4}$$

The pressure in the second half is

$$p_2 = p\left\{1 + \frac{e^{-\frac{S\bar{v}_O}{2V}t} - e^{-\frac{S\bar{v}_N}{2V}t}}{2}\right\}. \tag{5}$$

At $t = 0$ and $t = \infty$, (4) and (5) give $p_1 = p_2 = p$, as must be the case.

281. $n = n_0\sqrt{6\pi}$, where n is the density of the particles in the vessel, and n_0 in the beam.

282. The number of molecules lost per second by 1 cm^2 of the drop is $x = (n - n_\infty)\bar{v}/4$, where n and n_∞ are the numbers of molecules of saturated vapour over the drop and the plane surface of the liquid per cubic centimetre. The difference between them is found from the relationships:

$$p = nkT; \quad p_\infty = n_\infty kT; \quad p - p_\infty = \frac{2\sigma}{r}\frac{\varrho_v}{\varrho_l - \varrho_v},$$

which give

$$x = \frac{1}{2kT}\frac{\sigma}{r}\frac{\varrho_v}{\varrho_l - \varrho_v}\bar{v} = \frac{\sigma N}{r}\frac{\varrho_v}{\varrho_l - \varrho_v}\sqrt{\frac{2}{\pi\mu RT}},$$

where μ is the molecular weight, and N Avogradro's number. We can neglect ϱ_v in the denominator. We easily find for ϱ_v: $\varrho_v = 1{\cdot}73 \times 10^{-5}$ gcm^{-3}. After substituting the numerical values, we get $x = 4{\cdot}55 \times 10^{15}$ molecules cm^{-2} sec^{-1}.

284. $d = \sqrt{\frac{1}{\sqrt{2}\, n\pi\Lambda}} = 2{\cdot}5 \times 10^{-8}$ cm.

285. $\Lambda = \frac{3\eta}{\varrho v} = 0{\cdot}89 \times 10^{-5}$ cm.

286. $z = \sqrt{2}\,\pi d^2 \bar{v} n \approx 2{\cdot}2 \times 10^6$.

287. $p < 1{\cdot}1 \times 10^{-3}$ mm Hg.

288. $z \sim T^{-\frac{1}{2}}; \quad \Lambda \sim T$.

289. $\Lambda \sim p^{-1}; \quad z \sim p$.

290. $\Lambda \sim p^{-\frac{1}{\gamma}}; \quad z \sim p^{\frac{\gamma+1}{2\gamma}}$, where $\gamma = \frac{c_p}{c_v}$.

291. $$\eta = \frac{\pi p_2 d^4 \tau}{128 l V}\left[\ln\frac{(p_1 - p_2)(p_2 + p_3)}{(p_3 - p_2)(p_1 + p_2)}\right]^{-1}$$

$$\approx 14 \times 10^{-5} \text{ gcm}^{-1}\text{sec}^{-1},$$

$$d^2 = \frac{m\bar{v}}{3\sqrt{2}\,\pi\eta} = 14{\cdot}5 \times 10^{-16} \text{ cm}^2; \quad d = 3{\cdot}8 \times 10^{-8} \text{ cm}.$$

292. $$d^2 = \frac{c_v m v\sqrt{2}\,(t_1 - t_2)}{0{\cdot}72 i^2 R \ln\frac{r_2}{r_1}}; \quad d = 2{\cdot}3 \times 10^{-8} \text{ cm}.$$

293. $\varphi = \dfrac{\pi\eta\omega}{2fh} R^4 = 81°$.

294. We consider a ring of inner radius r and outer radius $r + dr$ on the rotating disc. The number of molecules reflected per second from the area of this ring is $(nv/4) \cdot 2\pi r \, dr$. Each of these loses angular momentum $mr^2\omega$, which is transmitted to the fixed disc. The total angular momentum transmitted per second to the disc is easily found by integration. On equating it to the moment $f\varphi'$ of the force acting from the twisted thread, we obtain for the angle of twist:

$$\varphi' = \frac{3\pi p}{8vf} \omega R^4 = \frac{3}{4} \frac{ph}{\eta v} \varphi \approx 1°,$$

where φ is the angle of twist corresponding to the case when the distance between the discs is small compared with the mean free path of a molecule (see the previous problem).

296. Since the distance between the walls is small compared with their dimensions, we can regard the walls as plane for the purposes of calculation. The temperature of one wall can be taken as equal to the temperature of the surrounding air T_0, and of the other to the temperature T of the liquid air. The molecules reflected from the outer wall will be described as "hot", and those reflected from the inner wall as "cold". Let the numbers of these molecules per cubic centimetre be n_0 and n, and their velocities v_0 and v respectively. The number of molecules reflected from 1 cm^2 of the hot wall per second is $n_0v_0/4 = nv/4$. These molecules transmit the mount of heat $(n_0v_0/4) \cdot 5kT_0/2$ to the cold wall; conversely they lose the amount of heat $(n_0v_0/4) \cdot 5kT/2$. Consequently $M = 5n_0v_0kS(T_0 - T)t/8q$. The pressure of the residual gas, if its temperature is T_0, is $p = (n + n_0)kT_0$. We finally obtain without difficulty:

$$M = \frac{5}{8q} Sp \sqrt{\frac{3RT}{\mu T_0}} \left(\sqrt{T_0} - \sqrt{T}\right) t \approx 110 \text{ g}.$$

297. When estimating the effect, it can be assumed that one sixth of the molecules of air moves to the right, and one sixth to the left. The molecules moving parallel to the plane of the disc can be neglected. We shall assume that the molecule velocities v are the same. Let the disc move uniformly with velocity u with the cooler surface forward. The number of collisions per square centimetre of this surface per second is $n(v + u)/6$. To estimate the effect, we can assume that, in a coordinate system moving with the disc, a molecule is reflected with velocity v_2 corresponding to the temperature T_2 of the surface. In a fixed co-ordinate system the velocity of the reflected molecule is $v_2 + u$, and its change in velocity is $v_2 + u + v$. The gas pressure on the cooler surface is therefore

$$p_2 = mn(v + u)(v_2 + u + v)/6.$$

Similarly, the pressure on the warmer surface is

$$p_1 = nm(v - u)(v_1 + v - u)/6.$$

With steady-state motion, $p_2 = p_1$. We easily find from this condition that

$$u = \frac{v_1 - v_2}{4v + v_1 + v_2} v \approx \frac{v_1 - v_2}{6} \approx \frac{v}{12} \frac{v_1^2 - v_2^2}{v^2}$$

$$\approx \frac{1}{12}\sqrt{\frac{3RT}{\mu}} \frac{T_1 - T_2}{T} \approx 1{\cdot}4 \text{ m/sec.}$$

298. The gas will flow into the vessel with the higher temperature:

$$m = \frac{\sqrt{T_1 T_2}}{T_1 + T_2} \frac{\sqrt{T_1} - \sqrt{T_2}}{\sqrt{T_1} + \sqrt{T_2}} M = \frac{2}{15} M.$$

299. $E = 5pV/2 = 375$ kg m.

300. About 55 cal.

301. About 0·75 cal g^{-1} deg^{-1}.

302. $\gamma = \dfrac{7 + 3\alpha}{5 + \alpha}$.

304. $c_v = 6R$ for XY and $c_v = 9R$ for XY_2.

Each atom of a molecule has three degrees of freedom. If the molecules form a solid, the atoms perform small vibrations about their equilibrium positions. According to classical theory the mean kinetic energy per degree of freedom is $\frac{1}{2}kT$. Since the mean kinetic and potential energies in a harmonic vibration are equal, the total energy per atom is $3kT$ on the average. If there are n atoms per molecule, the mean energy per molecule is $3nkT$, and the molar specific heat is $3nR$.

305. $c_v = \frac{27}{32} R = 1{\cdot}68 \text{ cal g}^{-1} \text{deg}^{-1}$.

306. $p_{\text{bomb}} = N\varrho ZkT/A \approx 7{\cdot}5 \times 10^{10}$ atm, where N is Avogadro's number, $Z = 92$ is the atomic number of uranium, $A = 238$ is its atomic weight; $p_{\text{earth}} = \frac{1}{2}\varrho_{\text{earth}} gR \approx 1{\cdot}7 \times 10^6$ atm, where R is the Earth's radius.

307. In the c.g.s. system:

$$Q = (3\gamma M^2/5)(1/R_2 - 1/R_1) = (3\gamma M^2/5)((R_1 - R_2)/R_1R_2).$$

If $R_2 = 0{\cdot}9R_1$, then $Q = 3\gamma M^2/50R_1 = 2{\cdot}3 \times 10^{47}$ erg. The energy radiated by the Sun in a year is about $1{\cdot}2 \times 10^{41}$ erg. The heat released when the Sun is contracting would be sufficient for about $1{\cdot}9 \times 10^6$ years. If the Sun were suddenly compressed by one-tenth its initial radius, its temperature would rise by approximately $4{\cdot}6 \times 10^5$ deg.

We first calculate the heat of formation W of the Sun from infinitely rarefied matter. We take an infinitesimally thin spherical layer of mass dm whose centre coincides with the Sun's centre. The resultant of all the gravitational forces acting on an elementary mass of the layer and produced by all the mass situated further away from the Sun's centre is zero. The matter closer to the Sun's centre acts as though its mass were concentrated at the centre. If its total mass is m, the work done by the gravitational forces when the layer is moved from infinity to a distance r from the Sun's centre is

$$\gamma \frac{m\, dm}{r} = \frac{4\pi}{3} \gamma \delta r^2 dm,$$

where δ is the density of the Sun. Suppose now that the process of formation of the Sun from infinitely rarefied matter has been completed. Then $dm = 4\pi r^2 \delta\, dr$, and we obtain for the heat of formation:

$$W(R) = \int_0^R \frac{4\pi}{3} \gamma \delta r^2 4\pi r^2 \delta\, dr = \frac{16}{15} \pi^2 \gamma \delta^2 R^5 = \frac{3}{5} \gamma \frac{M^2}{R},$$

where R is the Sun's radius. Similarly, the heat Q released on a decrease of the Sun's radius is obviously equal to

$$Q = W(R_2) - W(R_1).$$

If the Sun consisted only of hydrogen, the hydrogen would obviously be not only dissociated but also totally ionised. There would thus be $2N$ particles per gram of the Sun's mass: N electrons and N protons. The mean kinetic energy of their thermal motion is $2N \cdot (3kT/2) = 3RT$. The specific heat of the solar material would in this case be equal to $c_v = 3R \approx 6 \text{ cal g}^{-1} \text{deg}^{-1}$.

308. The figure for the specific heat must be less than the classical value.

The hydrogen molecule H_2 has six degrees of freedom: three translational, two rotational and one vibrational degree of freedom. If the interaction forces can be neglected, the translational motion of the molecules can be regarded as free motion. Such motion is not quantised—its energy can take any value. On the contrary, the vibrational and rotational motions are quantised—their energies can only take a series of discrete values. At ordinary temperatures the quantised values of the energy of the vibrational motion are large compared with the mean kinetic energy $3kT/2$ of the translational motion of the molecules. The thermal motion of the molecules is too weak for them to move from lower energy levels (zero) of the vibrational motion to higher levels. Almost all the molecules are in the lowest vibrational energy level. Under these circumstances the energy of the vibrational motion is almost independent of temperature, and this motion has no effect on the specific heat of the gas. The quantised energies of the rotational motion are usually much smaller than the corresponding values for the vibrational motion. All the possible quantised rotations are thus excited even at ordinary temperatures, and the mean energy per degree of freedom of the rotational motion is the same as per degree of freedom of the translational motion. However, if the gas temperature is so low that the mean energy of the thermal motion of the molecules is small compared with the differences between the energy levels of the rotational motion, rotations at high levels cease to be excited, and the rotational degrees of freedom will have no effect on the specific heat of the gas. Hydrogen begins to behave as a monatomic gas.

309. $$\bar{E} = N\frac{\varepsilon_1 e^{-\frac{\varepsilon_1}{kT}} + \varepsilon_2 e^{-\frac{\varepsilon_2}{kT}}}{e^{-\frac{\varepsilon_1}{kT}} + e^{-\frac{\varepsilon_2}{kT}}} + \frac{3}{2}RT.$$

If $\varepsilon_2 - \varepsilon_1 \gg kT$, then $\bar{E} \approx \varepsilon_1 N + \frac{3}{2} RT$.

310. $\overline{\varphi^2}$ is diminished α times; $\overline{\varphi^2}$ is increased β/γ^4 times. It must be noted that $\overline{\varphi^2}$ is independent of the moment of inertia of the mirror;

$$N = \frac{RT}{D\overline{\varphi^2}} \approx 6{\cdot}04 \times 10^{23}.$$

311. $D\overline{\varphi^2}_{qu} = I\overline{\dot{\varphi}^2}_{qu} = h\nu/(e^{h\nu/kT} - 1) \approx kT(1 - \frac{1}{2}h\nu/kT)$, where $\nu = (1/2\pi)\sqrt{D/I}$. The classical formulae are applicable for $h\nu/kT \ll 1$. For the mirror, $h\nu/kT \approx 2{\cdot}5 \times 10^{-18}$.

312. $N = \dfrac{RT \ln \alpha}{\frac{4}{3}\pi r^3(\varrho - \varrho_0)gl} = 65 \times 10^{23}.$

313. $\mu = \dfrac{2RT\varrho \ln \alpha}{\omega^2(\varrho - \varrho_0)(r_2^2 - r_1^2)}.$

315. If we take the z-axis vertically upwards, we can write $m\ddot{z} + mg = 0$. On multiplying this by z and noting that $z\ddot{z} = d(z\dot{z})/dt - \dot{z}^2$, we obtain:

$$\frac{d}{dt}(mz\dot{z}) + mgz - m\dot{z}^2 = 0.$$

We integrate this relationship over the period of the motion. The integral of the first term gives zero, and we find the required relation:

$$\bar{\varepsilon}_{pot} = 2\bar{\varepsilon}_{kin}.$$

In the case of the molecules of a monatomic gas, if we take account of collisions, we get $\bar{\varepsilon}_{pot} = 2\bar{\varepsilon}_{kin}/3$. For a diatomic gas, by the theorem on the uniform distribution of the kinetic energy over the degrees of freedom, $\bar{\varepsilon}_{pot} = 2\bar{\varepsilon}_{kin}/5$. The total energy of a mole of gas in a gravitational field is $E = N(\bar{\varepsilon}_{kin} + \bar{\varepsilon}_{pot}) = 7N\bar{\varepsilon}_{kin}/5 = 7RT/2$. Its derivative with respect to T is c_p, whereas c_v is the derivative of the kinetic energy only: $N\bar{\varepsilon}_{kin} = 5RT/2$. This gives $c_p - c_v = R$. This argument is easily extended to monatomic and poly-atomic gases.

316. $c = c_v + \dfrac{R}{12}\left(\dfrac{\mu g H}{RT}\right)^2.$

317. It is unchanged. The free fall of the vessel is equivalent to a removal of the gravity forces. At the instant of removal we have a non-uniform distribution of the gas density. After a certain time the gas molecules will be uniformly distributed throughout the volume of the vessel. But obviously, their total kinetic energy, which determines the temperature of the ideal gas, is unchanged. The experiment is similar to the familiar Gay-Lussac experiment of the expansion of a gas into a vacuum.

318. The number dn of molecules whose co-ordinates lie between r and $r + dr$, z and $z + dz$, is equal to

$$dn = \frac{ng}{\left(1 - e^{-\frac{mgl}{kT}}\right)\left(e^{\frac{m\omega^2R^2}{2kT}} - 1\right)}\left(\frac{m\omega}{kT}\right)^2 e^{-\frac{mgz}{kT}} \cdot e^{\frac{m\omega^2r^2}{2kT}}\, r\, dr\, dz,$$

where n is the total number of molecules in the vessel. The z axis is directed vertically upwards.

319. We consider a group of Brownian particles, each of which undergoes a displacement $\Delta\boldsymbol{r}_i$ in time τ. Let $n_i(z)$ denote the concentration of these particles, i.e. the number per cm^3. Let σ be a small area perpendicular to the z axis (Fig. 27). We denote by $\boldsymbol{r}$ the radius vector of the centre of this area. The number $\sigma\tau N_i$ of Brownian particles of the group in question passing through the area σ in time τ as a result of diffusion is equal to the number of these particles in the parallelepiped drawn in Fig. 27. If the parallelepiped is sufficiently small, the number in question can be taken equal to the concentration $n_i(\boldsymbol{r} - \frac{1}{2}\Delta\boldsymbol{r}_i)$ at the centre of the parallelepiped, multiplied by its volume $\sigma\Delta z_i$. Thus

$$\sigma\tau N_i = \sigma\Delta z_i n_i\left(\boldsymbol{r} - \frac{\Delta\boldsymbol{r}_i}{2}\right).$$

On expanding in powers of Δz_i, confining ourselves to first order terms and observing that n_i depends on z but not on x and y, we obtain:

$$N_i = \frac{1}{\tau}\Delta z_i n_i(\boldsymbol{r}) - \frac{1}{2\tau}\frac{\partial n_i}{\partial z}(\Delta z_i)^2.$$

The total diffusional flux N of Brownian particles per square centimetre per second is found by summing this expression over all i, i.e. over all the groups of particles. This gives:

$$N = \frac{1}{\tau}\sum \Delta z_i n_i(\mathbf{r}) - \frac{1}{2\tau}\sum (\Delta z_i)^2 \frac{\partial n_i}{\partial z}.$$

The first term vanishes on the average, since the probabilities of a particle being displaced upwards or downwards from a given position are the same. Let n denote the total number of Brownian particles per cubic centimetre. Then

$$n = \sum n_i, \quad n\overline{(\Delta z)^2} = \sum (\Delta z_i)^2 n_i.$$

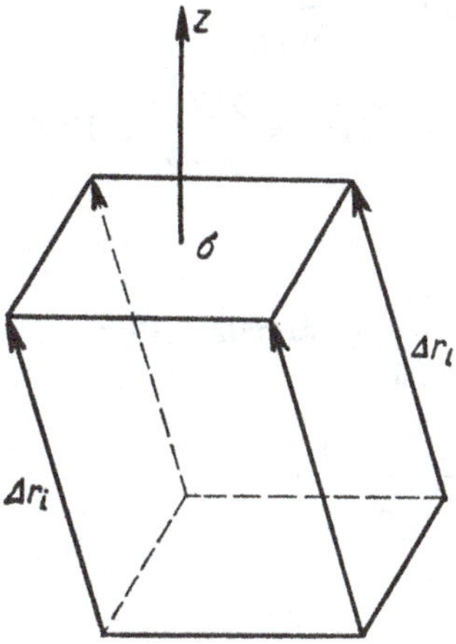

FIG. 27

The Δz_i, as independent variables are independent of z. The quantity $\overline{(\Delta z)^2}$ is also independent of z, since it is assumed that the concentration of Brownian particles is small, so that interaction between them plays no part. Thus differentiation of the last formula with respect to z gives $\overline{(\Delta z)^2}\,(\partial n/\partial z) = \sum(\Delta z_i)^2\,(\partial n_i/\partial z)$, and consequently $N = -(\overline{(\Delta z)^2}/2\tau)\,(\partial n/\partial z)$. On comparing this equation with $N = -D(\partial n/\partial z)$, which defines the diffusion coefficient D, we finally obtain

$$D = \frac{1}{2\tau}\overline{(\Delta z)^2}.$$

It follows from the context that $\overline{(\Delta z)^2}$ has to be understood as the "average over a set of particles". But since the particles are the same and interactions between them are absent, this average can be replaced by the "time average" for a single particle.

320. The density of the total flux of particles in the positive direction of the z axis is $nBf - D(\partial n/\partial z)$, where f is the resultant of the gravity force and the upward thrust of the hydrostatic pressure acting on the particle (the z axis is directed vertically downwards). On equating this expression to zero and noting that $n = n_0 e^{fz/kT}$, we obtain finally: $D = kT \cdot B$ (Einstein's formula).

321. $\overline{(\Delta z)^2} = 2kTB\tau = \dfrac{kT}{3\pi\eta a}\tau.$

322. $\overline{\Delta^2} = \overline{(\Delta x)^2} + \overline{(\Delta y)^2} = \dfrac{2kT\tau}{3\pi\eta a} \approx 10^{-6}\ \text{cm}^2;$

$\sqrt{\overline{\Delta^2}} \approx 10\ \mu.$

323. $N = \dfrac{RT\tau}{3\pi a\eta \cdot \overline{(\Delta x)^2}} \approx 6{\cdot}02 \times 10^{23}.$

324. $Ne = \dfrac{2RT(v_1 + v_2)}{E\overline{(\Delta x)^2}}\tau.$

325. $N = 5{\cdot}88 \times 10^{23}.$

326. $\tau \approx \dfrac{R^2}{6D} \approx \dfrac{R^2}{2lv} \approx \dfrac{R^2}{2lc} \approx 1{\cdot}4 \times 10^{14}\ \text{sec} \approx 4{\cdot}4 \times 10^6\ \text{years},$

where v is the velocity of a cosmic particle, which is close to the velocity c of light *in vacuo*. (See the solution to Problem 319).

327. When the wavelength is of the order of the mean free path.

328. Deflexion of an electron to larger angles when it collides with an ion can occur when the kinetic energy of the electron $\frac{1}{2}mv^2$ is comparable with the potential energy Ze^2/r of the interaction of these particles at their point of nearest approach (Ze is the charge on the ion). If we equate these expressions, we can find r, and thus an approximate expression for the cross-section:

$$\sigma = \pi r^2 \approx 4\pi\left(\frac{Ze^2}{mv^2}\right)^2 \approx \left(\frac{Ze^2}{kT}\right)^2. \qquad (1)$$

We have taken no account here of interactions at large distances, accompanied by deviations through small angles. Due to the accumulation of small deflexions in such interactions the momentum of an electron can vary by a finite amount. In typical cases the remote interactions are more important than the near-by interactions. They have no effect on the form of formula (1), however; they merely alter the numerical coefficient, which is of the order 10–20. Thus use can be made of (1) for rough estimates and qualitative discussions.

329. The arguments encountered in the elementary theory of electrical conduction in metals are applicable to a plasma. According to Drude's formula, $\lambda = e^2 nl/2m\bar{v}$, where $l = 1/n\sigma$ is the mean free path of an electron, $\bar{v} = \sqrt{3kT/m}$ is the mean velocity of its thermal motion, n is the number of electrons per cubic centimetre. On substituting the expression obtained in the previous problem for σ, we get

$$\lambda \approx \frac{(kT)^{3/2}}{2\sqrt{3m}\, e^2} = 6{\cdot}73 \times 10^7 \cdot T^{3/2} \text{ sec}^{-1}$$

$$= 7{\cdot}47 \times 10^{-5}\, T^{3/2} \text{ ohm}^{-1}\text{cm}^{-1}.$$

A more accurate (though still approximate) theory, that takes account of multiple scattering, gives

$$\lambda = (1{\cdot}55 \times 10^8/L)T^{3/2} \text{ sec}^{-1} = (1{\cdot}72 \times 10^{-4}/L)T^{3/2} \text{ ohm}^{-1}\text{cm}^{-1},$$

where L is the so-called coulomb logarithm, defined by the following formulae:

$$L = 9 - \tfrac{1}{2}\ln n + \tfrac{3}{2}\ln T \quad \text{for} \quad T \leqslant 16 \times 10^4 \text{ degrees},$$

$$L = 15 - \tfrac{1}{2}\ln n + \ln T \quad \text{for} \quad T \geqslant 16 \times 10^4 \text{ degrees},$$

where T is the temperature in degrees Kelvin and n is the concentration of the plasma, i.e. the number of electrons per cubic centimetre. We obtain for the specific resistance:

$$\varrho = 0{\cdot}58L \times 10^4 \times T^{-3/2} \text{ ohm cm}$$

$$= 0{\cdot}145L \times 10^{-6}\, T_{\text{kev}}^{-3/2} \text{ ohm cm}.$$

The coulomb logarithm L is weakly dependent on the temperature and the plasma concentration. It can be regarded as constant over a wide range of temperatures and concentrations. In this approximation the electrical conductivity and specific resistance are independent of the plasma concentration. The conductivity is directly proportional, and the specific resistance inversely proportional to $T^{3/2}$. These results refer to the case when the linear dimensions of the plasma are large compared with the mean free path of an electron.

330. $T \approx 1{\cdot}7° \times 10^7 \approx 1{\cdot}5$ keV.

331. The Wiedemann–Franz law is applicable to the plasma and gives

$$\varkappa = \frac{3k^2}{e^2} T\lambda \sim T^{5/2}.$$

The thermal conductivity of the plasma is independent of its concentration and proportional to $T^{5/2}$.

§ 7. Heat Radiation

332. We locate the layer inside a cavity, the walls of which are maintained at a temperature T. In the state of thermal equilibrium, an equilibrium (black) radiation is now established in the cavity. We consider a beam of this radiation of intensity I_0, incident on the layer at an angle φ (Fig. 28). After passing through the layer the

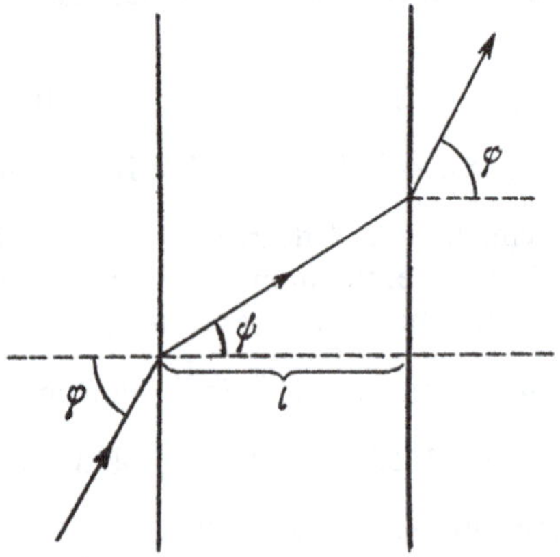

Fig. 28

intensity of the beam is reduced to $I_0 \exp(-\alpha l/\cos\psi)$, where ψ is the angle of refraction. The total intensity of the beam leaving the layer at an angle φ is, on the one hand, equal to

$$I + I_0 \exp(-\alpha l/\cos\psi),$$

where I is the intensity of the thermal radiation of the layer at the angle φ. On the other hand, the intensity of the same radiation must be equal to I_0, i.e. the intensity of radiation of a black body of temperature T. This gives:

$$I = I_0\left(1 - e^{-\frac{\alpha l}{\cos\psi}}\right).$$

333. $I = I_0(1-\varrho)(1-e^{-\delta})/(1-\varrho e^{-\delta})$, where $\delta = \alpha l/\cos\psi$, and ϱ is the coefficient of reflexion at the boundary of the layer. Both these quantities are functions of the wavelength.

334. $I = I_0(1-\varrho)$.

335. The intensity of the thermal radiation of the plate, issuing from left to right, is equal to the intensity of the corresponding linearly polarised component of the radiation of an ideally black body at the temperature T; the intensity of the radiation issuing in the opposite direction is zero.

338. $S = 4aT^3V/3$, where a is the constant in the Stefan–Boltzmann law.

339. $U = aT^4$, where a is the constant in the Stefan–Boltzmann law.

340. $c_v = 4aT^3$.

341. $VT^3 = \text{const.}$

342. $\sigma \approx 5 \times 10^{-5}\,\text{erg}\,\text{sec}^{-1}\text{cm}^{-2}\text{deg}^{-4}$. According to modern data:

$$\sigma = (5{\cdot}6697 \pm 0{\cdot}0010) \times 10^{-5}\,\text{erg}\,\text{sec}^{-1}\,\text{cm}^{-2}\,\text{deg}^{-4}.$$

343. $t \approx 1{\cdot}64$ hr.

344. $T \approx 400$°K.

345. $U = \dfrac{4\pi}{c} I;\quad S = \dfrac{c}{4} U,\quad S = \pi I.$

346. $dN(\nu) = \frac{2z}{c}\,d\nu$, where c is the wave propagation velocity along the string.

347. $dN(\nu) = \frac{2\pi\nu\,d\nu}{c^2}\,z^2$, where c is the wave propagation velocity over the membrane.

348. $dN(\nu) = \frac{8\pi\nu^2 d\nu V}{c^3}$, where c is the wave propagation velocity in the parallelepiped.

349. If $h\nu \gg kT$, then $U_\nu \approx (8\pi h\nu^3/c^3)\exp(-h\nu/kT)$ (Wien's formula).

If $h\nu \ll kT$, then $U_\nu \approx (8\pi\nu^2/c^3)\,kT$ (Rayleigh–Jeans formula).

350. The black radiation energy density is

$$U = \frac{8\pi h}{c^3}\int_0^\infty \frac{\nu^3 d\nu}{e^{\frac{h\nu}{kT}} - 1} = \frac{8\pi k^4 T^4}{c^3 h^3}\int_0^\infty \frac{x^3}{e^x - 1}\,dx.$$

The integral appearing in this is equal to

$$\int_0^\infty \frac{x^3}{e^x - 1}\,dx = \int_0^\infty \frac{x^3 e^{-x}}{1 - e^{-x}}\,dx = \int_0^\infty x^3 e^{-x}(1 + e^{-x} + e^{-2x} + \cdots)\,dx$$

$$= 6\left(1 + \frac{1}{2^4} + \frac{1}{3^4} + \cdots\right) = \frac{\pi^4}{15},$$

since the sum of the series in brackets is $\pi^4/90$. Hence

$$U = \frac{8\pi^5 k^4}{15c^3 h^3}\,T^4.$$

On using the relationships given in the answer to Problem 345, we find that $S = cU/4 = \sigma T^4$, where

$$\sigma = \frac{2\pi^5 k^4}{15c^2 h^3} = 5{\cdot}6687 \times 10^{-5}\ \text{erg}\,\text{cm}^{-2}\,\text{deg}^{-4}\,\text{sec}^{-1}.$$

To determine the constant α in Wien's law $\lambda_{max}\,T = \alpha$, we write Planck's formula in the form

$$U_\nu d\nu = U_\lambda\,d\lambda = \frac{8\pi hc}{\lambda^5}\cdot\frac{d\lambda}{e^{\frac{hc}{\lambda kT}} - 1}.$$

The problem amounts to finding the value of λ_{max} for which the function $\lambda^5(\exp(hc/\lambda kT) - 1)$ has a minimum. On introducing the new unknown $\beta = hc/kT\lambda_{max}$ and proceeding in the usual way, we arrive at the transcendental equation

$$e^{-\beta} + \frac{\beta}{5} - 1 = 0,$$

the root of which is $\beta = 4{\cdot}96511423$. Hence

$$\lambda_{max}T = \alpha = \frac{hc}{k\beta} = 0{\cdot}289782 \text{ cm deg.}$$

351. $T \approx 6000\,°\text{K}$.

352. $\lambda_{max} \approx 29$ Å.

353. $T = \dfrac{1}{\sqrt[4]{\epsilon_T}} T_r$.

354. No, since the radiating capacity of any body is less than the radiating capacity of a black body.

355. 5370 W.

356. $W \approx 1900$ W; $T_r = 2700\,°\text{K}$.

357. $$T_r = \frac{C_2}{\lambda \ln\left(1 + \dfrac{C_1}{E_c(T)\lambda^5}\right)},$$

where T_r is the brightness temperature for the wavelength λ; T is the true temperature; C_1 and C_2 are constants; $E_c(T)$ is the radiating capacity of the grey body.

358. $\lambda_{max}T = \dfrac{C_2}{5} = 0{\cdot}28776$ cm deg.

(See the answer to Problem 350.)

359. $T < \dfrac{hc}{\lambda k \ln 100} = \dfrac{3{\cdot}11 \times 10^7}{\lambda} \approx 4150\,°\text{K}$ (for $\lambda = 7500$ Å)

(λ is in Ångströms).

360. $U_\nu = \frac{8\pi h\nu^3}{c^3} e^{-\frac{h\nu}{kT}}$ (Wien's formula).

361. The probabilities of absorption and induced radiation are equal. Hence $\varkappa$ is proportional to $N_1 - N_2$, where N_1, N_2 are the numbers of molecules at the lower and higher levels. By Boltzmann's formula,

$$N_2 = N_1 e^{-\frac{E_2 - E_1}{kT}} = N_1 e^{-\frac{h\nu}{kT}},$$

whence $N_1 - N_2 = N_1[1 - \exp(-h\nu/kT)]$. Consequently,

$$\varkappa(T) = \varkappa_0\left(1 - e^{-\frac{h\nu}{kT}}\right).$$

(1) If $h\nu/kT \ll 1$, then $\varkappa(T) = \varkappa_0 h\nu/kT$, so that $\varkappa(T) \ll \varkappa_0$. This case is realised in the radio band. For instance, even at $\lambda = 1$ mm, $T = 300$°K we have $h\nu/kT \approx \frac{1}{20}$.

(2) If $h\nu/kT \gg 1$, then $\varkappa(T) = \varkappa_0$. This case holds in the optical region. For instance, when $\lambda = 5000$ Å, $T = 1500$°K, we have $h\nu/kT \approx 20$.

362. $p = \frac{U}{3} = \frac{4\sigma}{3c} T^4 = 4{\cdot}6 \times 10^{17}$ dyne cm^{-2} $= 4{\cdot}6 \times 10^{11}$ atm.

363. $T_{eff} = = T(1 - e^{-\alpha l})$. (See Problem 332.)

364. According to the Rayleigh–Jeans formula

$$S = \frac{2\pi kT}{\lambda^2}\left(\frac{r}{R}\right)^2 = \frac{8{\cdot}67 \times 10^{-17} \times T}{\lambda^2}\left(\frac{r}{R}\right)^2 \text{W} \cdot \text{m}^{-2}\,(\text{mc/s})^{-1}$$

$$\approx \frac{1{\cdot}86 \times 10^{-15}}{\lambda^2} \text{W} \cdot \text{m}^{-2}\,(\text{mc/s})^{-1},$$

where λ is in metres, $R = 1{\cdot}5 \times 10^8$ km is the radius of the Earth's orbit, r is the "effective radius" of the corona, which we have put for purposes of estimation equal to the radius of the photosphere $r = 6{\cdot}95 \times 10^5$ km.

365. $I = I_0 e^{-\varkappa z}$, where $\varkappa = A(N_1 - N_2)$, A is a constant. Amplification of the wave is possible if the concentration N_2 of particles at the higher energy level is greater than the concentration N_1 at the lower level.

CHAPTER II

ATOMIC AND NUCLEAR PHYSICS

§ 8. STRUCTURE OF THE ATOM AND SPECTRA

366. $\nu = (1/2\pi)\sqrt{e^2/ma^3}$, where a is the radius of the positively charged sphere, i.e. the radius of the Thomson atom, e is the charge and m the mass of the electron.

367. A harmonically oscillating electron radiates one frequency.

$$a = \left(\frac{e^2\lambda^2}{4\pi^2c^2m}\right)^{1/3} = 2 \cdot 6 \times 10^{-8} \text{ cm}.$$

368. $c_v = \frac{9}{2}R$.

369. The equations of the conservation of energy and angular momentum have the form in polar coordinates (Fig. 29): $\frac{1}{2}m\dot{r}^2$

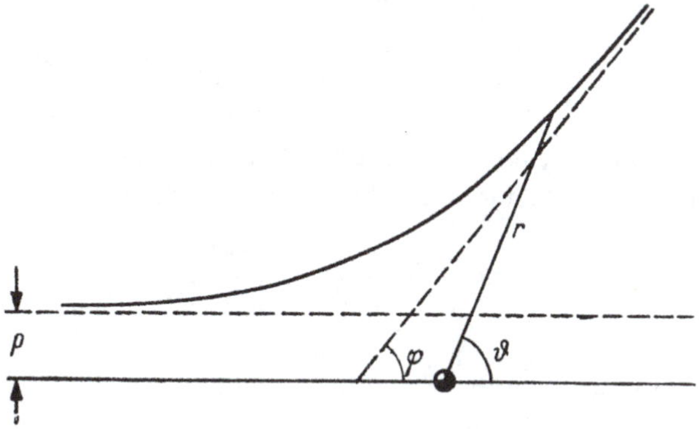

FIG. 29

$+ \frac{1}{2}mr^2\dot{\vartheta}^2 + (2Ze^2/r) = \frac{1}{2}mv^2$, $r^2\dot{\vartheta} = pv$, since the charge of the α-particle is $2e$. We eliminate $\dot{\vartheta}$ by noticing that $\dot{r} = \dot{\vartheta}dr/d\vartheta$, then make the substitution $r = 1/\varrho$. We obtain after simple calculations:

$$\left(\frac{d\varrho}{d\vartheta}\right)^2 + \left(\varrho + \frac{2Ze^2}{mp^2v^2}\right)^2 - \frac{4Z^2e^4}{m^2p^4v^4} = \frac{1}{p^2}. \tag{1}$$

On differentiating this equation with respect to ϑ and cancelling through by $d\varrho/d\vartheta$, we obtain:

$$\frac{d^2\varrho}{d\vartheta^2} + \varrho + \frac{2Ze^2}{mp^2v^2} = 0.$$

Hence

$$\varrho = A\cos\vartheta + B\sin\vartheta - \frac{2Ze^2}{mp^2v^2}, \tag{2}$$

where A and B are constants of integration. They are not independent of one another, however, but, from (1), are connected by the relationship

$$A^2 + B^2 = \frac{1}{p^2} + \frac{4Z^2e^4}{m^2p^4v^4}. \tag{3}$$

The initial condition: $\varrho \equiv 1/r = 0$ for $\vartheta = \pi$ gives

$$A = -2Ze^2/m^2p^4v^4.$$

Hence we obtain from (3): $B^2 = 1/p^2$. Equation (2) now transforms to

$$\varrho = A(1 + \cos\vartheta) + B\sin\vartheta \quad \text{or}$$

$$\frac{1}{r} = 2\left(A\cos\frac{\vartheta}{2} + B\sin\frac{\vartheta}{2}\right)\cos\frac{\vartheta}{2}. \tag{4}$$

r becomes infinite when $\cos\vartheta/2 = 0$ or $\vartheta = \pi$ (we have already made use of this) and when $\vartheta = \varphi$, where φ is given by

$$\cot\frac{\varphi}{2} = -\frac{B}{A} = \frac{mpv^2}{2Ze^2}. \tag{5}$$

370. $d\sigma = 2\pi \dfrac{Z^2e^4\sin\varphi}{m^2v^4\sin^4\dfrac{\varphi}{2}}\,d\varphi.$

371. $\Delta n = n\dfrac{V\varrho N}{A}\dfrac{2\pi Z^2e^4\sin\varphi}{m^2v^4\sin^4\dfrac{\varphi}{2}}\,d\varphi \approx 13$ particles, where $\varrho = 8{\cdot}9\,\mathrm{g\,cm^{-3}}$ is the density of copper, $A = 63{\cdot}57$ is its atomic weight, $Z = 29$ is its atomic number, N is Avogadro's number, V is the scattering volume.

372. $$\frac{u_{\mathrm{grav}}}{u_{\mathrm{el.st}}} = \gamma\left(\frac{m}{e}\right)^2 = \begin{cases} 2{\cdot}4 \times 10^{-43} \text{ for an electron} \\ 8{\cdot}1 \times 10^{-37} \text{ for a proton.} \end{cases}$$

373. If the electron displacement is $x = a\cos\omega t$, then

$$v = -\omega a \sin\omega t,\; \dot{v} = -\omega^2 a \cos\omega t.$$

The total energy of the electron is $W = \frac{1}{2}m\omega^2 a^2$. The mean energy loss per second is $2e^2\overline{\dot{v}^2}/3c^3 = e^2\omega^4 a^2/3c^3 = (2e^2\omega^2/3mc^3)W$. We can therefore write for the average electron energy change:

$$\frac{dW}{dt} = -\frac{2}{3}\frac{e^2\omega^2}{mc^3}W.$$

On writing W_0 for the initial energy, we obtain from this:

$$t = \frac{3mc^3}{2e^2\omega^2}\ln\frac{W_0}{W} \approx 1{\cdot}9 \times 10^{-8}\text{ sec.}$$

374. $$\Delta t = \frac{a_0^3 c^3 m^2}{4e^4} = 1{\cdot}5 \times 10^{-11}\text{ sec.}$$

375. It will radiate one frequency ν, if we neglect the change in state of the motion of the electron. The intensity of the radiation should be greater in the first orbit.

376. $$a = \frac{h^2 n^2}{4\pi^2 m Z e^2};\quad a_0 = 0{\cdot}53 \times 10^{-8}\text{ cm}\quad (n = 1,\ Z = 1);$$

$$v = \frac{2\pi e^2 Z}{hn};\quad v_0 = \frac{1}{137}c = 2{\cdot}183 \times 10^8\text{ cm sec}^{-1}.$$

377. $E = (e/a^2)\,300\,\mathrm{V\,cm^{-1}}$, where a is the orbit radius.

$$E_1 = 5{\cdot}13 \times 10^9\ \mathrm{V\,cm^{-1}},$$

$$E_4 = 2 \times 10^7\ \mathrm{V\,cm^{-1}}.$$

378. $F = 8 \times 10^{-3}$ dyne: the gravitational force is about 2×10^{39} times smaller.

380. $\frac{1}{\lambda} = R\left(\frac{1}{2^2} - \frac{1}{n^2}\right);$

$$H_\alpha = 6563\ \text{Å};\quad H_\beta = 4861\ \text{Å};\quad H_\gamma = 4340\ \text{Å}.$$

381. $\lambda_L = 1216\text{Å}$; $\lambda_{Pasch} = 18751\text{Å}$; $\lambda_{Br} = 4{\cdot}05 \times 10^{-4}$ cm $= 4{\cdot}05\ \mu$; $\lambda_{Pf} = 7{\cdot}40 \times 10^{-4}$ cm $= 7{\cdot}40\ \mu$.

382. $\lambda = \frac{4}{R} \approx 3647\ \text{Å}.$

383. The least number of levels is obtained for transitions between neighbouring levels, when

$$\frac{1}{\lambda} = R\left(\frac{1}{(n-1)^2} - \frac{1}{n^2}\right) \simeq \frac{2R}{n^3},$$

since $n \gg 1$ in the radio band.

Hence $n = \sqrt[3]{2R\lambda} \simeq 60\sqrt[3]{\lambda}$, where λ is measured in centimetres. We obtain with the aid of this formula:

λ	$\nu = c/\lambda$	n
1 cm	3×10^{10} c/s	60
10 cm	3×10^{9} c/s	130
1 m	3×10^{8} c/s	280
10 m	3×10^{7} c/s	600

384. $E = hcR = 2{\cdot}153 \times 10^{-11}$ erg,

$$V_i = \frac{E}{e} = 13{\cdot}5\ \text{V}.$$

385. 312 cal mole^{-1}.

386. 14300°K and 16300°K.

387. $n_1 : n_2 : n_3 = 1 : e^{-\frac{3Rch}{4kT}} : e^{-\frac{8}{9}\frac{Rch}{kT}} = 1 : 10^{-22,6} : 10^{-26,7}$.

388. $V = 10{\cdot}15$ V.

389. $\nu = Rc(1/1^2 - 1/n^2)$, where R is Rydberg's constant and c is the velocity of light.

390. Absorption of the frequency $2Rc$ takes place and is accompanied by ionisation of the atom (photoeffect in the atom).

391. $\lambda = 1216$ Å, $\lambda = 1026$ Å and $\lambda = 6562{\cdot}8$ Å.

392. All the lines of the line spectrum of hydrogen.

393. All the terms of the spectral series are present in the recombination spectrum, and there is a continuous emission spectrum beyond the limits of the series.

394. $V_{He} = 54$ V; $V_{Li} = 122$ V.

395. $\lambda = 303{\cdot}75$ Å.

396. $R_\infty = \dfrac{2\pi^2 me^4}{h^3 c} = 109737{\cdot}31\ \text{cm}^{-1}$.

397. $E = R_\infty Z^2 \dfrac{M}{M+m}$ (M is the mass of the nucleus and m the mass of the electron).

398. $\dfrac{m_H}{m} = 1838{\cdot}2$; $\dfrac{m_{He}}{m_H} = 3.97$.

399. $H_\alpha - D_\alpha = 1{\cdot}8$ Å; $H_\gamma - D_\gamma \approx 1{\cdot}3$ Å.

400. $\Delta V = 0{\cdot}00366$ V, $\Delta E = 84{\cdot}5$ cal mole^{-1}.

401. The transition from the $n = 6$ to the $n = 4$ level.

402. $\Delta\lambda = 2{\cdot}62$ Å.

403. Rydberg's constants for hydrogen and deuterium are

$$R_H = \frac{R_\infty}{1 + \dfrac{m}{M_H}}; \quad R_D = \frac{R_\infty}{1 + \dfrac{m}{M_D}},$$

where M_H and M_D are the masses of the hydrogen and deuterium nuclei. We obtain from this:

$$\frac{1}{m} = \frac{1}{R_D - R_H}\left(\frac{R_H}{M_H} - \frac{R_D}{M_D}\right).$$

On multiplying both sides of this equation by e and noting that $(M_H + m) N = H$, $(M_D + m) N = D$, $Ne = F$, we find that

$$\frac{e}{m} = \frac{F}{R_D - R_H}\left(\frac{R_H}{H - Nm} - \frac{R_D}{D - Nm}\right).$$

Since the atomic mass Nm of the electron is small compared with H and D, it does not need to be known to high accuracy when computing $H - Nm$ and $D - Nm$. We have: $Nm = 6{\cdot}025 \times \times 10^{23} \times 9{\cdot}108 \times 10^{-28} = 5{\cdot}49 \times 10^{-4}$; $H - Nm = 1{\cdot}007593$; $D - Nm = 2{\cdot}014186$. On substituting these values in the previous formula, we obtain:

$$\frac{e}{m} = 5{\cdot}2732 \times 10^{17} \text{ e.s.u.} = 1{\cdot}7590 \times 10^{7} \text{ e.m.u.}$$

404. We neglect the thermal velocity of the atoms. The maximum velocity of an atom reflected elastically from a satellite occurs on head-on impact and is equal to $2V$, whilst its kinetic energy is $2mV^2$. This energy is not entirely transmitted to another atom with which the atom in question collides. Maximum energy transfer also occurs in a head-on collision. In this case, by the laws of conservation of energy and momentum:

$$2mV^2 = \frac{mv^2}{2} + \frac{m'v'^2}{2} + E,$$

$$2mV = mv + m'v',$$

where v and v' are the velocities of the atoms after impact, m and m' their masses, and E the ionisation energy of the second atom. On eliminating v', we get a quadratic equation in v^2. For ionisation to be possible, it is necessary and sufficient that the roots of the quadratic equation be real. When $m = m'$ this condition has the form $mV^2 > E$. For hydrogen, nitrogen and oxygen atoms the energies mV^2 in electron volts are respectively 0·668; 9·35; 10·7. Ionisation is thus impossible in all three cases. This conclusion has to be modified if account is taken of the thermal motion of the atoms. Ionisation may occur in the case of single atoms, moving in the opposite direction to the satellite with large thermal velocities and colliding elastically with it.

405. $\mu = \dfrac{eh}{4\pi mc} = 0{\cdot}92 \times 10^{-20}$ ergoersted^{-1}.

406. $\dfrac{\mu}{l} = \dfrac{e}{2mc}$.

408. $E = \dfrac{\mu^2}{r^3} \approx 3 \times 10^{-24}$ erg.

409. $\omega = 2nl/J\,\text{sec}^{-1}$, where n is the number of atoms in the cylinder and J is the moment of inertia of the cylinder.

410. $\alpha = \dfrac{\mu}{l} = \dfrac{2M}{\omega J}$, where $M = n\mu$ is the magnetic moment of the cylinder.

411. $\omega = 2NhL\varrho/Mm^2 = 1{\cdot}12 \times 10^{-3}\,\text{sec}^{-1}$. Here m is the mass of the cylinder, L is its length, M is the atomic weight of iron, ϱ is its density, N is Avogadro's number.

412. $l = \dfrac{h}{4\pi} = 0{\cdot}52 \times 10^{-27}$ ergsec^{-1};

$$\mu = \frac{eh}{4\pi mc} = 0{\cdot}92 \times 10^{-20}\ \text{ergoersted}^{-1};$$

$$\alpha = \frac{\mu}{l} = \frac{e}{mc} = 1{\cdot}76 \times 10^{8}\ \text{oersted}^{-1}\,\text{sec}.$$

413. H: 2; Li: 2; Fe: 1, 3, 5, 7, 9; Cl: 2, 4, 6, 8; He: 1, 3; Mg: 1, 3; Hg: 1, 3; U: 1, 3, 5, 7.

414. Sr^{+}:2; Li^{+}:1, 3; Ca^{+}:2; C^{++}:1, 3; O^{++++}:1, 3.

415. 4.

416. $\Delta E = \dfrac{eh}{4\pi mc} H$; the number of levels is seven.

417. Into three components (by virtue of the selection rule, $\Delta m = 0, \pm 1$.)

418. $\Delta E = \dfrac{Ze}{2mca_n^3} \dfrac{h}{2\pi} l \dfrac{e}{mc} \dfrac{h}{2\pi} S \cos(\widehat{ls})$.

$Z = 1, n = 2, l = 1, S = \frac{1}{2}, \cos(\widehat{ls}) = \pm 1, a_2^3 = 4^3 a_0^3,$

$\Delta E = 2 \times 10^{-17}$ erg.

419. $\Delta\lambda = 0{\cdot}003$ Å.

420. If $\Delta\nu$ is the interval between the components with internal quantum numbers j and $j' = j + 1$, then $\Delta\nu$ is proportional to j'.

421. $2j + 1$.

422. Into two.

423. $E = E_0 + mgehH/4\pi mc$, where E is the energy in the field, E_0 the energy without the field, $m = -j, -j + 1, \ldots, +j$ and $g = (2j + 1)/(2l + 1)$.

424. Into 18.

425. 6.

426. $2n^2$.

428. $2(2l + 1)$.

429. Hyperfine splitting in hydrogen leads to the formation of two sublevels from one level.

The order of magnitude is $\Delta E \sim \mu_e \mu_p / r^3 \sim 10^{-18}$ erg (here the magnetic moments of the electron and proton are $\mu_e = eh/2mc = 9 \times 10^{-21}$ erg oersted^{-1}, $\mu_p \simeq 3e\hbar/2Mc \sim 1{\cdot}4 \times 10^{-23}$ erg oersted^{-1} and $r \sim 5 \times 10^{-9}$ cm is the radius of the first Bohr orbit).

This estimate leads to too low a value of ΔE since the electron comes closer to the nucleus in actual fact than according to Bohr's theory. When $r \sim 2 \times 10^{-9}$ cm the estimate agrees well with an accurate calculation.

430. $\nu = \Delta E/h \sim 10^9$ cycle sec^{-1}, $\lambda = c/\nu \sim 30$ cm. Actually, $\lambda = 21$ cm. The 21 cm radiation of neutral hydrogen is one of the most important methods in modern astrophysics of investigating interstellar space.

431. 10^9.

432. $\dfrac{n}{n_0} \approx 5 \times 10^{-6}$.

433. $t = \dfrac{1}{n} e^{-\frac{h\nu}{kT}} \approx 2{\cdot}5 \times 10^{-9}$ sec.

434. $r \sim (Dd/2)\sqrt{P/hc\lambda n} \sim 0{\cdot}1$ light year.

435. (1) $T_{\text{eff}} = E\lambda^4/8\pi ckS\tau\Delta\lambda = 4{\cdot}4 \times 10^8\,°\text{K}$.

(2) $T_{\text{eff}} \simeq E\lambda^2/8\pi ck\tau\,\Delta\lambda \simeq 10^{17}\,°\text{K}$.

436. (1) $p = E(1 + R)/c\tau S = 2(1 + R)/3$ dyne cm^{-2}, where R is the reflexion coefficient of the surface.

(2) $p \simeq E/c\tau\lambda^2 \simeq 150\,(1 + R)$ atm.

(3) $E \simeq (1/\lambda)\sqrt{8\pi E/c\tau} \simeq 6 \times 10^4$ e.s.u. $\simeq 1{\cdot}8 \times 10^7\ \text{V cm}^{-1}$.

437. The equation of motion of the particle is $m dv/dt = eE$, where E is the electric field-strength; it is not necessary to take into account the action of the Lorentz force, since it is compensated by the forces which lead to the motion of the particle round a circle of given radius r. By the law of induction, $2\pi rE = -\pi r^2(dH/dt)/c$. On combining these equations and integrating, we obtain $m(v - v_0) = -(e/2c)r\,(H - H_0)$. Hence the change in velocity is $v - v_0 = \omega_L r$, where $\omega_L = -eHr/2mc$ is the change in the angular velocity (prior to its variation, the field is assumed to be $H_0 = 0$).

438. As shown in the solution of the previous problem, as a result of switching on the field $m(v - v_0) = -(e/2c)r(H - H_0) = -(e/2\pi rc)\,(\Phi - \Phi_0)$, where $\Phi = \pi r^2 H$ is the magnetic flux. If the change $m(v - v_0)r$ in mrv is quantised and equal to $nh/2\pi$, the change is $\Phi - \Phi_0 = nhc/e$, i.e. it is also quantised and depends on the particle charge e. But one electron (or a small number) cannot have a significant effect on the flux of the external magnetic field. Hence it is clear that, in the presence of a magnetic field, mvr is not quantised. This result is connected with the fact that, in the presence of a magnetic field, the particle momentum p is not equal to mv. On the contrary, given certain conditions relevant to the region of applicability of Bohr's quantisation rule, the rule $pr = nh/2\pi$ is valid.

439. In a superconductor the current only flows in a thin surface layer whose thickness does not usually exceed 10^{-5} cm. In the body of the superconductor the current is zero and hence the velocity v of the ordered motion of the electrons is $v = 0$. Hence on a circle of radius r slightly larger than, but virtually equal to, the radius of the aperture in the cylinder, $pr = |e^*|\,\Phi/2\pi c = nh/2\pi$, whence $\Phi = nhc/|e^*|$.

§ 9. X-Rays

440. It all depends on the polarisation of the scattered radiation. If the incident beam is not polarised, but the oscillations in it are transverse, the beam scattered by the body A and travelling in the direction of B, will be polarised, in such a way that the plane of its oscillations coincides with the plane of the figure. The forced oscillations of the electrons of the body B thus occur in a direction parallel to BC. No electrons are radiated in this direction, which explains the absence of scattered radiation in the direction in question.

Materials with high atomic weights are unsuitable because they yield a hard characteristic radiation of their own, which is of considerable intensity. The natural radiations of carbon, paraffin, etc. are weak and soft, and are absorbed after travelling a few centimetres in air; they thus have no disturbing effect on the experiment.

441. $$\nu = Rc(Z-1)^2\left(\frac{1}{1} - \frac{1}{2^2}\right) = 4{\cdot}16 \times 10^{18}\ \text{sec}^{-1};$$

$$\lambda_\alpha = 0{\cdot}72\,\text{Å (in fact } \lambda_\alpha = 0{\cdot}71\,\text{Å).}$$

$$E = h\nu = 2{\cdot}72 \times 10^{-8}\ \text{erg} = 17{\cdot}100\ \text{eV}.$$

442. $V = 12{,}340/\lambda$ V; $V_{Mo} \approx 23$ kV, $V_{Cu} \approx 10$ kV, $V_{Fe} \approx 8{\cdot}5$kV. The true values of V are respectively

$$V_{Mo} = 20\ \text{kV}, \quad V_{Cu} = 8{\cdot}9\ \text{kV} \quad V_{Fe} = 7{\cdot}1\ \text{kV}.$$

443. $\lambda_{Mo} \approx 0{\cdot}62$Å, $\lambda_{Fe} \approx 1{\cdot}7$Å, $\lambda_{Cu} \approx 1{\cdot}4$Å.

444. Radiation is excited from chromium but not from cobalt.

445. All the lines of all the series, except the K-series, are excited.

446. Zirconium and molybdenum; the element niobium lies between them.

447. Sodium.

448. 60,000 V.

449. $\lambda \approx 1{\cdot}54$ Å.

450. $v \approx 5 \times 10^9$ cm sec^{-1}.

451. $a \cos\alpha = n\lambda$, where n is an integer. A system of hyperbolas is observed in the focal plane.

452. (1) $a(\cos\alpha - \cos\alpha_0) = n\lambda$.

(2) The distance D from the screen must satisfy

$$D \gg \frac{(L\cos\alpha)^2}{\lambda} = N^2 n^2 \lambda$$

(N is the number of scattering centres).

453. A system of concentric rings.

454. $a\cos\alpha = n_1\lambda$, $b\cos\beta = n_2\lambda$, where n_1, n_2 are integers, and α, β are the angles between the direction of the diffracted ray and the mutually perpendicular linear chains of points of which the plane grating is composed. The diffraction pattern consists of spots, at the points of intersection of two families of hyperbolas: one family corresponds to the diffraction pattern from one linear chain of points, the other from the chain perpendicular to it.

455. $a\cos\alpha = n_1\lambda$, $b\cos\beta = n_2\lambda$, $c(1 - \cos\gamma) = n_3\lambda$, where γ is the angle between the direction of the incident rays and the diffracted ray. The maxima on the screen are at the places where the concentric circles, corresponding to diffraction from the linear chain parallel to the direction of the incident rays, pass through the points of intersection of the hyperbolas, corresponding to diffraction from the plane grating. Generally speaking, the maxima will not be observed for any λ; λ must satisfy the condition

$$\left(\frac{n_1}{a}\right)^2 + \left(\frac{n_2}{b}\right)^2 + \left(\frac{n_3}{b}\right)^2 = \frac{4\sin^2\dfrac{\gamma}{2}}{\lambda^2}.$$

456. $$\left.\begin{aligned} a(\cos\alpha - \cos\alpha_0) &= n_1\lambda, \\ a(\cos\beta - \cos\beta_0) &= n_2\lambda, \\ a(\cos\gamma - \cos\gamma_0) &= n_3\lambda, \end{aligned}\right\}\text{ Laue conditions}$$

$$\lambda = -2a\,\frac{n_1\cos\alpha_0 + n_2\cos\beta_0 + n_3\cos\gamma_0}{n_1^2 + n_2^2 + n_3^2}$$

457. $$\frac{2a}{\sqrt{n_1^2 + n_2^2 + n_3^2}}\sin\vartheta = \lambda.$$

459. Diffraction is always possible in principle, but the diffraction angle is negligibly small, especially when the beam is normally incident to the lattice.

Furthermore, the incident beam must be accurately parallel. In practice, no X-ray diffraction is observed from a grating when the angle of incidence is significantly different from 90°. The above-mentioned difficulties are only overcome when the angle of incidence approaches 90°. The angle of incidence is usually chosen to be greater than the limiting angle of total internal reflection. It is then possible to obtain clear diffraction of X-rays from ordinary reflecting gratings.

460. A system of concentric rings will be observed (the centre is the track of the primary beam).

$$\tan 2\vartheta = \frac{z}{R}, \quad 2d\sin\vartheta = n\lambda.$$

461. 1; 2; 4.

462. $$a_{\text{NaCl}} = \sqrt[3]{\frac{\mu}{2Z\varrho}} = 2{\cdot}814\,\text{Å};$$

$$a_{\text{Fe}} = \sqrt[3]{\frac{2\mu}{Z\varrho}} = 2{\cdot}87\,\text{Å}$$

(Z is the Loschmidt number and μ is the molecular weight).

463. $\lambda = 1{\cdot}47\,\text{Å}$.

464. $d = 6{\cdot}28\,\text{Å}$.

465. Nickel.

§ 10. THE QUANTUM NATURE OF LIGHT. THE WAVE PROPERTIES OF PARTICLES

466. $m = \frac{h\nu}{c^2} = \frac{h}{c\lambda} \approx 0{\cdot}44 \times 10^{-32}$ g.

467. $\lambda = h/mc = 0{\cdot}02426$Å (the Compton shift for 90°).

468. The photon momentum is

$$p = h\nu/c = h/\lambda \approx 1{\cdot}3 \times 10^{-22}\,\text{g cm sec}^{-1}.$$

The hydrogen molecule momentum is

$$P \approx \sqrt{3kTM} \approx 5{\cdot}4 \times 10^{-19}\,\text{g cm sec}^{-1}.$$

469. $\lambda = \frac{h}{P} \approx 1{\cdot}2$Å.

470. The energy of a photon of visual light is $h\nu = hc/\lambda \approx 4 \times 10^{-12}$ erg, the energy of a hydrogen molecule $\approx 3kT/2 \approx 6 \times 10^{-14}$ erg.

471. The number of photons $\approx 1{\cdot}2 \times 10^{21}$.

472. $E = \frac{p^2}{m}\left(m = \frac{h\nu}{c^2}\right)$.

474. Let M be the mass of the source and v its velocity. The energy of the source is made up of the kinetic energy $\frac{1}{2}Mv^2$ and the internal energy E of the excited atoms. When one photon is emitted, the internal energy E changes by a well-defined amount (the energy is quantised!): $E' - E = -h\nu_0$, where ν_0 is the frequency of the photon emitted by the fixed source. When a photon is emitted the body suffers a recoil, and its velocity changes. By the law of conservation of energy,

$$\tfrac{1}{2}Mv^2 + E = \tfrac{1}{2}Mv'^2 + E' + h\nu,$$

where ν is the frequency of the photon emitted by the moving source. On writing the law of conservation of momentum and projecting it onto the direction of the velocity v and onto the perpendicular direction, we obtain:

$$Mv = Mv' \cos\alpha + \frac{h\nu}{c} \cos\Theta,$$

$$0 = Mv' \sin\alpha - \frac{h\nu}{c} \sin\Theta,$$

where Θ and α are the angles between the direction of the velocity v and the directions of the momenta of the emitted photon and the source after emission. On eliminating v' and α, we get

$$2hM(\nu - \nu_0) - 2Mv \frac{h\nu}{c} \cos\Theta + \frac{h^2\nu^2}{c^2} = 0.$$

If the mass M of the source is sufficiently large, the last term can be neglected, and we get

$$\nu = \frac{\nu_0}{1 - \frac{v}{c}\cos\Theta}.$$

475. In the relativistic case it is meaningless to distinguish the internal energy of the source, because its variation is automatically looked after by the change in the rest mass of the source. Let the rest masses of the source before and after radiation be M and M'. The laws of conservation of momentum and energy can now be written in the form

$$\frac{Mv}{\sqrt{1-\beta^2}} = \frac{M'v'}{\sqrt{1-\beta'^2}} \cos\alpha + \frac{h\nu}{c} \cos\Theta,$$

$$0 = \frac{M'v'}{\sqrt{1-\beta'^2}} \sin\alpha - \frac{h\nu}{c} \sin\Theta,$$

$$\frac{Mc^2}{\sqrt{1-\beta^2}} = \frac{M'c^2}{\sqrt{1-\beta'^2}} + h\nu.$$

We have the additional relationship

$$(M - M')\,c^2 = h\nu_0.$$

On eliminating α, v', M' from these equations, we get

$$\frac{Mc^2\nu}{\sqrt{1-\beta^2}}(1-\beta\cos\Theta) = Mc^2\nu_0 - \frac{h\nu_0^2}{2}$$

or, on neglecting the last term:

$$\nu = \nu_0\frac{\sqrt{1-\beta^2}}{1-\beta\cos\Theta}.$$

476. When $\Theta = 0$, $\nu(0) = \nu_0\dfrac{\sqrt{1-\beta^2}}{1-\beta}$. When $\Theta = \dfrac{\pi}{2}$, $\nu\left(\dfrac{\pi}{2}\right)$ $= \nu_0\sqrt{1-\beta^2}$. If $\beta \to 1$, then $\nu(0) \gg \nu(\frac{1}{2}\pi)$. Hence it is clear that, in a narrow neighbourhood of the angle $\Theta = 0$ the frequency of the emitted light is particularly large. Let us find the angle Θ for which $\nu(\Theta) = \alpha\nu(0)$, where $\alpha < 1$. We easily obtain for this angle:

$$\cos\Theta \approx 1 - \frac{\Theta^2}{2} = \frac{1 - \dfrac{1-\beta}{\alpha}}{1-(1-\beta)} \approx 1 - \frac{1-\alpha}{\alpha}(1-\beta),$$

whence $\Theta^2 = 2(1-\alpha)(1-\beta)/\alpha$. Since $\sqrt{1-\beta^2} = mc^2/E$, where E is the total energy of the particle, we have $1-\beta \approx \frac{1}{2}(mc^2/E)^2$. This gives $\Theta = \sqrt{(1-\alpha)/\alpha}\,(mc^2/E)$. When $\alpha = \frac{1}{2}$ we get $\Theta = mc^2/E$.

477. $\Delta E = \hbar\omega = (2E/mc^2)^2\,\hbar\omega_0/(1 + 4E_0\hbar\omega_0/m^2c^4)$. If $E_0 \ll mc^2(mc^2/4\hbar\omega_0)$, then $\hbar\omega \simeq (2E/mc^2)^2\,\hbar\omega_0 \ll E_0$; in the opposite limiting case $\hbar\omega \simeq E_0$. In the example given, $\hbar\omega = 10^8$ eV.

478. Using the formula for the Doppler effect,

$$\omega_0 = \omega\sqrt{1-v^2/c^2}\,/[1+(v/c)]$$

(the photon and electron are assumed to be moving in opposite directions, the velocity of the electron being v). It follows that, in the ultra-relativistic case, $\omega_0 = \omega mc^2/2E_0$ and the condition $\hbar\omega \ll mc^2$ becomes $E_0 \ll \dfrac{(mc^2)^2}{2\hbar\omega_0}$.

479. In the case concerned the scattering cross-section of the photons by electrons is the Thomson cross-section:

$$\sigma = (8\pi/3)(e^2/mc^2)^2 = 6{\cdot}65 \times 10^{-25}\,\text{cm}^2.$$

At a collision the photon loses an average recoil energy $(E/mc^2)^2 \times \times \hbar\omega_0$. Thus

$$-\left(\frac{dE}{dt}\right)_{\text{Compton}} = \sigma\left(\frac{E}{mc^2}\right)^2 \hbar\cdot\omega_0 n_\Phi c \simeq 2\times 10^{-14} W_\Phi\left(\frac{E}{mc^2}\right)^2,$$

where n_Φ is the concentration of photons with energy $\hbar\omega_0$ and $W_\Phi = n_\Phi\cdot\hbar\omega_0$ is the radiation energy density. If W_Φ is measured in electron volts per cubic centimetre, the formula gives $-(dE/dt)_{\text{Compton}}$ in electron volts per second.

480. $E = E_0/(1 + aE_0 t), a = \sigma W_\Phi/m^2c^3 \simeq 10^{-25}\,\text{eV}^{-1}\,\text{sec}^{-1}$ (See the solution to Problem 477). In 10^6 years the electron energy diminishes by 3 per cent, and in 10^8 years it is equal to $E_0/4 = 2{\cdot}5 \times 10^9$ eV. To know the temperature of the radiation is only possible if the inequality $E_0 \ll mc^2(mc^2/\hbar\omega_0)$ be true for the majority of photons (see Problem 478).

481. On approaching the Sun the electron energy varies according to $\dfrac{1}{E(r)} - \dfrac{1}{E_0} = 4\sigma W_\Phi(r_\odot)\, r_\odot^2/m^2c^3cr$ (in this case the collisions are always head-on). Hence

$$E(r_\odot) = \frac{E_0}{1 + \dfrac{4\sigma}{m^2c^3}\, W_\Phi(r_\odot)\,\dfrac{r_\odot}{c}\, E_0}$$

and $E_0 - E(r_\odot) \simeq 10^{-2}E_0 = 10^8$ eV, since $r_\odot = 7\times 10^{10}$ cm and $W_\Phi(r_\odot) = S(r_\odot)/c = 2{\cdot}1$ erg cm^{-3} $= 1{\cdot}3 \times 10^7$ eV cm^{-3}, where $S(r_\odot) = 6{\cdot}35 \times 10^{10}$ erg cm^{-2} sec^{-1} is the flux of solar radiation at $r = r_\odot$ ($r_\odot$ is the radius of the photosphere).

482. $$\nu = \frac{\nu_0}{1 - \dfrac{vn(\nu)}{c}\cos\Theta + \dfrac{hn^2(\nu)}{2M}\dfrac{\nu}{c^2}},$$

or, neglecting the last term in the denominator,

$$\nu = \frac{\nu_0}{1 - \frac{vn(\nu)}{c} \cos \Theta}.$$

483. Using the same arguments as when solving Problem 475, we can write:

$$\frac{Mv}{\sqrt{1-\beta^2}} = \frac{M'v'}{\sqrt{1-\beta'^2}} \cos \alpha + n \frac{h\nu}{c} \cos \Theta,$$

$$0 = \frac{M'v'}{\sqrt{1-\beta'^2}} \sin \alpha - n \frac{h\nu}{c} \sin \Theta,$$

$$\frac{Mc^2}{\sqrt{1-\beta^2}} = \frac{M'c^2}{\sqrt{1-\beta'^2}} + h\nu.$$

Hence

$$\nu = \frac{(M - M')\frac{c^2}{h}\sqrt{1-\beta^2}\left(1 - \frac{M-M'}{2M}\right)}{1 - \beta n(\nu) \cos \Theta + \frac{h\nu}{2Mc^2}\sqrt{1-\beta^2}\,[n^2(\nu) - 1]}. \quad (1)$$

Two cases are possible.

1. The denominator in (1) is positive. The quantum emission $h\nu$ is now only possible on condition that $M - M' = h\nu_0/c^2 > 0$, i.e. the atom passes from a higher to a lower energy level as a result of the emission. In this case

$$\nu = \frac{\nu_0 \sqrt{1-\beta^2}\left(1 - \frac{h\nu_0}{2Mc^2}\right)}{1 - \beta n(\nu) \cos \Theta + \frac{h\nu}{2Mc^2}\sqrt{1-\beta^2}\,[n^2(\nu) - 1]}, \quad (2)$$

or, neglecting quantum corrections,

$$\nu = \frac{\nu_0\sqrt{1-\beta^2}}{1 - \beta n(\nu) \cos \Theta}. \quad (3)$$

2. The denominator in (1) is negative. Quantum emission $h\nu$ is only possible if $M' - M = h\nu_0/c^2 > 0$, i.e. as a result of the emission the atom passes to a higher energy level. The energy of the emitted quantum is taken from the kinetic energy of the emitting atom. In this case

$$\nu = \frac{\nu_0 \sqrt{1-\beta^2}\left(1 + \dfrac{h\nu_0}{2Mc^2}\right)}{\beta n(\nu)\cos\Theta - 1 - \dfrac{h\nu}{2Mc^2}\sqrt{1-\beta^2}\,[n^2(\nu) - 1]} \tag{4}$$

or, neglecting the quantum corrections,

$$\nu = \frac{\nu_0\sqrt{1-\beta^2}}{\beta n(\nu)\cos\Theta - 1}. \tag{5}$$

Let us confine ourselves for the sake of brevity to the simplified expressions (3) and (5). If $1 - \beta n(\nu) > 0$, i.e. $v < c/n(\nu)$ (the source velocity is less than the phase velocity of light in the medium), only the first case can be realised, i.e. when a photon is emitted the atom passes to a lower energy level. In particular, an unexcited atom cannot radiate in this case.

If $1 - \beta n(\nu) < 0$, i.e. $v > c/n(\nu)$ (the source velocity is greater than the phase velocity of light in the medium, and it is possible to speak of a "superlight" Doppler effect), both cases are possible. The atom passes to the lower energy level if the angle Θ at which the photon is radiated satisfies the condition $\cos\Theta < 1/\beta n(\nu)$, in other words, the radiation is directed outside the Cherenkov cone: $\cos\Theta = 1/\beta n(\nu)$. The atom passes to the higher energy level if the direction of the radiation is inside this cone. In particular, an unexcited atom can radiate in this direction. Finally, radiation is possible at the angle $\cos\Theta = 1/\beta n(\nu)$ without a quantum transition of the atom from one energy level to another.

484. In case (a) there is a narrow region around the angle Θ_0 defined by the equation $\cos\Theta_0 = 1/\beta n(\nu)$, in which the frequencies of the radiated light are very high. In case (b) there is no such angle or region.

485. $$\cos\Theta(v) = \frac{c}{n(\nu)v}\left[1 + \frac{h\nu}{2Mc^2}\sqrt{1 - \frac{v^2}{c^2}(n^2(\nu) - 1)}\right].$$

Radiation is possible if the right-hand side of this formula does not exceed unity (this condition is in practice the same as the condition obtained from interference considerations).

486. At the frequency for which the refractive index $n(\nu)$ is a maximum.

487. At the frequency $\nu = 0$. (See the answer to Problem 485.)

488. When the channel radius $a \ll \lambda$. When $a \gg \lambda$ the radiation intensity falls sharply.

489. We use the conservation laws

$$\Delta E = \hbar\omega + l\hbar\omega_0$$

$$\Delta \boldsymbol{p} = \left(\frac{\hbar\omega}{c}\right)\sqrt{\varepsilon_0}\,\frac{\boldsymbol{k}}{k} + l\hbar\boldsymbol{k}_0$$

where ΔE is the energy reduction, and $\Delta \boldsymbol{p}$ is the reduction in the particle momentum. They are connected by $\Delta E = (\boldsymbol{v} \cdot \Delta \boldsymbol{p})$ Using this, we obtain:

(a) when $l = 0$, $\cos\vartheta = c/\sqrt{\varepsilon_0}\, v$ (the Cherenkov radiation condition),

(b) when $l \neq 0$, $\omega = l[\boldsymbol{k}_0 \cdot \boldsymbol{v}) - \omega_0]/[1 - (v/c)\sqrt{\varepsilon_0}\cos\vartheta]$, where ϑ is the angle between $\boldsymbol{k}$ and $\boldsymbol{v}$.

The frequency ω is always positive, which introduces the usual restrictions. The values $l < 0$ correspond to a reduction (and not an increase, as in the case $l > 0$) in the energy of the medium.

490. It is possible, but only if the medium is non-linear and the Cherenkov condition $c/n(\omega)v \leqslant 1$ is satisfied, where the role of the velocity v is played by the group velocity of propagation of the electromagnetic field exciting the Cherenkov radiation with frequency ω (the simplest picture is obtained when the exciting field is the field of a wave packet, moving with the group velocity v; in this case, when account is taken of the non-linearity of the medium, an excitation travels in it with velocity v, leading to Cherenkov radiation of waves with frequencies satisfying the condition $\cos\vartheta = c/n(\omega)\,v \leqslant 1$. There is no radiation without nonlinearity, as is clear from the fact that the principle of superposition holds (see also Problem 491).

491. From the conservation laws,

$$\omega_0 = \omega + \Omega, \quad \boldsymbol{k}_0 = \boldsymbol{k} + \boldsymbol{K},$$

it follows that

$$\cos\vartheta = \frac{\omega_0^2 n_0^2 - \omega^2 n^2 + \Omega^2 N^2}{2\omega_0 \Omega n_0 N},$$

where ϑ is the angle between the vectors $\boldsymbol{k}_0$ and $\boldsymbol{K}$, ω and $\boldsymbol{k}$ are the frequency and wave vector of the scattered X-ray quantum, n_0, n and N are the refractive indices of the initial and scattered X-ray quanta and the optical photon respectively. If the medium is anisotropic, $N = N(\Omega, \boldsymbol{K}/K)$ can take two values, corresponding to the two possible polarisations of the photon. The probability of Raman scattering, which has not yet been observed, is very small even in an anisotropic medium, and it is generally practically zero in an optically isotropic medium. If we neglect the square of the frequency Ω, we have

$$\cos\vartheta = \frac{1}{N}\,\frac{d(\omega n)}{d\omega} = \frac{c}{N(\Omega)\, v_{gr}(\omega_0)},$$

where $v_{gr}(\omega_0) = c/(d(n\omega)/d\omega)$ is the group velocity of the radiation with frequency ω_0. It is clear from this last expression for $\cos\vartheta$ that we can speak here of Cherenkov radiation (see also Problem 490).

492*. We seek (e.g. graphically) the points of intersection of the curve $n^2\cos^2\vartheta = \varepsilon_\perp|\varepsilon_\parallel|\cos^2\vartheta/(-\varepsilon_\perp\sin^2\vartheta + |\varepsilon_\parallel|\cos^2\vartheta)$ with the straight line $1/\beta^2 = c^2/v^2$ in case (1), with the straight line $(1/\beta^2) \times (1-(\Omega/\omega))^2 = c^2/v^2 (\Omega/\omega \leqslant 1)$ in case (2a), and with the straight line $(1/\beta^2)(1+(\Omega/\omega))^2 = c^2/v^2$ in case (2b). If there are points of intersection, radiation of the given type exists; if there are none, there is no radiation. The answers are:

(1) $\beta^2\varepsilon_\perp < 1$,

(2) (a) $(1/\beta^2)(1-(\Omega/\omega))^2 > \varepsilon_\perp$,

(b) $(1/\beta^2)(1+(\Omega/\omega))^2 > \varepsilon_\perp$,

(3) $(1+(\Omega/\omega))^2 > \beta^2\varepsilon_\perp > 1$.

* See also Problem 483.

493. The atom is ionised. The fact is that, when n = const, there is a finite probability of radiation inside the Cherekov cone, with the atom passing to a higher energy level (see Problems 483 and 488). Transitions in the reverse direction are also possible. In the case of an infinite channel length, however, the atom passes to a higher energy state in the long run, i.e. it is ionised.

494. $$\Delta\lambda = \frac{2h}{mc}\sin^2\frac{\varphi}{2} = \frac{h}{mc} = 0{\cdot}02426\,\text{Å}.$$

495. $$\tan\vartheta = \frac{mc^2}{mc^2 + h\nu}\cot\frac{\varphi}{2}.$$

496. $$E = 2h\nu\frac{h\nu\sin^2\dfrac{\varphi}{2}}{mc^2 + 2h\nu\sin^2\dfrac{\varphi}{2}} = h\nu\frac{h\nu}{mc^2 + h\nu}.$$

497. $\Delta\lambda_{max} = 2\lambda_{Compton}(m/M) = 2{\cdot}64 \times 10^{-5}$ Å, where $\lambda_{Compton}$ is the Compton wavelength for the electron, M and m are the masses of the proton and electron.

498. $\Delta\lambda = h/2Mc = 0{\cdot}66 \times 10^{-5}$ Å (M is the mass of the nucleus).

499. About 450 sec.

500. $t \approx 2$ hr.

501. $\Delta\nu = -\nu\gamma M/Rc^2$, where γ is the gravitational constant, M is the mass of the star and R is its radius.

502. $$\Delta\lambda = \lambda\frac{\gamma M}{Rc^2} = 0{\cdot}012\,\text{Å}.$$

503. $\Delta\lambda/\lambda \simeq \gamma M/c^2 r_0 \simeq 0{\cdot}075$, where γ is the gravitational constant, and $r_0 \simeq 2 \times 10^6$ cm is the radius of the star.

504. $\Delta\varphi = 2\gamma M/Rc^2$, where R is the distance of the light ray from the centre of the Sun. According to the general theory of relativity, the effect must be twice as great. If the ray passes close to the edge of the sun (R is the Sun's radius), then $2\Delta\varphi = 4\gamma M/Rc^2 = 1{\cdot}75''$.

505. $E = h\nu_{ac}$, $p = h\nu_{ac}/v_{ac}$.

506. The scattering of light is a process of absorption or emission of a phonon by a photon. Using the laws of conservation of energy and momentum, we can write for such a process:

$$h\nu' = h\nu \pm h\nu_{ac},$$

$$\frac{nh\nu'}{c}\cos\vartheta = \frac{nh\nu}{c} \pm \frac{h\nu_{ac}}{v_{ac}}\cos\alpha,$$

$$\frac{nh\nu'}{c}\sin\vartheta = \pm\frac{h\nu_{ac}}{v_{ac}}\sin\alpha,$$

where ϑ is the angle between the directions of motion of the incident and scattered photons; α is the angle between the directions of motion of the incident photon and the corresponding phonon. The plus sign refers to absorption, the minus sign to emission of a phonon. Planck's constant falls out of the equations, which indicates the possibility of a classical interpretation of the phenomenon. The elimination of α and ν' leads to a quadratic equation in ν_{ac}:

$$\left(\frac{1}{v_{ac}^2} - \frac{n^2}{c^2}\right)\nu_{ac}^2 \pm \frac{4n^2\nu\nu_{ac}}{c^2}\sin^2\frac{\vartheta}{2} - \frac{4n^2\nu^2}{c^2}\sin^2\frac{\vartheta}{2} = 0.$$

On neglecting the second term by comparison with the last, and neglecting n^2/c^2 by comparison with $1/v_{ac}^2$, we get

$$\nu_{ac} = \frac{2n\nu}{c}v_{ac}\sin\frac{\vartheta}{2}.$$

507. $\lambda = \dfrac{h}{mv} = \sqrt{\dfrac{150}{V}}\,10^{-8}$ cm, where V is the energy in volts,

$\lambda_1 = 12{\cdot}2$ Å, $\lambda_2 = 0{\cdot}122$ Å, $\lambda_3 = 0{\cdot}039$ Å.

508. $\lambda = \sqrt{\dfrac{150}{V}}\,\dfrac{1}{\sqrt{1 + 9{\cdot}78 \times 10^{-7}\,V}}$ where V is in volts, λ in Ångströms; $\lambda_1 = 0{\cdot}037$ Å, $\lambda_2 = 12{\cdot}35 \times 10^{-7}$ Å, $\lambda_3 = 12{\cdot}35 \times 10^{-13}$ Å.

509. We obtain for hydrogen: $\lambda_1 = 0{\cdot}284\,\text{Å}$, $\lambda_2 = 2{\cdot}84 \times 10^{-4}\,\text{Å}$, $\lambda_3 = 1{\cdot}51\,\text{Å}$; we obtain for mercury: $\lambda_1 = 0{\cdot}02\,\text{Å}$, $\lambda_2 = 2 \times 10^{-5}\,\text{Å}$, $\lambda_3 = 0{\cdot}107\,\text{Å}$.

510. $\mu = \dfrac{\lambda_0}{\lambda'} = \sqrt{\dfrac{E + U_0}{E}} = \sqrt{1 + \dfrac{V_0}{V}}$ (E and V are respectively the electron energy *in vacuo* and the potential difference corresponding to it).

512. $2d\sqrt{\mu^2 - \cos^2\vartheta} = n\lambda_0$, where λ_0 is the wavelength *in vacuo*, μ is the refractive index, ϑ is the glancing angle.

513. $V_0 = \dfrac{150}{4a^2}m^2 - V\sin^2\vartheta = 15\,\text{V}$, where V is in volts, a in Ångströms, m the order of the reflexion.

514. $a(\cos\alpha - \cos\alpha_0) = h\sqrt{\dfrac{150}{V}}$,

$$a(\cos\beta - \cos\beta_0) = k\sqrt{\frac{150}{V}},$$

$$a\left\{\sqrt{\cos^2\gamma + \frac{V_0}{V}} - \sqrt{\cos^2\gamma_0 + \frac{V_0}{V}}\right\} = l\sqrt{\frac{150}{V}},$$

where V is in volts, a in Ångströms, γ_0 and γ are the angles between the normals to the incident and diffracted waves (*in vacuo*) and the normal to the crystal surface.

515. $w = \dfrac{v}{2} + \dfrac{\text{const}}{v}$; $\quad h\nu = \frac{1}{2}mv^2 + \text{const}.$

By Rayleigh's formula, the group velocity $u = w - \lambda\, dw/d\lambda$. On putting here $\lambda = h/p = h/mv$, $u = v$ and considering the motion with non-relativistic velocities ($m = \text{const}$), we get

$$v = w + v\frac{dw}{dv} = \frac{d}{dv}(wv),$$

whence

$$wv = \frac{v^2}{2} + \text{const}; \quad w = \frac{v}{2} + \frac{\text{const}}{v}.$$

Further,

$$\nu = \frac{w}{\lambda} = \frac{\dfrac{v}{2} + \dfrac{\text{const}}{v}}{\dfrac{h}{mv}} = \frac{\dfrac{mv^2}{2} + \text{const}}{h}.$$

The arbitrary constants in the expressions for v and w play no part in any phenomena. They can be put equal to zero.

Obviously, the solution can be extended to motion with relativistic velocities (when m depends on v). In this case, if we neglect the constants of integration that play no part, the formulae become

$$w = \frac{c^2}{v}; \; mc^2 = \frac{m_0 c^2}{\sqrt{1 - \dfrac{v^2}{c^2}}} = h\nu.$$

516. We take the optical axis of the microscope as the y axis and take the x axis perpendicular to it. The electron momentum changes as a result of the Compton effect:

$$\Delta p_x = \frac{h\nu}{c} \sin\alpha, \Delta p_y = \frac{h\nu}{c} \cos\alpha,$$

where α is the aperture; the values given represent upper limits for Δp_x and Δp_y.

517. $\Delta x > \dfrac{\lambda}{\sin\alpha}$, $\quad \Delta p_x \Delta x > h$.

518. Δx is of the order d, Δp_x of the order $(h/\lambda)\sin\alpha$, where $\sin\alpha \approx \lambda/d$. Hence $\Delta p_x \Delta x$ is of the order h.

519. $\Delta v_{sph} \approx 6{\cdot}62 \times 10^{-25}$ cm sec^{-1}, $\Delta v_{el} = 7{\cdot}3 \times 10^{2}$ cm sec^{-1}.

520. $\Delta x \approx 10^{-8}$ cm, $\Delta v > 7 \times 10^{8}$ cm sec^{-1}.

521. In the stationary state the quantum mechanical averages of the kinetic and potential energies of the system are connected by

$$\bar{T} + \bar{U} = E,$$

where E is the total energy of the system.

In the case of a diatomic molecule (neglecting its rotation),

$$\bar{T} = \frac{\overline{p^2}}{2\mu}, \quad \bar{U} = \frac{1}{2}\mu\omega_0^2\overline{x^2},$$

where, by virtue of the Heisenberg relation,

$$\overline{p^2} \cdot \overline{x^2} \geqslant \frac{\hbar^2}{4}.$$

Hence

$$\frac{1}{2}\mu\omega_0^2\overline{x^2} + \frac{\hbar^2}{8\mu\overline{x^2}} \leqslant E.$$

The left-hand side has a minimum for $\overline{x^2} = \hbar/2\mu\omega_0$. Consequently,

$$E \geqslant \tfrac{1}{2}\hbar\omega_0.$$

If we assume that the minimum is reached (this can be proved by solving Schrödinger's equation) in the ground state, we have for this state:

$$E = \frac{1}{2}\hbar\omega_0, \quad \overline{x^2} = \frac{\hbar}{2\mu\omega_0}.$$

The molecular size $\approx\sqrt{\hbar/2\mu\omega_0}$.

A similar argument cannot be used with the same degree of precision in the case of a hydrogen atom. In this case

$$\bar{U} = -e^2\overline{(1/r)}.$$

If the atom is in the s-state, then

$$T = \frac{\overline{p^2}}{2\mu}, \quad \overline{p^2}\overline{r^2} \geqslant \frac{\hbar^2}{4}.$$

To order of magnitude,

$$\bar{r} \approx \sqrt{\overline{r^2}}, \quad \overline{(1/r)} \approx 1/\bar{r}.$$

Hence

$$E \gtrsim \frac{\hbar^2}{8\mu(\bar{r})^2} - \frac{e^2}{\bar{r}}.$$

The right-hand side has a minimum for

$$\bar{r} = \frac{\hbar^2}{4\mu e^2},$$

which determines the order of magnitude of the hydrogen atom diameter in the fundamental state. The corresponding energy is

$$E \gtrsim -\frac{2\mu e^4}{\hbar^2}.$$

522. $\nu = \dfrac{1}{2\pi}\sqrt{\dfrac{4\pi n e^2}{m}} \approx 2{\cdot}6 \times 10^{15}\ \text{sec}^{-1}$,

$$E = h\nu \approx 1{\cdot}7 \times 10^{-11}\ \text{erg} \approx 10{\cdot}8\ \text{eV}.$$

Here e and m are the charge and mass of an electron, $n \approx 8{\cdot}4 \times 10^{22}$ is the number of atoms per cubic centimetre of copper.

§ 11. Nuclear Physics

523. $m = \mu \dfrac{pV}{RT} \approx 0{\cdot}2$ g.

524. $T_2 = T_1 K^{1-\gamma} \approx 268\,°\text{K}$, $t_2 = -5\,°\text{C}$.

525. By definition, $S = \varrho_1/\varrho_2$, where $\varrho_1 = m_1/V_1$, $\varrho_2 = m_2/V_2$. Here m_1 is the mass of vapour saturating the compressed volume V_1 of the chamber at the temperature T_1, and m_2 is the mass of vapour saturating the expanded volume V_2 of the chamber at the temperature T_2. Hence $S = m_1V_2/m_2V_1$. From the perfect gas law for the vapour before and after expansion of the chamber:

$$p_1V_1 = \frac{m_1}{\mu}RT_1, \quad p_2V_2 = \frac{m_2}{\mu}RT_2.$$

The second of these equations refers to the case when the excess vapour is condensed, where we have neglected as insignificant the temperature rise due to condensation. We find from these equations, using the equation of the adiabat $T_1 V_1^{\gamma-1} = T_2 V_2^{\gamma-1}$:

$$S = \frac{p_1}{p_2}\left(\frac{V_1}{V_2}\right)^{\gamma-1} = \frac{p_1}{p_2} k^{1-\gamma}.$$

526. For water (1) 2·9, (2) 3·0; for alcohol (1) 1·7, (2) 2·7.

527. $S = 6{\cdot}8$.

528. $R_{cr} = 2\sigma/(p_v - p_l) \approx 4 \times 10^{-7}$ cm. We have neglected the dependence of the saturated vapour pressure on the surface curvature. This is easily shown to be permissible.

529. The energy E of the δ-electron must be not less than the energy of formation of the bubble with radius R_{cr} (see the previous problem). The latter energy is made up of the surface energy of the bubble and the heat of vaporisation of the liquid in the bubble. Hence

$$E \geqslant 4\pi\sigma R_{cr}^2 + \frac{4\pi}{3} R_{cr}^3 nq \approx 196 \text{ eV},$$

since the number of moles per unit volume of vapour at the pressure p_v and the critical radius are respectively equal to $n = p_v/RT = 5{\cdot}4 \times 10^{-4}$, $R_{cr} = 2\sigma/(p_v - p_l) = 9 \times 10^{-7}$ cm.

530. 10^{-7}.

532. The γ-quanta have moved upwards. Two pairs (electron and positron) produced by the γ-quanta are clearly visible on the photograph.

533. The single "heavy" track on one of the photographs belongs to the ${}_2He^3$ nucleus formed as a result of the reaction

$$\gamma + {}_2He^4 \rightarrow {}_2He^3 + {}_0n^1.$$

On the other photograph the reaction

$$\gamma + {}_2He^4 \rightarrow {}_1p^1 + {}_1T^3,$$

is recorded, where the "heavier" track corresponds to the triton and the thin track to the proton.

534. The central track is due to a meson. In fact, it cannot be the track of an electron since the energy of the particle producing it is greater than the energy of the electrons, and the track thickness is wider. Neither can it be the track of a proton, since it is clear from the photograph that the track bends slightly in the magnetic field of the chamber, so that its energy cannot be very large. The track of a proton would be much thicker at small energies.

535. About 76,000 photographs.

536. The number of fissions $n = n_C n_{ph} \sigma$, where n_C is the number of carbon nuclei in the propane irradiated by the flux of photons from n_{ph} effective quanta. This gives:

$$\sigma = \frac{n}{n_C n_{ph}} = 4{\cdot}4 \times 10^{-28} \text{ cm}^2.$$

537. $E \approx 600$ MeV.

538. $E_{tot} = Mc^2 \sqrt{1 + \left(\frac{eH\varrho}{Mc^2}\right)^2} = 1120$ MeV.

$E_{kin} = E_{tot} - Mc^2 = 178$ MeV, where M is the mass of a proton, e is its charge, c is the velocity of light, $\varrho = a^2/8h$ is the radius of curvature of the track.

539. The mass of a meson in units of the electron mass (m_e) is 200. In the other cases: (1) 230 m_e, (2) 210 m_e, (3) 230 m_e, (4) 184 m_e.

540. (1) 204 m_e, (2) 350 m_e, (3) 184 m_e, (4) 220 m_e.

541. (1) 161 m_e, (2) 250 m_e, (3) 226 m_e.

542. (a) The ionisation losses of the particle increase as its velocity falls. The number of grains per unit length of track therefore increase in the direction of motion of the particle.

(b) At equal velocities, the specific losses for protons, deuterons and α-particles are in the ratio $1:1:4$, and at equal energies, in the ration $1:2:16$.

(c) $\approx 1:1{\cdot}5:4$. The grain densities are much less distinct, which makes it difficult to distinguish one of the charged particles after they have travelled equal distances.

543. (a) The fact that the grain densities are equal indicates that the particle velocities are equal (see Problem 542). It follows from the given formula that the residual paths of single-charged particles with equal velocities are in the ratio of the masses of the particles, i.e. $R_p : R_d : R_t = 1:2:3$. Obviously, $E_p : E_d : E_t = 1:2:3$.

(b) If the particles denoted by the subscripts a and b have the same velocities, it follows from the formula in the text of the problem that

$$R_b(E) = \left(\frac{Z_a}{Z_b}\right)^2 \left(\frac{M_b}{M_a}\right) R_a\left(\frac{M_a}{M_b}E\right).$$

This relationship is accurate for particles with equal charges. (In the case of particles with different charges, it will remain accurate if Z_a, Z_b are replaced by certain effective charges.) Using this relationship and knowing $R_a = f(E)$ for a particle with mass M_a, we can easily obtain $R_b = f(E)$ for the particle with mass M_b. The results for tritons are given in Table IV (page 235).

(c) We have to determine the number N of grains on the same section τ of track segment in the emulsion; we then find the range from $N = f(R)$, and from $E = f(R)$ the energy of the proton which corresponds to the same grain density. Given the same grain density (equal velocity) the deuteron and triton energies will be respectively 2 and 3 times the proton energy.

544. After measuring the number N of grains on successive sections (τ) of track, find the relationship $N = f(R)$ for each particle. Different residual ranges R_i of particles will correspond to an equal number of grains and equal velocities.

Determine the mean multiple scattering angle for the ith track at a distance R_i from the end of the track. Since the particle velocities are equal at these points, the ratio of scattering angles is equal to the inverse ratio of the masses.

545. Slow π^--mesons in the field of the nucleus occupy a Bohr orbit and, on interacting with the nucleus, are absorbed by it. Fission of the nucleus then occurs. In photographic emulsions, the track of a meson terminates in a star in the majority of cases (see Photographs VIII, X, XI). It must be borne in mind, however, that in emulsions, absorption of π^--mesons leads in about 30 per cent of cases to the emission of only neutral particles.

A slow π^+-meson disintegrates into a μ^+-meson with an energy of 4·1 MeV and a neutrino. The μ^+-meson disintegrates in turn into an electron and two neutrinos. Thus, in electron-sensitive photographic emulsions, a μ^+-meson track of definite length ($\approx 600\,\mu$) is observed at the end of the range of a π^+-meson, and an electron track at the end of the μ^+-meson track (see Photograph VI).

546. Two stars are shown on Photograph VII, corresponding to the reaction

$$C_6^{12} + \gamma \rightarrow He_2^4 + He_2^4 + He_2^4.$$

None of the other nuclei of the emulsion can provide a splitting into three like particles.

(a) The energy of particle 3 can be found from the law of conservation of momentum: $\boldsymbol{P}_3 = \boldsymbol{P}_1 + \boldsymbol{P}_2$. If $E_1 = E_2$, it follows that $E_3 = 2E_1(1 + \cos\alpha)$. We find from Table VI that the range $R = 15{\cdot}3\,\mu$ corresponds to an α-particle energy of 4 MeV. This gives $E_3 \approx 10$ MeV. The energy of the γ-quantum is $E_\gamma = E_1 + E_2 + E_3 + E_b'$. The binding energy E_b' is equal to the difference in mass between the initial and final states and in our case amounts to approx. 7·3 MeV. Consequently $E_\gamma \approx 25{\cdot}3$ MeV.

(b) If the reaction proceeds in two stages, the emission of the α-particle leads to the formation of a beryllium nucleus. This nucleus is unstable in the ground state and splits up into two α-particles. The excited state Be^8 is also well known, with an excitation energy $\approx 2{\cdot}9$ MeV. If we obtain this excitation energy as a result of the calculation, our assumption of a fission process $C^{12}(\gamma, 3\alpha)$ will thereby be proved. The general expression for the excitation energy of a nucleus splitting into two particles 1 and 2 is

$$E^*_{(1+2)} = E_1 + E_2 - E_3 \frac{m_3}{m_1 + m_2} + E_b'',$$

where m_1, m_2, m_3 are the masses of the particles, and E_b'' is the binding energy of the intermediate nucleus, equal to the difference in mass between this nucleus and the fission particles. It is obtained from the following relationships:

$$E^*_{(1+2)} = T_{(1+2)} + E_b'', \quad T_{(1+2)} = E_1^c + E_2^c,$$

$$E_\gamma + E_b' = E_3 + T_{(1+2)} + E^k_{(1+2)}, \quad E_\gamma - E_b' = E_1 + E_2 + E_3,$$

where E_1^c and E_2^c are the energies of particles 1 and 2 in the centre of mass system of the intermediate nucleus, $E^k_{(1+2)}$ is the kinetic energy of the intermediate nucleus. On observing that $\boldsymbol{P}_3 = \boldsymbol{P}_{(1+2)}$ i.e. $E^k_{(1+2)} = E_3 m_3/(m_1 + m_2)$, the relationship in question is easily obtained.) For Be^8, $E_b'' = -0{\cdot}1$ MeV, so that $E^*_{Be^8} \approx 2{\cdot}9$ MeV. The fission process $C^{12}(\gamma, 3\alpha)$ thus in fact proceeds with the formation of an intermediate Be^8 nucleus in the excited state with energy $\approx 2{\cdot}9$ MeV.

547. (a) Track 1 is due to a π^--meson (see Problem 545). Since photofission of deuterium takes place, the total charge of the two other particles must be equal to $+2e$, whilst their total mass is two atomic units of mass. Given the γ-quanta energies mentioned in the problem, we can only expect a reaction of the type

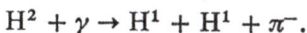

$$H^2 + \gamma \rightarrow H^1 + H^1 + \pi^-.$$

(b) Let the nucleus of mass m_3, at which scattering has occurred, have been initially at rest. Let E_3 be the energy of the nucleus, and E_2 the energy of the particle of mass m_2 after scattering. It follows from the law of conservation of momentum that

$$\cos\vartheta = \frac{E_3(m_2 - m_3)}{2\sqrt{m_2 m_3 E_2 E_3}},$$

where ϑ is the angle between the directions of motion of the scattered particles; $\vartheta = 90°$ for $m_2 = m_3$. This condition is satisfied by proton scattering by hydrogen and deuteron scattering by the deuterium with which the emulsion is filled. The latter is excluded, however, since deterons are not emitted in the reaction in question. In the case of proton scattering by deuterium with $E_3 = 2E_2, \vartheta = 120°$.

548. (a) $Li_3^8 \rightarrow e^- + \nu + Be_4^{8*}$; $Be_4^{8*} \rightarrow He_2^4 + He_2^4$.

Emission by the Li_3^8 nucleus of an electron and neutrino has occurred. A Be^8 nucleus in the excited state has been formed, and this has split into two α-particles. The "hammer" track could also have been produced by the process

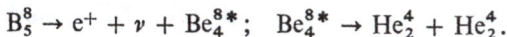

$$B_5^8 \rightarrow e^+ + \nu + Be_4^{8*};\quad Be_4^{8*} \rightarrow He_2^4 + He_2^4.$$

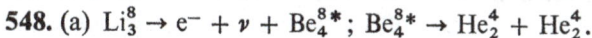

(b) Since decay of Li_3^8 has occurred at the end of the range, the maximum kinetic energy of the electron can be calculated from the difference in mass between the initial and final states, whilst taking into account the energy loss in excitation of the Be^8:

$$\Delta m = (m_{Li} + 3m_e) - [(m_{Be} + 4m_e) + m_e] + m_e \approx 16 \text{ MeV},$$

where m_{Li} and m_{Be} are the masses of the nuclei. The masses of the atoms are usually given in tables. The last term is equal to the number of orbital electrons in the initial and final states. Since the two α-particles travel in opposite directions, the kinetic energy of the Be^8 can be assumed zero, and the excitation energy of the Be^8 equal to $E^*_{Be} = E_{\alpha_1} + E_{\alpha_2} + E''_b \approx 2{\cdot}9$ MeV. Then $(E_{e^-})_{max} \approx 13{\cdot}1$ MeV. In 90 per cent of cases the decay of Li^8 proceeds to the 2·9 MeV Be^8 level.

549. The star on Photograph X is produced by the reaction

$$Be_4^9 + \pi^- \rightarrow Li_3^8 + n_0^1.$$

The rest energy of a π^--meson is 139·6 MeV. The binding energy, determined by the difference in mass, is 18·2 MeV. The energy E_0 distributed between the reaction products is 121·4 MeV. The laws of conservation of momentum and energy are

$$\frac{E_{Li}}{E_n^1} = \frac{m_n^1}{m_{Li}}, \quad E_0 = E_{Li} + E_{n'}.$$

In the non-relativistic approximation, the neutron energy is 108 MeV, the lithium energy 13·4 MeV.

550. (a) Neutrons with thermal velocities are regarded as slow in neutron physics. The neutron energy and momentum can therefore be neglected in the reactions in question. The stars mentioned in the problem will consist of two particle tracks in opposite directions. The particle energies can be found from the conservation laws. The energy distributed between the particles will be equal to the difference in mass between the initial and final states. In the case of the second reaction part of this energy goes into excitation of the Li^7.

First reaction: $E_0 = \Delta m = 4{\cdot}65$ MeV, $E_\alpha = 1{\cdot}98$ MeV, $E_{H^3} = 2{\cdot}66$ MeV, $R_\alpha + R_{H^3} \approx 42\ \mu$.

Second reaction: $E_0 = \Delta m = 2{\cdot}87$ MeV, $E_\alpha = 1{\cdot}51$ MeV, $E_{Li} = 0{\cdot}86$ MeV.

(b) The fast neutrons are scattered in the emulsion by hydrogen. It easily follows from the law of conservation of momentum (see the equation in the answer to Problem 547) that $E_n = E_p/\cos^2\beta$, where β is the angle between the directions of motion of the proton and neutron. In order to find the neutron energy, we have to measure the angle β and the range of the proton.

551. The K-meson splits into two π^+-mesons and one π^--meson. The charge of the K-meson is positive. On expressing the masses in energy units, we can write

$$m_K = 3m_\pi + E_{\pi_1} + E_{\pi_2} + E_{\pi_3} = 490{\cdot}3 \pm 3{\cdot}2 \text{ MeV}.$$

No account is taken of the error in determining the masses of the π-mesons. In atomic units of mass $m_K = (960 \pm 6{\cdot}3)m_e$. (According to recent data the mass of a K^+-meson is $493{\cdot}98 \pm 0{\cdot}14$ MeV.)

552. $4{\cdot}2 \times 10^{-14}$ amps.

553. The change in the collector potential is $\Delta V = Q/C$; the charge collected on it is $Q = \Delta V \cdot C = 2 \times 10^{-12}$ coulomb. The number of ion pairs produced in the chamber by the cosmic particles is $N = Q/e = 1{\cdot}25 \times 10^7$. The mean free path of the cosmic particles in the chamber is $2\pi/d$, where d is the chamber diameter. Thus one particle produces on the average 306 ion pairs. Consequently $1{\cdot}25 \times 10^7/306 = 4{\cdot}1 \times 10^4$ particles have passed through the chamber.

554. $$d_{\text{eff}} = \frac{d}{\overline{\cos\vartheta}}; \quad \overline{\cos\vartheta} = \frac{\int_0^{\pi/2} \cos\vartheta \sin\vartheta \, d\vartheta}{\int_0^{\pi/2} \sin\vartheta \, d\vartheta} = \frac{1}{2}; \quad d_{\text{eff}} = 2d.$$

555. $6{\cdot}1 \times 10^7$ ion pairs per second.

556. We obtain from the equation for I/I_{sat} : $0{\cdot}35r = \ln(1 + 0{\cdot}36r)$. By solving this equation graphically, we get $r = 0{\cdot}18$ roentgen. The maximum intensity measured by the chamber in the conditions given is about 3·1 roentgen.

557. 4·2 hr.

558. 2°·7.

559. $0{\cdot}8 \times 10^7$.

560. $\dfrac{E}{p} = \dfrac{E_p}{C} = 70$ eV.

561. $5{\cdot}6 \times 10^4$ photons.

562. Since the charged particle recording efficiency is 100 per cent, the scintillation counter must record every γ-quantum absorbed or (non-elastically) scattered in the counter. We easily obtain from this, for the counter efficiency required: $f = 1 - e^{-\mu d}$, where μ is the γ-quanta absorption coefficient in the crystal, and d is its thickness.

563. $N_\gamma = N/f \approx 18\,\gamma$-quanta per second. Here, N is the number of light pulses per second. The expression for f is given in the answer to the previous problem.

564. $V = \dfrac{Mne}{C} \approx 16$ V.

565. 40 V.

566. About 140 keV.

567. $0{\cdot}16 \times 10^{-9}$ amps.

568. $$V = V_a \ln \frac{\dfrac{r_k}{r_a}}{\ln \dfrac{r_a + \dfrac{\lambda_0}{p}}{r_a}} = 410 \text{ V}.$$

569. (a) The voltage pulse amplitude in the proportional counter is $V = QA/C$. Knowing the α-particle energy and the mean energy of formation of ion pairs, we can find the mean number of ion pairs formed by the α-particle over its complete range, and then per centimetre path of the α-particle. The latter number is $7{\cdot}3 \times 10^4$. Knowing the average path, traversed by the α-particle in the counter, we easily find that the mean number of ion pairs produced by the α-particle when it passes through the counter is $1{\cdot}1 \times 10^5$. The corresponding voltage pulse amplitude is 1·63 V.

(b) $1{\cdot}7 \times 10^{-3}$ V.

570. If the number of particles recorded by the counter is n, and its resolving time is τ, in a time $n\tau$ the counter will fail to record one of the particles entering it. The number of particles passing through the counter in this time is $Nn\tau$. Hence the total number of particles passing through the counter in unit time is $N = n + Nn\tau$, i.e. the sum of the recorded and the non-recorded particles. We thus obtain for the resolving time: $\tau = (N - n)/Nn$.

571. $$\tau = \frac{1}{n_{12}}\left[1 - \sqrt{1 - \frac{n_{12}(n_1 + n_2 - n_{12})}{n_1 n_2}}\right] = 2{\cdot}3 \times 10^{-4}\,\text{sec.}$$

572. $N = 1250$ pulse sec^{-1}.

573. Since the resolving time of the photomultiplier is less than the resolving time of the crystal, the photomultiplier records all the particles recorded by the crystal. Hence the number of recorded particles is determined solely by the de-excitation time of stilbene: $n = N/(1 + N\tau) = 3{\cdot}7 \times 10^7$ pulse sec^{-1}.

574. The number of particles recorded by the counter is $n_1 = N/(1 + N\tau_1)$. The number of counter pulses recorded by the recording device is

$$n = \frac{n_1}{1 + n_1\tau_2} = \frac{N}{1 + N(\tau_1 + \tau_2)} = 2{\cdot}1 \times 10^3 \text{ pulse sec}^{-1}.$$

575. The number of random coincidences is $\omega = 2\tau n_1 n_2$. The factor 2 is due to the fact that the discharge in the second counter may either precede or follow the discharge in the first counter within the interval τ sec.

576. The number of coincidences is $\omega = 2\tau n^2$, whence $n = 10^6$ particles.

577. The passage through the counter of a cosmic particle producing "background" can be regarded as a random event. We know that, if the probability of an event is proportional to the time during which this event is observed, the mean deviation $D = \sqrt{(n - \bar{n})^2} = \sqrt{n}$, where n is the observed number of events, and $\bar{n}$ is the true mean value of the number of events. If two independent events are observed, then $D_{12} = \sqrt{D_1^2 + D_2^2}$.

The relative error is equal to $\sqrt{D_1^2 + D_2^2}/n$. In our case $D_1^2 = n$ and $D_2^2 = 8n$. The relative error is therefore $3/\sqrt{n}$. We find from this that n must be not less than 900.

578. $5\frac{3}{4}$ min.

579. The measurement time in the first case (without using the coincidence circuit) is 67 min, and in the second case 10 sec.

580. $\nu = \dfrac{2mc^2}{h} = 2{\cdot}47 \times 10^{20}\ \text{sec}^{-1}, \quad \varepsilon = 1{\cdot}02\ \text{MeV}.$

581. (a) $E_{max} \leqslant E - 2mc^2 \approx 149$ MeV.

(b) $E_{max} \leqslant E - mc^2 \approx 79{\cdot}5$ MeV.

582. $v = c\sqrt{1 - \left(\dfrac{1}{1 + \dfrac{E}{mc^2}}\right)^2}$. For a positron, $v = 2{\cdot}82 \times 10^{10}$ cm sec^{-1}. In the case of α-particles and protons, $E \ll mc^2$, and we can use the approximate formula $v = \sqrt{2E/m}$. For a proton, $v \approx 1{\cdot}4 \times 10^9$ cm sec^{-1}. For an α-particle, $v \approx 7 \times 10^8$ cm sec^{-1}.

583. $V = \dfrac{m}{M}v = 2{\cdot}7 \times 10^7$ cm sec^{-1}. Here, m is the mass of an α-particle, v its velocity, M the mass of the RaB nucleus.

584. 10^9 erg · hour^{-1}. (See Hints on page 226.)

585. $Q = N\dfrac{mv^2}{2}\left(1 + \dfrac{m}{M}\right) = 24{\cdot}5$ cal hr^{-1}. Here, N is the number of disintegrations per hour, m and M are the masses of the α-particle and the recoil nucleus.

586. If W is the electron kinetic energy, then $dW/dt = (e\dot{\Phi}(R)/c) \times \times (\omega/2\pi)$, where $\omega = ecH(R)/E$ is the cyclotron frequency for the electron, and E is the total energy. The radius of the electron orbit in the magnetic field is $R = mcv/eH = E\beta/eH(R)$. We differentiate R:

$$\frac{dR}{dt} = \frac{R}{E\beta^2}\frac{dE}{dt} - R\left(\frac{\dot{H}}{H} + \frac{\partial H}{\partial R}\dot{R}\right).$$

On introducing the notation $n = -(R/H)\,\partial H/\partial R$ and recalling that $dE/dt = dW/dt$, we find after simple working that

$$\frac{(1-n)}{R}\frac{dR}{dt} = \frac{\dot{H}}{H}\left(\frac{\dot{\Phi}(R)}{2\pi R^2 \dot{H}} - 1\right).$$

The dot here denotes partial differentiation with respect to time.

587. A discussion of dynamic stability can be reduced to a statical problem by passing to a rotating coordinate system. In the rotating system, the centrifugal force mv^2/R and the Lorentz force $-eH(R)v/c$ act on the particle. The resultant is

$$f(R) = \frac{mv^2}{R} - \frac{eH(R)v}{c}.$$

Motion round a circle of constant radius R_0 in our system corresponds to the equilibrium position

$$f(R)_0 = \frac{mv^2}{R_0} - \frac{eH(R_0)v}{c} = 0.$$

In order for this equilibrium position to be stable, the force $f(R)$ must be a restoring force. This means that, when $R > R_0$, the force f must be less than zero, i.e. directed towards smaller radii. Conversely, when $R < R_0$, f must be greater than zero, i.e. directed towards greater radii. It is easily seen that this occurs if $H(R)$ decreases not faster than $1/R$. The above requirement imposed on f can be transferred to df/dR, since $f(R_0) = 0$, so that the function $f(R) = (\partial f/\partial R)(R - R_0)$ in the vicinity of R_0. We easily find from this that the necessary condition for stability is

$$-\frac{R}{H}\frac{\partial H}{\partial R} < 1.$$

588. The magnetic field, decreasing from the periphery of the magnet, has a "barrel" shape (Fig. 30). The arrows indicate the direction of the action of the Lorentz force on the ions located outside the central plane.

By considering the action on a charged particle of the field component directed along the radius, the motion is easily shown to be stable. Conversely, if the field increases from the periphery, the lines of force are pulled in inside the magnet, and the motion is unstable.

The analytic proof is as follows. The force in the direction of the z axis (the z axis coincides with the axis of symmetry of the field) is

$$f_z = \frac{e}{c} H_r(z, r) = \frac{e}{c} \frac{\partial H_r}{\partial z} z,$$

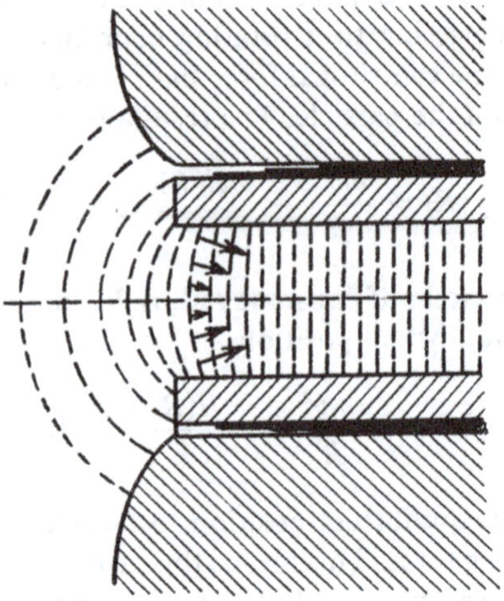

FIG. 30

since, from symmetry, $H_z(0, r) = 0$. The condition curl $\boldsymbol{H} = 0$ gives $\partial H_r/\partial z = \partial H_z/\partial r$. Hence

$$f_z = \frac{e}{c} \frac{\partial H_z}{\partial r} z.$$

In order for the force f_z to be a restoring force (see Problem 587), the derivative $\partial H_z/\partial r$ must be less than zero.

589. $|E_\varphi| = \dfrac{\dot{\Phi}}{2\pi Rc}$. It is easily shown that, if the betatron condition (see Problem 586) is fulfilled, $\partial E_\varphi/\partial R = 0$ and $\partial^2 E_\varphi/\partial R^2 > 0$, if $-(R/H)\,\partial H/\partial R < 1$.

Windings are mounted along different orbits in the betatron and the induced e.m.f. measured. A graph is drawn, showing the induced e.m.f. divided by $2\pi R$ on the axis of ordinates and the radius R of the winding on the axis of abscissae. The points plotted are joined by a smooth curve. Its minimum corresponds to the position of the equilibrium orbit.

590. The electron loses 12 eV by radiation at every revolution. With the conditions stated, the radiation loss during one revolution of the electron and the energy gained are equal at 292 MeV. The self-energy of the electron is 0·51 MeV.

591. In order for the detuning to be a minimum, the frequency of rotation and the frequency of the electric field must obviously coincide when the proton reaches half its final energy. In this case the frequency of rotation in the centre of the magnet will be greater than the frequency of the electric field. When the proton reaches half its maximum energy, the frequencies are the same. On reaching the final energy the rotation frequency will be less than the field frequency, the difference between them being precisely the same as their difference (with reversed sign) at the centre of the magnet. In our case the maximum energy W_1 is equal to 44·5 MeV.

In fact, $R^2 = E^2v^2/e^2H^2c^2 = (E^2 - E_0^2)/e^2H^2$, where $E = E_0 + W$ is the total energy of the proton, and $E_0 = 938{\cdot}1$ MeV is the rest mass energy of the proton. Hence

$$W = \sqrt{E_0^2 + e^2R^2H^2} - E_0.$$

The Larmor frequency $\omega = ecH/(E_0 + \frac{1}{2}W_1) = 1{\cdot}404 \times 10^5$ rad per second.

592. Let the deuteron acquire energy a in one revolution. The rate of increase of the energy is now $dE/dt = a\omega/2\pi$, where ω is the angular frequency of the deuteron revolution. The familiar expression $\omega = ecH/E$ for the frequency can be rewritten as

$$\omega\left(E_0 + \int_0^t \frac{a\omega}{2\pi}\, dt\right) = ecH,$$

where $E_0 = 18{\cdot}76 \times 10^8$ eV is the rest mass energy of the deuteron. On differentiating this relationship with respect to t and taking H = const, we obtain a differential equation for $\omega(t)$:

$$\frac{\dot{\omega}}{\omega^3} + \frac{a}{2\pi ecH} = 0.$$

We obtain as a result:

$$\omega(t) = \frac{\omega_{\text{init}}}{\sqrt{At+1}},$$

where

$$A = \frac{a\omega_{\text{init}}^2}{2\pi ecH}.$$

In our example $\omega_{\text{init}} = 0{\cdot}719 \times 10^8\ \text{sec}^{-1}$; $A = 92\ \text{sec}^{-1}$. The total frequency variation is $\Delta\omega/\omega_{\text{init}} = (E - E_0)/E_0 = 10{\cdot}65$ per cent.

593. $$R = \frac{c}{\omega_0}\sqrt{1 - \frac{\omega_0^2 E_0^2}{e^2c^2H_0^2 \sin^2 \Omega t}}.$$

594. (1) The change in the radius is 0·6 cm.

(2) 83 μsec after the magnetic field has passed through zero.

(3) When calculating the length of path in the betatron state it can be assumed that the magnetic field varies linearly with time, since the betatron state lasts 83 μsec. During this time the phase of the magnetic field changes by rather more than 1·5°. The energy acquired by the particle in one revolution is 136 eV. Hence, during the betatron state the electron has performed $1{\cdot}46 \times 10^4$ revolutions and has traversed a path equal to 27 km. In the synchrotron state, it can be assumed to a very high degree of accuracy that $v = c$. Hence we find that the path traversed by the electron in the synchrotron state is about 5000 km.

595. Since $T \gg t$, the counter cannot record more than one pulse in each cycle.

(1) Let $t = 2\tau$; then the number of random coincidences is

$$W_{\text{rand}} = \frac{N_1N_2}{f}.$$

(2) When $t > 2\tau$, the number of random coincidences is diminished in the ratio $2\tau/t$:

$$W_{\text{rand}} = \frac{2N_1N_2\tau}{ft};$$

(3) When $t < 2\tau$, W_{rand} does not vary until $\tau < 1/f$.

Thus with pulse loading of a counter the number of random coincidences increases rapidly by comparison with the case of continuous loading.

596. $\omega_0(t) = \dfrac{\omega_K}{\sqrt{L^2+1}}$, where $L = \dfrac{E_0}{eR_0H}$, $\omega_K = \dfrac{c}{R_0}$

is the frequency of revolution in the limiting case, when the particle velocity $v \approx c$ (c is the velocity of light, E_0 is the rest mass energy of the particle; for a proton, $E_0 = 938$ MeV, for an electron $E_0 = 0{\cdot}511$ MeV).

597. Since the acceleration takes place in an orbit of constant radius, the rate of increase in energy must be the same as in a betatron. Using this fact, we find that the proton acquires 191 eV in one revolution. The maximum energy $\approx 1{\cdot}3 \times 10^9$ eV. The path of the proton $\approx$ 1900 km.

598. In the presence of straight intervals the frequency ω_K is equal to $2\pi c/\Pi$, where Π is the orbit perimeter (see Problem 596). In our case $\omega_K = 2\pi \times 1{\cdot}44 \times 10^6$ sec^{-1}, whilst $L = 0{\cdot}28/t$, where t is the time in seconds, measured from the instant when the magnetic field becomes zero. (a) The magnetic field at the start of the acceleration process is $H = 155$ oersted. (b) When $\beta^2 \ll 1$ the error $\Delta\omega$ in the frequency displaces the orbit by the amount

$$\Delta R = -R\frac{\Delta\omega}{n\omega_0 F}, \quad \text{where} \quad F = 1 - \frac{\Pi - 2\pi R}{n\Pi}.$$

This expression is obtained by differentiating the relationship between ω_0 and H (Problem 596) on the assumption that $L \gg 1$; n is the index of the magnetic field, equal to $\frac{2}{3}$. In our case $|\Delta R| = 11$ cm.

599. About 20 MeV sec^{-1}.

600. (a) An observer sees individual radiation bursts, following one another at equal time intervals $T_H^* = 2\pi/\omega^*$, $\omega_H^* = eH \cdot mc^2/mcE$ (it is assumed that $\vartheta \gg \alpha$, where α is the angle between $\boldsymbol{v}$ and $\boldsymbol{H}$).

(b) The burst length is $\Delta t \simeq \Delta t'(1 - v/c) \sim \Delta t'(mc^2/E)^2$, where $\Delta t' \sim \vartheta/\omega_H^* \sim (1/\omega_H^*) \cdot mc^2/E = mc/eH$ is the time interval during which the electron moves in the direction of the observer (within the limits of the cone of angle ϑ). The factor $(1 - v/c)$ in the expression for Δt is due to the Doppler effect (the pulse is compressed by a amount $v\Delta t'$, so that its length diminishes by $v\Delta t'/c$). The spectrum consists of overtones of the electron revolution frequency ω_H^*, but when $E/mc^2 \gg 1$ it is practically continuous. In the frequency spectrum of a pulse of length Δt the greatest frequency is the cyclical frequency $\omega_{max} \sim 1/\Delta t \sim (eH/mc)(E/mc^2)^2$. To see this, we have to consider the Fourier expansion of the spacial pulse which has the form of a "spike" of length Δt, while the field in the spike changes sign (the time average of the field in the pulse vanishes).

An accurate calculation shows that the maximum occurs at the frequency $\nu_{max} = \omega_{max}/2\pi = 0{\cdot}216(eH/mc)(E/mc^2)^2 = 1{\cdot}8 \times 10^{18} HE^2$ (E in erg, H in oersted).

601. We use the formula of the previous problem, $\nu_{max} = 4{\cdot}6 \times \times 10^{-6} HE^2$, where E is measured in electron volts. When $E = 10^9$ eV, $\nu_{max} \sim 1{\cdot}5 \times 10^7$ c/s, $\lambda = c/\nu \sim 20$ cm; when $E = 3 \times 10^{14}$ eV, $\nu \sim 10^{18}$ c/s, $\lambda \sim 3$ Å.

602. The radiation in the wave is polarised predominantly along the electric field $\boldsymbol{E}$, directed perpendicularly to the external magnetic field ($\boldsymbol{E}$ is directed along the acceleration of the radiating charge).

603. In order for the particle to enter the accelerating field at the same value of the potential difference, the distance l_n between the centres of adjacent gaps must increase proportionally to the particle velocity:

$$l_n = \frac{v_n T}{2} = \frac{\lambda \beta_n}{2} = \frac{\lambda}{2}\sqrt{1 - \left(\frac{E_0}{E}\right)^2},$$

where λ is the wavelength of the electric field. In this case the time spent in passing between two gaps is $\frac{1}{2}T$. Let the electron acquire energy $eV_R \leqslant eV_0$ as it passes through each gap; then the length of the nth tube is

$$L_n = \frac{3}{8}\lambda\sqrt{1 - \left[\frac{E_0}{E_0 + W_{init} + eV_R n}\right]^2}.$$

In our example we can take $(W_{init} + eV_R n)/E_0 \ll 1$. Hence

$$L_n = \frac{3}{8}\lambda\sqrt{\frac{2W_{init}}{E_0}}\sqrt{1 + \frac{eV_R}{W_{init}} n} = 5{\cdot}2\sqrt{1 + 0{\cdot}25n}.$$

The tube length thus varies from 5·2 to 16·4 cm.

604. For the same accelerating field frequency, the tubes must be twice as long.

605. Let z denote the distance from the input aperture of the accelerator, and E_z the electric field-strength of the wave. The equation of motion

$$\frac{d}{dt}\left(\frac{m_0\dot{z}}{\sqrt{1-\frac{\dot{z}^2}{c^2}}}\right) = e\mathscr{E}_z$$

gives us

$$\frac{m_0\dot{z}}{\sqrt{1-\frac{\dot{z}^2}{c^2}}} = e\mathscr{E}_z t + A_1,$$

where A_1 is a constant of integration. On solving this equation for $\dot{z}$, we get

$$\dot{z} = \frac{(e\mathscr{E}_z t + A_1)c}{\sqrt{m_0^2c^2 + (e\mathscr{E}_z t + A_1)^2}}.$$

Integrating a second time, we get $z = \frac{\sqrt{E_0^2 + c^2(e\mathscr{E}_z t + A_1)^2}}{e\mathscr{E}_z}$ $+A_2$, where $E_0 = m_0c^2$. This easily gives us the wave phase velocity v and the particle energy W as functions of z:

$$v = c\frac{\sqrt{(e\mathscr{E}_z z + E_0 + W_{\text{init}})^2 - E_0^2}}{e\mathscr{E}_z z + E_0 + W_{\text{init}}}; \quad W = W_{\text{init}} + e\mathscr{E}_z z.$$

In a proton accelerator v varies by a factor of 9·5, and in an electron accelerator by a total of 0·6 per cent.

606. The electrostatics theorem in question says that there can be no position of stable equilibrium in systems in which only electrostatic forces are acting. Since in linear accelerators the phase velocity $v < c$, we can consider the motion in a coordinate system which moves at a given instant with velocity v, and thus reduce the problem to an electrostatic problem. The theorem in question shows that the possible equilibrium positions have the form of "saddle-points", i.e. if there is stability in one direction, there is no stability in the perpendicular direction. This implies for a linear accelerator that, if there is stability in the direction of wave propagation ("phasing"), i.e. the particle can be accelerated without its falling behind or outstripping the wave, stability is necessarily absent in the perpendicular direction and the beam deviates from the wave-guide wall. And conversely, if we arrange for "focusing", then "phasing" must be absent. This difficulty can be overcome by using a subsidiary constant magnetic field or by means of grids in the diaphragm apertures, in which electric charges appear. In this case the electrostatics theorem is inapplicable, since either a focusing magnetic field, or moving charges, appear in the moving coordinate system.

607. If we use the same methods of solution as in Problem 605, we find that the distance of the particle from the wave is

$$\Delta z = \frac{\sqrt{W_k^2 + 2E_0 W_k} - (W_{\text{init}} + E_0)\,\beta_{\text{init}} - (W_k - W_{\text{init}})}{e\mathscr{E}_0},$$

where $\beta_{\text{init}} = v_{\text{init}}/c$. In our case $((W_{\text{init}} + E_0)/E_0)^2 \gg 1$, so that

$$\Delta z \approx \frac{E_0}{2e\mathscr{E}_0}\left[\frac{E_0}{W_{\text{init}} + E_0} - \frac{E_0}{W_k}\right] = 2{\cdot}7\ \text{cm}.$$

608. As is clear from the answer to Problem 588, the equation of the particle oscillations in the vertical direction (i.e. in the direction perpendicular to the surfaces of the magnetic poles) can be written as

$$m\ddot{z} - \frac{e}{c}\frac{\partial H_z}{\partial z} z = 0. \qquad (1)$$

Since H_z varies as R^n in the first half of the sectors, (1) becomes

$$\ddot{z} - \omega^2 n z = 0. \qquad (2)$$

For the second half of the sectors:

$$\ddot{z} + \omega^2 n z = 0, \qquad (3)$$

where ω is the frequency of rotation round the orbit of radius R_0. The particle vibrations in the radial direction (i.e. in the central plane between the magnet poles) are described by the same equations (2) and (3) ($n \gg 1$), provided we interchange neighbouring sectors. Equations (2), (3) can be solved by a matching method. It is convenient to introduce the particle azimuth $\vartheta = \omega t$ instead of time t. The azimuth is measured from zero in each sector. Each pair of sectors forms a complete period of variation of the conditions of motion. Using this, we match the solutions for adjacent pairs of sectors. We obtain as a result:

$$\left.\begin{aligned} z_1 &= A \sin \sqrt{n}\, \vartheta + B \cos \sqrt{n}\, \vartheta, \\ z_2 &= (AC - BS) \sinh \sqrt{n}\, \vartheta + (AS + BC) \cosh \sqrt{n}\, \vartheta, \end{aligned}\right\} \tag{4}$$

where

$$C = \cos \sqrt{n} \frac{\pi}{N}, \quad S = \sin \sqrt{n} \frac{\pi}{N}. \tag{5}$$

On introducing for each pair of sectors an index m, running through all integral values, we obtain difference equations for the constants A_m and B_m in the mth and $(m+1)$th sectors:

$$\left.\begin{aligned} A_m[SC_2 + CS_2] + B_m[CC_2 - SS_2] &= B_{m+1}, \\ A_m[SS_2 + CC_2) + B_m[CS_2 - SC_2] &= A_{m+1}, \end{aligned}\right\} \tag{6}$$

where

$$C_2 = \cosh \sqrt{n} \frac{\pi}{N}, \quad S_2 = \sinh \sqrt{n} \frac{\pi}{N}.$$

We seek the solution of equations (6) in the form

$$A_m = De^{i\mu m}, \quad B_m = fDe^{i\mu m}. \tag{7}$$

On substituting (7) in (6), we easily obtain:

$$\cos \mu = CC_2$$

or, on expanding $\cos \mu$ in powers of $\sqrt{n}(\pi/N)$:

$$\cos \mu = 1 - \frac{n^2}{6}\left(\frac{\pi}{N}\right)^4.$$

For the solution to be stable, we must have $|\cos \mu| < 1$. At the centre of the stability region $\cos \mu = 0$, i.e.

$$n^2 = 6\left(\frac{N}{\pi}\right)^4.$$

Apart from the principal stability region, whose centre has been found, there is an infinite series of stability regions in the range of values n for which $\cos \sqrt{n}(\pi/N)$ vanishes. Only the principal region is of any practical importance.

609. The period of revolution of the particle T_0 is

$$T_0 = \frac{(2\pi R + l)}{c\beta},$$

where $\beta = v/c$. Hence $l = T_0 c\beta - 2\pi R$. The dependence of β on the orbit radius R and the magnetic field-strength is found in the same way as in Problem 596.

610. The radius of the trajectory in the cyclotron "gaps" is R/x. In the gaps the orbit rotates through the angle $l/(R/x)$, and in the sectors through the angle $2\pi - lx/R$. The perimeter of the trajectory is equal to $(2\pi - lx/R)R + l = 2\pi R + (1 - x)l$. The length l is thus increased by a factor of $1/(1 - x)$ compared with the length obtained in the previous problem (given the same radius R).

611. We use the familiar formula of relativity theory: $p^2c^2 = E^2 - E_0^2$, where p is the momentum of the particle (or of several particles), and E, E_0 are the total and rest mass energies of the particle (or particles). It follows from this formula that $E^2 - p^2c^2 - E_0^2$ is the same in all systems (due to the invariance of E_0). We consider two identical particles moving in opposite directions with energies E_v. Then

$$(2E_v)^2 = (E_j + E_0)^2 - p^2c^2,$$

where E_j is the energy of one of the particles in the system in which the other is at rest. Hence

$$p^2c^2 = E_j^2 - E_0^2.$$

Assuming that $E_v \gg E_0$, we get

$$E_j = \frac{2E_v^2}{E_0}.$$

(1) If we take E_0 as approximately 0·5 MeV for electrons, and 1000 MeV for protons (instead of the exact figure 938·1 MeV),

we obtain effective energies for electron accelerators of 40 GeV and 4000 GeV respectively, and (2) for proton accelerators 200 GeV and 20,000 GeV.

612. According to the Doppler effect formula: $\omega' = \omega(1+\beta)/\sqrt{1-\beta^2} = 2\omega E/E_0$. The energy of the protons is therefore $\hbar\omega' = 1{\cdot}78 \times 2{\cdot}4 \times 10^4 \approx 4{\cdot}3 \times 10^4$ eV. The electric field-strength increases by the same factor, i.e. it will be equal to 12,000 MV/cm.

613. The magnetic field should not have a preferred direction, so that particles of a given sign can rotate in different directions. A ring-type magnet has to be made up from $2N$ completely identical magnet sectors. The current must be arranged to flow in opposite

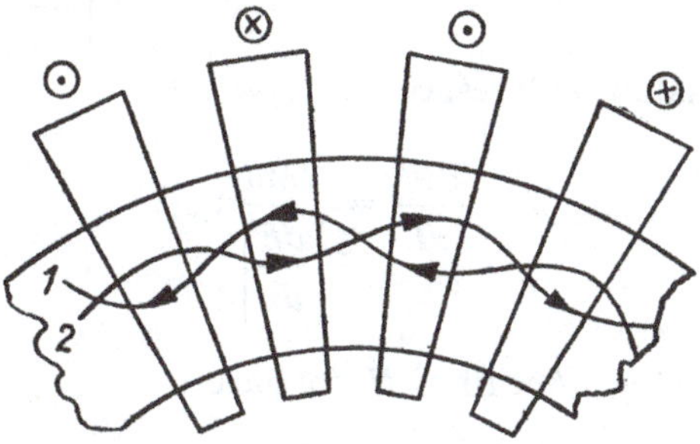

FIG. 31. Piece of ring magnet, consisting of two sectors with magnetic field directed towards us (the sectors marked ⊙) and two sectors with the field in the opposite direction. The figures 1 and 2 indicate the two possible orbits and the directions of motion for positive particles.

directions through the windings of adjacent sectors. In this case the direction of particle rotation round its orbit depends on the initial conditions, whilst the orbits themselves are similar but are turned through an angle π/N relative to one another, as shown in Fig. 31.

614. The resonance condition is the equality of the rate of change $d\varphi/dt$ of the phase of the wave ($\varphi = \omega t - kz$; $d\varphi/dt = \omega(1 - \dot{z}/c)$) and the rate of change $eH_0/\gamma m_0 c$ of the phase of the rotation in the magnetic field. If the resonance condition is fulfilled at the initial instant, it follows from the equations of motion that it will remain fulfilled. Let the plane wave have the components $E_x = A \sin\varphi$, $H_y = A \sin\varphi$; then $d(m_0\gamma\dot{z})/dt = (e/c)\dot{x}A\sin\varphi = (e/c)\dot{x}H_y$, and we have from the law of conservation of energy:

$$\frac{d(m_0\gamma c^2)}{dt} = e\dot{x}A\sin\varphi = e\dot{x}E_x.$$

This gives us $d(m_0\gamma c - m_0\gamma\dot{z})/dt = 0$, or $(1 - \dot{z}/c)\gamma = \text{const.}$

615. (a) We find the direction of the average radiation, i.e. we require that $\int n\,d\Omega = 4\pi[n(90°)]\,(1 + A/3) = 4\pi n(\vartheta_0)$; we therefore have to take $\cos^2\vartheta_0 = \frac{1}{3}$.

(b) The total output per primary deuteron is

$$N' = 2M\int_0^{x(E)} \sigma(x)\,dx = 2M\int_0^E \sigma(E)\frac{dE}{\left|\frac{dE}{dx}\right|}.$$

On differentiating with respect to E, we get

$$\frac{dN'}{dE} = \frac{2M\sigma}{\left|\frac{dE}{dx}\right|};$$

noting that $N' = 1{\cdot}6 \times 10^{-13}\,N$, we have

$$\sigma = 1{\cdot}6 \times 10^{-13}\frac{1}{2M}\frac{dE}{dx}\frac{dN}{dE} = \frac{1{\cdot}9 \times 10^{-23}}{\sqrt{E}}e^{-\frac{46}{\sqrt{E}}}.$$

616. The recoil proton energy is equal to $E\cos^2\vartheta = E_1$ (ϑ is the angle between the directions of travel of the neutron and the recoil proton).

The recoil proton production differential cross-section in the centre of mass system is proportional to the solid angle $d\cos\vartheta_0$, where ϑ_0 is the angle in the centre of mass system. But $\vartheta_0 = 2\vartheta$, so that $d\cos\vartheta_0 = 2d\cos^2\vartheta$. The cross-section is therefore proportional to dE_1. Hence the cross-section corresponding to production of a proton with energy $E_1 > E_0$ is $\sigma(E)\,(E - E_0)/E$, i.e. it is proportional to $E^{-1/2}(1 - E_0/E)$. The detector sensitivity is proportional to the same quantity.

617. The probability of fission of each uranium nucleus is $\omega_f = n\sigma_f/4\pi R^2 = 1{\cdot}47 \times 10^{-20}\,\text{sec}^{-1}$, and the probability of α-disintegration is $\omega_\alpha = (\ln 2)/\tau = 5 \times 10^{-18}\,\text{sec}^{-1}$. The ratio of the numbers of pulses is $\omega_\alpha/\omega_f = 340$, whilst the ratio of the energies released is $\omega_\alpha E_\alpha/\omega_f E_f = 18$.

In view of the large number of pulses from α-particles it is necessary to arrange for the sensitivity to be such that they are not counted.

618. (a) Neglecting the electron binding energy, we find that $Q = -931\,(7{\cdot}01824 + 1{\cdot}00816 - 7{\cdot}01916 - 1{\cdot}00899) = 1{\cdot}62\,\text{MeV}$.

(b) The total energy of the proton and lithium nucleus in the centre of mass system must be $E_0 = Q = 1{\cdot}62\,\text{MeV}$, $E_0 = \frac{1}{2}M_1v_1^2 + \frac{1}{2}M_pv_p^2$. Obviously, $v_p = 7v_1$ (since the momenta are the same but in opposite direction). Hence we find v_1 and v_p. The proton velocity in the laboratory coordinate system is $v_1 + v_p$, whilst the energy is $E_p = 8E_0/7 = 1{\cdot}85$ MeV.

619. 31·8 MeV.

620. 28·1 MeV.

621. $Q_a = 4{\cdot}0$ MeV; $Q_b = 3{\cdot}25$ MeV.

622. $Q_a = 18{\cdot}3$ MeV; $Q_b = 17{\cdot}6$ MeV.

623. It follows from the answers to Problems 621 and 622 that a deuteron releases an energy $\frac{1}{6}(4 + 3{\cdot}25 + 17{\cdot}6 + 18{\cdot}3) = 7{\cdot}2\,\text{MeV}$ per "burn-up". We easily find from this that a total energy of $3{\cdot}6 \times 10^3$ kWh is released by the total combustion of the deuterium contained in a litre of water; this is equal to the energy obtained by burning 277 kg of petrol.

624. The number of reactions per second per cubic centimetre is $\frac{1}{2}N^2\overline{\sigma(v)v}$, where the bar denotes averaging over all the values of the relative velocities of the deuterium atoms.

625. 2·9 W cm^{-3}.

626. $p = \dfrac{H^2}{8\pi} \approx 16$ atm.

627. $1{\cdot}6 \times 10^8$ cal.

628. $A_{\text{deuterium}} = 2{\cdot}01471$; $A_{\text{electron}} = 0{\cdot}0000548$; $A_{\text{deuteron}} = 2{\cdot}01416$.

629. 17·2 MeV.

630. The energies of the proton and neutron are equal and amount to 0·215 MeV. The proton and neutron move away in opposite directions.

631. $\Delta m = 0{\cdot}46 \times 10^{-9}$ g.

632. $4{\cdot}6 \times 10^{-9}$ g.

633. $\Delta m = 2{\cdot}4 \times 10^{-32}$ g.

634. About 4 million tons.

The Basic Relations of the Theory of Radioactive Decay (General Hints on the Solution of Problems 635–648)

If N is the number of radioactive atoms at the instant t, the number of disintegrations in time dt is $\lambda N\,dt$, where λ is a constant called the disintegration constant. The change in the number of radioactive atoms in time dt is

$$dN = -\lambda N\,dt. \qquad (1)$$

On integrating (1) with the initial condition $N = N_0$ at $t = 0$, we obtain the radioactive decay law

$$N = N_0 e^{-\lambda t}. \qquad (2)$$

On substituting in (1) $t = T = (\ln 2)/\lambda$, we see that the number of radioactive atoms is halved in time T. For this reason T is sometimes called the half-life of the radioactive substance.

The activity of a radioactive preparation is the number of disintegrations occurring in it per unit time: $n = -dN/dt$. On the basis of (1):

$$n = \lambda N; \qquad (3)$$

the activity (or intensity) of the preparation decreases according to the same exponential law as the number of radioactive atoms. The unit of activity is usually the curie: 1 curie $= 3{\cdot}7 \times 10^{10}$ disintegrations per sec, i.e. the number of disintegrations per second in 1 g of radium.

Let ν radioactive atoms possessing the disintegration constant λ be formed per unit time (under the influence of irradiation by neutrons or other particles, or as a result of decay of the parent substance). The change in the number of these atoms in time dt is dN:

$$dN = \nu\, dt - \lambda N\, dt,$$

whence (taking $N = 0$ at $t = 0$)

$$N = \frac{\nu}{\lambda}(1 - e^{-\lambda t}). \tag{4}$$

At first (when $t \ll T$) the number of radioactive atoms increases almost linearly; but the growth in the number of atoms gradually slows down and after an interval equal to several half-value periods, a saturation point is reached at which the number of new radioactive atoms forming per second is precisely equal to the number disintegrating in the same time, i.e.

$$\nu = \lambda N.$$

Let the half life T_1 of the parent substance be very large compared with the maximum of the half-lifes T_k of its subsequent disintegration products. In time $t \gg T_k$ the number of atoms of the decay products ceases to increase and, by (4), is equal to

$$N_i = \frac{\nu}{\lambda_i},$$

where ν = the number of disintegrations of the parent substance per unit time, equal to $\lambda_1 N_1$.

Thus, $\lambda_1 N_1 = \lambda_2 N_2 = \cdots = \lambda_i N_i$, i.e. the activity (number of disintegrations) of every member of the radioactive family is the same. This state is called the state of radioactive equilibrium.

635. $\lambda = 2{\cdot}9 \times 10^{-5}\ \text{sec}^{-1}$.

636. $\lambda = \dfrac{0{\cdot}693}{T} = 1{\cdot}42 \times 10^{-11}\ \text{sec}^{-1}$.

637. $\Delta N = 3{\cdot}80 \times 10^{10}$.

638. It may be seen from the shape of the graph that at least two radioactive elements are present. The long half-life can be determined directly; it is equal to 8 hr. The shorter half-life can be found as follows. We subtract from the counter readings the values corresponding to the long half-life, and draw the graph for the new values. The short half-life is 40 min.

639. In view of the radioactive equilibrium RaD, RaE and Po have the same number of disintegrations per sec, i.e. the number of β-particles emitted per sec by the RaD or RaE is equal to the number of α-particles emitted by the Po. The number of atoms of each type is found from the condition that the activities are equal:

$$\lambda_{RaD}N_{RaD} = \lambda_{RaE}N_{RaE} = \lambda_{Po}N_{Po} = 10^5 \text{ sec}^{-1}.$$

The half-life of RaD is found from the uranium–radium disintegration series table (Table VII, page 236): $T = 22 \text{ years} = 6{\cdot}9 \times 10^8$ sec, whence

$$\lambda_{RaD} = \frac{0{\cdot}693}{T_{RaD}} = \frac{0{\cdot}693}{6{\cdot}9 \times 10^8} = 10^{-9} \text{ sec}^{-1}$$

and

$$N_{RaD} = \frac{10^5}{10^{-9}} = 10^{14} \text{ atoms}.$$

640. The half-life of radium is 1550 years; 1 g radium contains

$$N_{Ra} = \frac{6{\cdot}02 \times 10^{23}}{226} = 2{\cdot}66 \times 10^{21} \text{ atoms}.$$

Using the same method as in the previous problem, we can find the number of disintegrations occurring per second in 1 g of radium, and the number of radon atoms in equilibrium with 1 g of radium (the half-life of radon is $T_{Rn} = 3{\cdot}82$ days):

$$\lambda_{Ra}N_{Ra} = 3{\cdot}7 \times 10^{10}; \quad N_{Rn} = \frac{\lambda_{Ra}N_{Ra}}{\lambda_{Rn}} = 1{\cdot}76 \times 10^{16}.$$

Since 1 mole of gas occupies a volume of 22,400 cm³ in normal circumstances, the volume of radon in equilibrium with 1 g of radium is equal to

$$V_{Rn} = 22400 \frac{N_{Rn}}{6{\cdot}02 \times 10^{23}} = 6{\cdot}5 \times 10^{-4} \text{ cm}^3 = 0{\cdot}65 \text{ mm}^3$$

641. ≈ 43 mm³. No account is taken in the calculation of the release of helium by products of radium decay.

642. $\lambda = 4{\cdot}5 \times 10^{-18} \text{ sec}^{-1}$.

643. In view of the radioactive equilibrium between U^{238} and U^{234}, $\lambda_{234} \cdot N_{234} = \lambda_{238} \cdot N_{238}$, whence

$$\frac{T_{234}}{T_{238}} = \frac{\lambda_{238}}{\lambda_{234}} = \frac{N_{234}}{N_{238}} = 6 \times 10^{-5}; \quad T_{234} = 2{\cdot}7 \times 10^5 \text{ years.}$$

The half-life of U^{234} is much smaller than the age of the Earth ($\approx 10^9$ years); hence our assumption of the existence of radioactive equilibrium between U^{238} and U^{234} is justified.

644. The activity of the compound, like the number of active atoms, decreases in accordance with the law: $e^{-\lambda t} = 2^{-t/T}$. The activity of the P^{32} compound 10 days after its preparation is

$$I = I_0 \cdot 2^{-\frac{t}{T}} = 100 \times 2^{-\frac{10}{15}} = 63 \text{ mcurie.}$$

645. $T_{UI} = 4{\cdot}5 \times 10^9$ years.

646. $Z = 90$; $A = 230$; ionium is an isotope of thorium.

647. $T \approx 1{\cdot}5 \times 10^9$ years.

648. On irradiation to saturation the number of iodine atoms disintegrating per second (i.e. the activity of the preparation) is equal to the number of atoms forming per second, i.e.

$$n_{sat} = 10^7 \text{ disintegrations per second.}$$

The number of iodine atoms in the case of activation to saturation is

$$N_{sat} = \frac{n}{\lambda} = 10^7; \quad \frac{0{\cdot}693}{25 \times 24 \times 3600} = 3{\cdot}1 \times 10^{13} \text{ atoms.}$$

The number of iodine atoms in time t after irradiation is

$$N = N_{sat}(1 - e^{-\lambda t}),$$

or, for small t ($t \ll T$),

$$N = N_{sat}\lambda t = nt.$$

When $t = 1$ min,

$$N = nt = 10^7 \times 60 = 6 \times 10^8 \text{ atoms.}$$

When $t = 25$ min,

$$N = N_{sat}(1 - e^{-\lambda t}) = 1{\cdot}55 \times 10^{13} \text{ atoms.}$$

649. If an intermediate process exists, then in the co-ordinate system in which ω is at rest, its rest energy E_ω^0 is equal to the sum of the energies of the particles into which ω disintegrates:

$$E_\omega^0 = E'_{\pi^+} + E'_{\pi^-} + E'_{\pi^0} = E',$$

whilst the total momentum of the disintegrating particles is

$$\boldsymbol{P}' = \boldsymbol{P}'_{\pi^+} + \boldsymbol{P}'_{\pi^-} + \boldsymbol{P}'_{\pi^0} = 0.$$

Since the quantity $E^2 - P^2c^2$ is invariant on passing to another system, we have in the laboratory system $E^2 - P^2c^2 = (E_\omega^0)^2$, where E and P are the total energy and momentum of the three particles (π^-, π^0 and π^+) in the laboratory system.

On considering a large number of decay reactions and evaluating $E^2 - P^2c^2$, we should obtain each time the same quantity $(E_\omega^0)^2$, if the particle ω exists.

650. Reactions 2, 4 are impossible because of the non-conservation of the lepton charge, and reaction 8 because of the non-conservation of the baryon charge.

651. Reactions 2, 3, 6, 8, 9 are impossible. A comparison of reactions 5 and 6 when investigating the interaction of neutrinos obtained by reaction 1 with protons has shown that reaction 5 occurs, but not 6, although the latter is more suitable energy-wise. The existence of two neutrinos was proved by this means.

652. In reactions 1, 6, 8, 10, 12, 14, $|\Delta S| = 0$ and they proceed through strong interaction. In reactions 2, 3, 4, 7, 9, 11, $|\Delta S| = 1$. Hence disintegrations 3, 4 have relatively small probabilities, whilst reactions 2, 7, 9, 11, are not observed in practice. In the disintegration 5 and reaction 13, $|\Delta S| = 2$. Thus they are not observed. Cascade hyperons decay in accordance with reaction 4, and afterwards Λ decays in accordance with reaction 3.

653. The kinetic energy can only be completely used for particle production in a centre of mass system of colliding particles, since it is only in this system that all the particles can be at rest after the reaction (at the energy threshold). Hence the problem of finding the threshold energy amounts to the problem of determining the connexion between the kinetic energy in the laboratory system W and in the centre of mass system W_c. Let E_1 denote the rest mass energy of the approaching particle and E_2 the rest mass energy of the nucleon ($E_2 = 938$ MeV). We now find from the condition for invariance of $(E + W)^2 - c^2p^2$ in all systems that

$$(E_1 + E_2 + W)^2 - c^2p_1^2 = (E_1 + E_2 + W_c)^2,$$
$$(E_1 + W)^2 - c^2p_1^2 = E_1^2.$$

These two equations give

$$W = W_c\left(1 + \frac{2E_1 + W_c}{2E_2}\right).$$

The threshold value W for production of a π-meson is obtained by setting $W_c = m_\pi c^2 = 140$ MeV. We find as a result that the π-meson production threshold for a γ-quantum or electron impinging on a nucleon is 150 MeV, and for a nucleon impinging on a nucleon is 290 MeV.

654. We consider the reaction of an electron and positron in the centre of mass system. The conservation law shows that the momentum of the γ-quantum is equal to zero in this system, which is obviously impossible.

655. If the energy of the proton is sufficiently large it can radiate π^0 and π^+ mesons, and also positrons (the reactions $p \to p + \pi^0$, $p \to n + \pi^+$, $p \to n + e^+ + \nu$). π^--mesons and electrons cannot be radiated.

656. $I_\gamma = 2\sigma I_{cr} N(L)$.

I_γ, centre $\simeq 5 \times 10^{-4}$ photons $\text{cm}^{-2} \cdot \text{sec} \cdot \text{steradian}$

I_γ, anticentre $\simeq 10^{-4}$ photons $\text{cm}^{-2} \cdot \text{sec} \cdot \text{steradian}$

I_γ, pole $\simeq 10^{-5}$ photons $\text{cm}^{-2} \cdot \text{sec} \cdot \text{steradian}$

657. $I_{cr} \simeq I_\gamma / 2\sigma n R_{ph} \simeq 400\, I_\gamma$ particles $\text{cm}^{-2} \cdot \text{sec} \cdot \text{steradian}$. The photometric radius of the Metagalaxy is $R_{ph} \simeq 5 \times 10^{27}$ cm and is approximately determined from the condition $u \approx \frac{1}{2}c$.

658. The laws of conservation of energy and momentum must be satisfied when a γ-quantum is emitted:

$$E_{12} = \hbar\omega + R,$$

$$\frac{\hbar\omega}{c} = p_R = \frac{1}{c}\sqrt{R(2Mc^2 + R)},$$

where p_R is the momentum of the nucleus after emission of a γ-quantum.

We obtain on solving these equations:

$$R = \frac{E_{12}^2}{2(Mc^2 + E_{12})} \approx \frac{E_{12}^2}{2Mc^2}.$$

Hence $\hbar\omega = E_{12} - R$; $\Delta\omega = -R/\hbar$, whilst $\Delta\lambda \approx 2\pi\hbar/2Mc^2$, which is the same as the answer to Problem 498. We obtain for the Ir^{191} nucleus: $R = 0{\cdot}046$ eV.

659. We obtain by analogy with the previous problem:

$$R = \frac{E_{12}^2}{2Mc^2}; \quad \hbar\omega = E_{12} + R.$$

660. It may be seen from the solutions to Problems 658 and 659 that the difference between the energies of the emission and absorption lines of free nuclei is $2R \approx E_{12}^2/Mc^2$. It is more convenient to compare the relative line widths: Γ/E_{12}, $\sqrt{2kT/Mc^2}$ and $2R/E_{12}$. The required temperature is $T_0 = E_{12}^2/2Mc^2k$. We obtain the following table for the nuclei quoted in the problem:

Nucleus	Tu^{169}	Fe^{57}	Dy^{161}	Ir^{193}	Au^{197}	Er^{166}	Zn^{67}	Hf^{177}	W^{182}	Ir^{191}	Re^{187}
$\left(\frac{2R}{E_{12}}\right) \times 10^7$	0·53	2·7	1·7	4·1	4·2	5·2	15·4	6·9	5·9	7·2	10·7
T_0	3	22	26	172	186	241	825	340	449	535	1152

It will be seen from this table that the natural line widths are many orders less than the difference between the γ-quantum emission and absorption lines, whilst T_0 is fairly large for most nuclei. These factors lead to difficulties in observing the resonance absorption of γ-quanta by free nuclei.

661. The γ-quantum energy shift due to the Doppler effect is

$$\Delta E = \frac{Ev}{c}.$$

We find from this, on putting $\Delta E = \Gamma/6$, that $v/c = 6 \times 10^{-12}$, and $v = 0{\cdot}18$ cm sec^{-1}.

662. On expressing the energy E_{12} in keV, we find that

$$E_{12} < 5\sqrt{\frac{T_D A}{160}} \text{ keV}.$$

Hence, when $A = 225$ and $T_D = 480\,°K$,

$$E_{12} < 75\sqrt{3} \text{ keV}.$$

When $A = 64$ and $T_D = 160\,°K$,

$$E_{12} < 40.$$

We can conclude from this that, to observe the Mössbauer effect, we want to confine ourselves to γ-quanta energies of the order of 100 keV or less and mass numbers 50 or larger.

663. $h = \Gamma c^2/100g\, E_{12} \approx 28$ m.

664. The undisplaced line of γ-radiation (its existence was discovered by Mössbauer) results from the fact that the recoil momentum is transmitted to the crystal as a whole. But the mass of a nucleus when it emits a γ-quantum of energy $E_{12} = h\nu$ is diminished by $\Delta M = E_{12}/c^2$, so that its mean kinetic energy, connected with the thermal motion, changes by $\Delta E = \Delta M u^2/2 = E_{12}u^2/2c^2 = 3kTE/2Mc^2$, where M is the mass of the nucleus and the mean value $\overline{u^2}$ is $3kT/M$. Thus the frequency of the emitted γ-quantum is diminished by $\Delta\nu = \Delta E/h = 3kT\nu/2Mc^2$. If the temperature difference between the radiator and the receiver is δT, the emission and absorption frequencies are displaced for this reason by $\delta\nu = 3k\delta T\nu/2Mc^2$. The frequency shift due to the height difference is $\Delta\nu = gh\nu/c^2$, so that $\delta T = 1°$ corresponds to a height difference $\delta h = 3k\delta T/2Mg \approx 22$ m.

From the classical view point the temperature-dependent variation in the absorption of γ-radiation is due to the quadratic Doppler effect.

TABLE I. WATER AND ETHYL ALCOHOL VAPOUR PRESSURES AT DIFFERENT TEMPERATURES

Temperature in °C	Pressure in mm Hg		Temperature in °C	Pressure in mm Hg	
	water	ethyl alcohol		water	ethyl alcohol
35	42·188	—	5	6·54	17·70
30	31·834	78·41	4	6·01	16·62
28	28·35	70·09	3	5·68	15·69
25	23·76	59·03	2	5·29	14·60
24	22·38	55·70	1	4·92	13·65
23	21·07	52·54	0	4·58	12·73
22	19·83	49·54	−1	4·25	—
21	18·65	46·69	−2	3·95	—
20	17·54	44·00	−2·8	—	9·49
19	16·48	41·45	−3·0	3·67	—
18	15·48	39·05	−4·0	3·40	—
17	14·53	36·77	−5·0	3·16	—
16	13·64	34·62	−6·0	2·93	—
15	12·79	32·60	−7·0	2·71	—
14	11·99	30·69	−8·0	2·51	—
13	11·23	28·89	−9·0	2·32	—
12	10·52	27·19	−10·0	2·14	6·47
11	9·84	25·59	−10·6	—	5·20
10	9·21	24·08	−11.0	1·98	—
9	8·61	22·66	−12·0	1·83	—
8	8·05	21·31	−13·0	1·68	—
7	7·51	20·04	−16·5	—	3·23
6	7·01	18·84	−24·5	—	1·72

TABLE II. $-\left(\frac{dE}{dx}\right)_{\text{ion}} = f\left(\frac{\beta}{(1-\beta^2)^{1/2}}\right)$

$\frac{\beta}{(1-\beta^2)^{1/2}}$	f in 10^3 eV per cm air	$\frac{\beta}{(1-\beta^2)^{1/2}}$	f in 10^3 eV per cm air
0·126	45·2	0·894	3·28
0·18	25·9	1·15	2·83
0·255	14·8	1·39	2·69
0·315	10·8	1·61	2·52
0·366	8·7	2·68	2·41
0·411	7·4	4·74	2·49
0·60	4·68		

TABLE III. $\frac{Rm}{M} = g$ AS A FUNCTION OF $\left(\frac{\beta}{(1-\beta^2)^{1/2}}\right)$ (R = RANGE OF PARTICLE)

$\frac{\beta}{(1-\beta^2)^{1/2}}$	$g\left(\frac{\beta}{(1-\beta^2)^{1/2}}\right)\cdot 10^2$ expressed in cm air in standard conditions	$\frac{\beta}{(1-\beta^2)^{1/2}}$	$g\left(\frac{\beta}{(1-\beta^2)^{1/2}}\right)\cdot 10^2$ expressed in cm air in standard conditions
0·02	0·05	0·18	12·35
0·04	0·10	0·25	21·00
0·06	0·275	0·30	41
0·08	0·70	0·35	61
0·10	1·60	0·40	102
0·12	3·0	0·45	183
0·14	5·25	0·50	265
0·16	8·40		

TABLE IV. RANGE–ENERGY RELATIONSHIPS FOR PARTICLES IN EMULSIONS

Range (microns)	Energy (MeV)				Range (microns)	Energy (MeV)			
	p	d	t	α		p	d	t	α
5	0·47	0·58	0·63	1·50	60	2·60	3·37	3·80	10·30
10	0·78	0·98	1·10	2·84	70	2·88	3·79	4·20	11·35
20	1·26	1·60	1·82	4·86	80	3·10	4·05	4·60	12·35
30	1·66	2·10	2·40	6·47	90	3·35	4·35	5·00	13·25
40	2·00	2·55	2·89	7·85	100	2·60	4·65	5·30	14·23
50	2·32	2·97	3·37	9·10	150	4·60	6·00	7·00	18·15

TABLE V. $\frac{d(Hr)}{dx}$ IN LEAD AS A FUNCTION OF $\frac{\beta}{(1-\beta^2)^{1/2}}$

β	$\frac{\beta}{(1-\beta^2)^{1/2}}$	$\frac{d(Hr)}{dx}\cdot 10^{-5}$ in oersted cm^{-1} per cm lead	β	$\frac{\beta}{(1-\beta^2)^{1/2}}$	$\frac{d(Hr)}{dx}\cdot 10^{-5}$ in oersted cm^{-1} per cm lead
0·3	0·288	8·33	1·0	0·706	0·80
0·4	0·372	4·33	1·1	0·739	0·72
0·5	0·449	2·71	1·2	0·768	0·67
0·6	0·515	1·91	1·3	0·793	0·62
0·7	0·574	1·45	1·4	0·814	0·56
0·8	0·625	1·15	1·5	0·832	0·545
0·9	0·667	0·94	1·6	0·848	0·543
			1·8	0·874	0·542

TABLE VI. MASSES OF NEUTRAL ATOMS IN AMU

n_0^1	1·0089860 ± 10	Li^7	7·0182389 ± 42
H^1	1·0881451 ± 2	Li^8	8·0250425 ± 44
H^2	2·0147425 ± 6	Be^7	7·0191625 ± 33
H^3	3·0170013 ± 29	Be^8	8·0078563 ± 38
He^3	3·0169807 ± 18	Be^9	9·0150566 ± 36
He^4	4·0038761 ± 13	B^{10}	10·0161236 ± 39
Li^6	6·0170404 ± 44	C^{12}	12·0038156 ± 4

TABLE VII. THE URANIUM–RADIUM RADIOACTIVE SERIES

Name	Z	A	Decay	Half-life	Particle energy in MeV
Uranium U I	92	238	α	4,5 · 10⁹ years	4·21
UX_1	90	234	β	23 days	0·13
UX_2	91	234	β	1·14 min	2·32
Uranium U II	92	234	α	2·7 · 10⁵ years	4·75
Ionium Io	90	230	α	8·3 · 10⁴ years	4·66
Radium Ra	88	226	α	1550 years	4·79
Radon Rn	86	222	α	3·82 days	5·49
RaA	84	218	α	3 min	6·00
RaB	82	214	β	26·8 min	0·65
RaC	83	214	β (99,96%) α (0·04%)	19·7 min	3·2 5·5
RaC′	84	214	α	1·5 · 10⁻⁴ sec	7·68
RaC″	81	210	β	1·3 min	1·80
RaD	82	210	β	22 years	0·025
RaE	83	210	β	5 days	1·17
Polonium Po	84	210	α	140 days	5·30
Lead Pb	82	206	stable		

Made in the USA
Monee, IL
04 February 2025

11495347R00144